FRANK WILCZEK
50 Years of Theoretical Physics

FRANK WILCZEK
50 Years of Theoretical Physics

Edited by

Antti Niemi
Nordita, Sweden

Kok Khoo Phua
Institute of Advanced Studies, Singapore

Alfred Shapere
University of Kentucky, USA

World Scientific

NEW JERSEY · LONDON · SINGAPORE · BEIJING · SHANGHAI · HONG KONG · TAIPEI · CHENNAI · TOKYO

Published by

World Scientific Publishing Co. Pte. Ltd.

5 Toh Tuck Link, Singapore 596224

USA office: 27 Warren Street, Suite 401-402, Hackensack, NJ 07601

UK office: 57 Shelton Street, Covent Garden, London WC2H 9HE

Library of Congress Cataloging-in-Publication Data

Names: Niemi, Antti J., editor. | Phua, K. K., editor. | Shapere, Alfred, editor.
Title: Frank Wilczek : 50 years of theoretical physics / edited by Antti Niemi, Nordita, Sweden,
    Kok Khoo Phua, Institute of Advanced Studies, Singapore, Alfred Shapere, University of Kentucky, USA.
Description: First edition. | New Jersey : World Scientific Publishing Co. Pte. Ltd., [2022] |
    Includes bibliographical references.
Identifiers: LCCN 2022000997 (print) | LCCN 2022000998 (ebook) | ISBN 9789811255175 (hardcover) |
    ISBN 9789811251948 (ebook for institutions) | ISBN 9789811255182 (ebook for individuals)
Subjects: LCSH: Wilczek, Frank. | Wilczek, Frank--Influence. | Physicists--United States--Biography. |
    Mathematical physics.
Classification: LCC QC16.W545 F73 2022 (print) | LCC QC16.W545 (ebook) |
    DDC 530.092 [B]--dc23/eng20220315
LC record available at https://lccn.loc.gov/2022000997
LC ebook record available at https://lccn.loc.gov/2022000998

British Library Cataloguing-in-Publication Data
A catalogue record for this book is available from the British Library.

For any available supplementary material, please visit
https://www.worldscientific.com/worldscibooks/10.1142/12713#t=suppl

Preface

This commemorative volume in honor of Frank Wilczek marks both his 70th birthday and the first half century of his extraordinary career as a physicist. Beginning with the 1973 co-discovery of asymptotic freedom in gauge theories, for which he received the 2004 Nobel Prize, his career has been defined by transformative ideas and discoveries that have impacted virtually every corner of physics. To a remarkable degree, these contributions have aged very well; in many cases their significance and impact has only grown with time.

Wilczek's work with David Gross on asymptotic freedom was quickly followed by their proposal of Quantum Chromodynamics (QCD) as the theory of the strong interaction and, thus, as the completion of the Standard Model. The predictions and tests they proposed would set the stage for much future experimental work, eventually helping to establish the Standard Model as a complete, predictive theory. Among these predictions, the gluon fusion vertex, which Wilczek identified in 1977 as the dominant coupling of the Higgs boson to gluons, presciently turned out to be the key process in the 2012 discovery of the Higgs, and continues to play a central role in searches for particles beyond the Standard Model.

Following the spectacular success of QCD and the Standard Model, Wilczek turned his attention to extensions of the Standard Model motivated by unification and the cosmology of the very early universe. His discovery with Dimopoulos and Rabi, that the gauge couplings in the minimal supersymmetric Standard Model unify with much higher accuracy than their Standard Model counterparts, remains one of the most compelling motivations for supersymmetry and grand unification.

Another fundamental extension of the Standard Model, proposed independently by Wilczek and Steven Weinberg as a solution of the strong CP problem, is the axion. This particle (which he named) was quickly realized by him and others to have remarkable cosmological implication. Over time, it has become one of the leading dark matter candidates, whose position has been strengthened by the failure of LHC to observe any sign of dark matter. Wilczek is currently involved in several major axion detection efforts.

Wilczek's later work on extreme phases of QCD has also transformed our understanding of the strong interaction. Beginning in the late 90s, he made fundamental contributions to mapping out the phase diagram of QCD at high temperatures and densities. In particular, his discovery that cold quark matter at high densities exhibits color superconductivity and color flavor-locking has had important applications to the astrophysics of neutron stars.

In condensed matter physics, Wilczek's work on fractional statistics and the quantum Hall effect has had a far-reaching, long-term impact. In 1982 he showed how gauge theories in $2+1$ dimensions could accommodate particles with fractional statistics, a discovery that was to have profound implications in condensed matter physics. Although previous, independent work had introduced the principle of fractional statistics, Wilczek was the first to show that such particles, which he called "anyons", could be realized as charge-flux composites, sourced by a Chern–Simons term. In 1984, with Daniel Arovas and J. Robert Schrieffer, he demonstrated the existence of anyons in the fractional Hall effect. In subsequent work with various collaborators, he explored and elucidated the rich phenomenology and dynamics of anyonic matter, and of quantum Hall states in particular. The 2020 observation of fractional statistics in quantum Hall systems is a striking validation of Wilczek's pioneering work and is bound to lead to many applications in the future.

Among numerous other contributions in condensed matter physics is his proposal of a new class of phases of matter, in a 1987 paper that laid the foundations for the subject of topological insulators. Wilczek and Zee's non-Abelian generalization of Berry's phase, with applications to fluids and molecular physics has also had widespread influence. More recently, his 2012 proposal and subsequent development of "time crystals", systems in which time-translation symmetry is broken spontaneously, have inspired a significant and rapidly expanding literature. Recent high-profile experiments have discovered time crystal phases in nonequilibrium atomic and condensed matter systems.

In a more theoretical vein, Wilczek's work on quantum gravity and string theory includes the discovery of T-duality as an exact symmetry of string theory; pioneering work on the microscopic approach to black hole entropy in string theory; and the definition and first computations of entanglement entropy in a nontrivial field theory. The latter computations established a link between entanglement entropy of a conformally invariant system and its central charge, which has informed much subsequent theoretical development, from quantum information theory to quantum gravity.

In recent years, Wilczek has continued to produce work of extraordinary depth and originality. Highlights include a new design concept for axion detection based on exploiting resonance with plasma oscillations; a fast and efficient method for measuring the quantum state of entangled many-body systems; an experimental protocol for sharp, detailed tests of the suggested emergence of a gauge theory in the low-energy dynamics of quantum spin ice; experimental studies of interference between light of different wavelengths (a possibility suggested in his earlier work); and a proposal for observing quantum gravity effects in gravitational wave detectors, which won First Prize in the 2020 Gravity Research Foundation essay competition.

Wilczek continues to be an active spokesman for science to the educated public, through his regular "Wilczek's Universe" columns in the *Wall Street Journal* as well as occasional solicited articles in *Nature* journals, *Scientific American* and *Quanta*. He is also the author of several nontechnical books on particle physics, including the bestselling 2021 book *Fundamentals*, which has earned wide critical acclaim.

This volume includes contributions from many of Wilczek's collaborators, students, and friends, some of whom participated in a special meeting in his honor, "Quantum Connections 2021", that took place in June 2021 in Stockholm. The articles include reminiscences as well as original work reflecting Wilczek's current interests and the continuing relevance of his scientific contributions.

On behalf of the contributors and the innumerable other colleagues and students who have had the pleasure of working with Frank Wilczek over the years, we humbly offer this collection of articles as a small tribute to his enormous legacy.

Antti Niemi
Alfred Shapere

Young Frank Wilczek displaying his scientific curiosity. (Courtesy of Betsy Devine.)

Wilczek as a graduate student in 1973, the year he and David Gross discovered asymptotic freedom. (Courtesy of Betsy Devine.)

Leaving for work on October 6, 2004 after receiving a phone call from Sweden. (Courtesy of Betsy Devine.)

Nobel Prize diploma, artwork, and medal. (Courtesy of Betsy Devine.)

At home with physics. (Courtesy of Betsy Devine.)

Nobel Symposium on Graphene, May 2010.

From Shanghai Jiao Tong University.

From dinner hosted by Stockholm University.

Betsy and Frank at Högberga.

Mid-summer celebration at Högberga/*Quantum Connections 2018*.

Quantum Connections 2018 participants.

Quantum Connections 2019 participants.

https://doi.org/10.1142/9789811251948_fmatter

Contents

Professor Wilczek Comes to Harvard

Mark Alford

Physics Department, Washington University, Saint Louis, MO 63130, USA
alford@physics.wustl.edu

How Frank changed my life as soon as I met him

When Frank Wilczek arrived as a visiting professor at Harvard in fall 1987, I was a drifting graduate student in the theoretical physics program. I had narrowly avoided being kicked out after I decided to switch from experiment to theory. I had been rescued by Sidney Coleman, with whom I had written one paper on an obscure variant of his "Q-ball" solitons. Sidney was a kind and profoundly insightful physicist, but his students had to come up with their own ideas for publishable research. I had not come up with anything promising. Meanwhile, other students working with Harvard faculty like Howard Georgi were powering along, following their advisors' well established research programs and writing papers.

Frank's way of doing physics was different from anything we had seen before. His mind boiled with ideas which bubbled out in every conversation. Several of us, including John March-Russell, Yi-hong Chen, and Martin Greiter, gravitated to him. Frank hosted movie nights at his house on Fridays, where we would talk about physics for a little while then watch a movie on his TV, for which someone had to bring a rented video cassette tape. We knew that in principle the other faculty had houses and families off in some orthogonal dimension, but Frank's house quickly became a regular part of our lives. Betsy was a warm welcoming presence, and his very young daughters Mira and Amity scampered around cheerfully, although they weren't that interested in a bunch of physicists talking about superconducting anyons and unstable vacua.

Frank was full of ideas and he was enthusiastic about all of them. For graduate students who hung around him the main challenge was to pick out which of them were the best ones to pursue. Sidney Coleman was a perfect complement. I tried to contribute as best I could, but sometimes it felt as if my main role was to act as a sort of broker, telling Sidney about Frank's creative suggestions, returning to Frank with Sidney's insights, going back and forth until we had a paper. Over the next few months John March-Russell and I worked with Frank on sphalerons, Aharonov-Bohm interactions between particles and cosmic strings, particle production by cosmic strings, screening of magnetic monopole charge, the behavior of anyon dielectrics, and probably other topics too.

Being around Frank was a great education for young students. Up to that point we had been trained in classroom physics, taught to solve pre-digested problems where the overriding imperative was not to make any mistakes. In some way it was like learning to drive a car by pointing it downhill and only using the brake. Frank taught us about the gas pedal: the power of uninhibited creation that can take you up hills and over mountains to the unexplored territory beyond. We learned to balance "you can't..." with "what if...?"; to replace "that's wrong" with "that's funny...".

The most successful project from that time for me was Frank's idea that cosmic strings arising from Grand Unified Theories, which contain exotic magnetic fields associated with the spontaneously broken (or, as Sidney would more accurately call them, "hidden") GUT symmetries, could interact significantly with surrounding matter via the Aharonov-Bohm effect. This turned out to be an enormously instructive project for a young physicist to work on.

The first great lesson was not to treat peer-reviewed literature as scripture. There was already a paper on the scattering of particles off cosmic strings, written by a well-regarded cosmologist, which said there was no Aharonov-Bohm interaction because you could do a gauge transformation and "hide" the gauge potential behind the string. Frank saw immediately that this was not right, but it took me a while to really believe that something published in *Physical Review*, reproduced and extended in *Physics Reports*, could be completely wrong.

Nudged along by Frank, I found that if you scatter a GUT-charged particle off the cosmic string then the interaction cross-section is just given by the momentum of the particle. It isn't suppressed by the small size of the string core, and actually in the lowest angular momentum state the wavefunction diverges at the string core.

In the process I gained some experience of navigating the storms that can arise in research. One day we received an unwelcome message from a student of Roman Jackiw at MIT. They had been working on similar Aharonov-Bohm phenomena, and he told us we had missed an essential aspect: there was a "self-adjoint extension" to the Hamiltonian that arose from a choice one could make in the boundary conditions at the origin, the center of the string core. I was panicked, but Frank was always confident that we had done things correctly. After a week or two, John March-Russell and I were able to show that the boundary condition we had chosen was the right one for any physically reasonable profile of magnetic flux in the string core. There were some tense exchanges with the MIT group, but in the end I think we all agreed it was just a matter of emphasis: they were interested in the mathematical formalism, we were interested in the possible cosmological phenomenon. Panic over.

One final lesson from this wonderfully instructive project: after issuing a preprint (which in those days meant someone had to mail out hundreds of photocopies to a list of institutions) and submitting the paper to *Physical Review Letters*, we heard from Ryan Rohm at Boston University that he had done the same calculation in his thesis a few years before, but never published it in a journal. We checked and it was true. You can never be sure where the precursors or parallels to your pet project may be lurking.

We all knew that Frank's visiting position was part of Harvard's effort to recruit him to their faculty, but other places were in the running too, and he accepted a position at the Institute for Advanced Study in Princeton. John March-Russell and I were deep into our work with Frank on Aharonov-Bohm and cosmic strings, and we were excited when Frank invited us down to Princeton to visit the IAS and work with him for a few days. I don't remember what we worked on, but the visit really reinforced our impression of Frank's ultra-egalitarian ethos. Here is how it went. John, his new wife Virginia Samuels, and I rented a car and drove down to Princeton. Frank, as part of his hiring deal with the IAS, had been given Einstein's house on Mercer Street, and he let me stay there overnight. At the end of the day I went upstairs to sleep in an old bed that had been in the house when they bought it, a legacy from Margot Einstein. I don't know if Albert himself had ever slept in that bed, but its mattress reminded me of the classic elastic-sheet pictures of the gravitational well around a black hole. I sank into the deep valley and slept well. There was no event horizon: I was able to get out of it again in the morning.

Frank needed to be back in Boston to give a talk at Northeastern, and he asked us to give him a ride on Saturday. But Virginia needed to go back on Friday night for a Saturday rehearsal. We expected that Frank would bail on us but he didn't. He asked if one of us could give him a place to stay in Boston on Friday night, I offered a bed in the Somerville apartment I shared with three other people, and the deal was done. Betsy reminded him to give us some money for gas, and I drove our rented car back to Boston that night, three grad students plus Frank Wilczek, future Nobel prize winner, dozing in the passenger seat. Although John and I were graduate students and Frank was a permanent member of one of the greatest physics institutes in the world, to him we were all physicists, all on the same level.

I graduated from Harvard in 1990. A few years later Frank made another big impact on my life when he recruited me to a postdoc position at the Institute for Advanced Study, and got me and Krishna Rajagopal working on the idea of Cooper pairing in quark matter. That turned out to be a career-creating project for me, a much bigger deal than Aharonov-Bohm scattering by cosmic strings. But nothing will ever match the wisdom I absorbed from that one year as a graduate student at Harvard working with Frank.

© 2022 World Scientific Publishing Company
https://doi.org/10.1142/9789811251948_0002

Pre-K Memories of Frank Wilczek

Daniel P. Arovas

Department of Physics
University of California at San Diego
San Diego, CA 92093-0319, USA
darovas@ucsd.edu

I regret having failed to produce an original scientific contribution for this Festschrift for Frank Wilczek. Frank is of course a physicist of exceptional breadth, and with many extraordinary accomplishments. On a personal note, Frank was also an early and strongly positive influence on my own career. So I much appreciate the opportunity to contribute some memories of Frank from his "pre-K" days, which is to say from the mid-1980s, when he was a permanent member of the original Institute for Theoretical Physics in Santa Barbara (*i.e.* before ITP became KITP).

Prior to occupying the Director's office, Bob Schrieffer, who was my thesis advisor, was Frank's office neighbor at the west end of the top floor of Ellison Hall — ITP's original venue. At that time, in the spring of 1984, Frank and Bob spoke often as their physics interests had substantially overlapped in the area of fractional quantum numbers. Su, Schrieffer, and Heeger [1] had shown that soliton excitations in the one-dimensional long-chain polymer polyacetylene exhibit reversed spin-charge relations, *i.e.* $Q = \pm e$ and $S = 0$ or $Q = 0$ and $S = \frac{1}{2}$. Strikingly, for a model of *spinless* electrons, the solitons have *fractional charge* $Q = \pm\frac{1}{2}e$. This aspect continued to fascinate Bob for the next several years [2]. Meanwhile, on January 8, 1982, *Physical Review Letters* received two manuscripts from Frank, which were published back-to-back [3,4], outlining the basic quantum mechanics of charge-flux composites and their connection to fractional charge of magnetic monopoles in CP non-conserving field theories, first discussed by Witten [5]. (By the way, the published figures from Ref. [3] look as if they were scrawled on a napkin during a lunchtime discussion.) The fact that these charge-flux composites exhibited the phenomenon of fractional statistics in $(2+1)$-dimensions prompted Wilczek to name them *anyons* [6]. Earlier work by Leinaas and Myrheim [7], which articulated several key aspects of this construction, eventually and rightly came to be widely recognized.

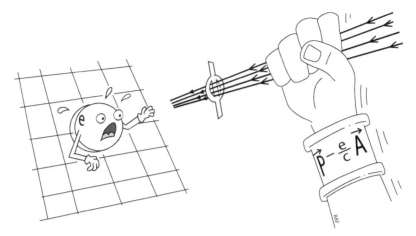

Fig. 1.   Artist's conception of a charged particle — flux tube composite. From my Ph.D. thesis (UC Santa Barbara, 1986). Sketch by Roger A. Freedman.

At this time, the fractional quantum Hall effect was probably the most exciting topic in all of physics. Laughlin's astonishing description of a many-body wavefunction for an incompressible quantum fluid with fractionally charged quasiparticle excitations had electrified the condensed matter community [8]. In a masterstroke of intuition and creativity, Bertrand Halperin proposed [9] that Laughlin's quasiparticles behaved as Wilczek's anyons, and argued how this feature could explain the hierarchy of fractional quantum Hall states, with anyonic quasiparticles previously described as either bosons (Haldane) [10] or fermions (Laughlin). Concomitant with all this excitement, Michael Berry published a paper with the unassuming title, "Quantal phase factors accompanying adiabatic changes" [11] which would prove to have enormous impact. I remember talking with Bob in his office one day when Frank excitedly burst in waving Berry's preprint, saying that it must hold the key for proving that Laughlin's quasiparticles were indeed anyons. At this point, the story becomes anticlimactic, because it took all of about 30 minutes to sketch out the simple argument for the braiding statistics on Schrieffer's blackboard [12]. Compelling experimental evidence of anyonic braiding statistics of Laughlin quasiparticles was announced in 2020 [13].

It was around this time that I did a bit of intellectual backfill and started reading Frank's various papers related to fractional statistics. I was intrigued by a draft that he and Tony Zee had written where they sought to describe how physical properties of a gas of anyons would evolve from bosonic to fermionic character as the statistics angle θ was continuously varied. They sketched how they imagined the second virial coefficient would

 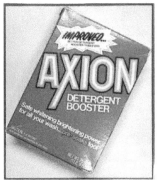

Fig. 2. Left: Shell's super unleaded nonabelian gasoline. Right: a box of axions.

interpolate between the Bose and Fermi values of $\mp\frac{1}{4}\lambda_T^2$, with λ_T the thermal wavelength. But there was no calculation! I recalled learning about quantum virial coefficients in John Cardy's statistical mechanics class the previous year and set myself on working it out for anyons. When I finished, I had found the same result using two different methods, but my interpolation curve had a cusp at the bosonic values of $\theta = 2\pi n$, whereas Wilczek and Zee's curve was smooth. So I went to talk to Bob about it, and he said, "well, let's see what Frank has to say." I nervously followed him into Frank's office to present my results. Frank listened intently, asked questions, thought briefly, and then to my great relief said, "this is right." So Frank, Bob, and I had our second paper, along with Tony [14]. For a second year graduate student intimidated to be in such heady company, this was a tremendously empowering experience, and Frank's interest and approval meant the world to me.

I want to conclude with two small stories about Frank's sense of humor. Another thing which happened in the year 1984 was that Shell Oil introduced a new super unleaded gasoline called "SU 2000." An advertising campaign was built around the new product, and at one of the local Shell stations they were giving out free bumper stickers which read "SU 2000 — Go with it!" (It would have been better had they named it SU(2000), but I suppose one can't let such details get in the way of a good joke.) I immediately thought of Frank, who was renowned for his work on nonabelian gauge theories, and I presented him with the bumper sticker that very day. I was delighted to see that by the next morning, Frank had affixed it to his ITP office door.

The second story is about the axion, another hypothetical particle named by Wilczek. Not long after the anyon excitement, Frank's postdoc John Moody was scheduled to give a lecture at the ITP on some axion physics he and Frank had been working on. The name "axion" was familiar to me from the laundry products aisle at the local supermarket since there was a detergent by the same name. I assumed that Frank could not possibly know this. Perhaps I should have known better, given the whimsical name "anyon," but I presumed that the name "axion" had some staid, technical physics reasoning behind it, likely having something to do with axial currents, a collocation I had heard in the hallways from time to time. I also suspected that Frank might be the sort of genius physics nerd who had never so much as seen a washing machine, and that since exiting the birth canal someone else had been doing his laundry. But by this time I did know that Frank had a pretty good sense of humor, so I bought a box of the Axion detergent, and worked it out with John that at some point early on in his talk, after he first uttered the magic word, he asked his audience, rhetorically, "And what is an axion?", whereupon he brought out the box of detergent from underneath the lectern, poured some in a plastic cup, and had it passed around the audience so we could all see what axions looked like. (Turns out axions are little blue spheres a few mm in diameter — who knew?) Frank was delighted, and John later presented him with the framed detergent box. But it turns out that the joke here ultimately was on me, because as I found out for the first time only in mid-February 2020, at a dinner celebrating a distinguished lecture Frank gave at UC San Diego, in fact the axion *was* named after the laundry detergent [15].

References

[1] W. P. Su, J. R. Schrieffer, and A. J. Heeger, Solitons in polyacetylene, *Phys. Rev. Lett.* **42**, 1698–1701 (1979).

[2] S. Kivelson and J. R. Schrieffer, Fractional charge, a sharp quantum observable, *Phys. Rev. B.* **25**, 6447–6451 (1982).

[3] F. Wilczek, Magnetic flux, angular momentum, and statistics, *Phys. Rev. Lett.* **48**, 1144–1146 (1982).

[4] F. Wilczek, Remarks on dyons, *Phys. Rev. Lett.* **48**, 1146–1149 (1982).

[5] E. Witten, Dyons of charge $e\theta/2\pi$, *Phys. Lett. B.* **86**(3), 283–287 (1979).

[6] F. Wilczek, Quantum mechanics of fractional-spin particles, *Phys. Rev. Lett.* **49**, 957–959 (1982).

[7] J. M. Leinaas and J. Myrheim, On the theory of identical particles, *Il Nuovo Cimento B.* **37**(1), 1–23 (1977).

[8] R. B. Laughlin, Anomalous quantum Hall effect: An incompressible quantum fluid with fractionally charged excitations, *Phys. Rev. Lett.* **50**, 1395–1398 (1983).

[9] B. I. Halperin, Statistics of quasiparticles and the hierarchy of fractional quantized Hall states, *Phys. Rev. Lett.* **52**, 1583–1586 (1984).

[10] F. D. M. Haldane, Fractional quantization of the Hall effect: a hierarchy of incompressible quantum fluid states, *Phys. Rev. Lett.* **51**, 605–608 (1983).

[11] M. V. Berry, Quantal phase factors accompanying adiabatic changes, *Proc. R. Soc. Lond. A.* **392**, 45–57 (1984).

[12] D. Arovas, J. R. Schrieffer, and F. Wilczek, Fractional statistics and the quantum Hall effect, *Phys. Rev. Lett.* **53**, 722–723 (1984).

[13] J. Nakamura, S. Liang, G. C. Gardner, and M. J. Manfra, Direct observation of anyonic braiding statistics, *Nature Physics* **16**(9), 931–936 (2020).

[14] D. P. Arovas, R. Schrieffer, F. Wilczek, and A. Zee, Statistical mechanics of anyons, *Nucl. Phys. B* **251**, 117–126 (1985).

[15] F. Wilczek, Time's (almost) reversible arrow, *Quanta Magazine* (2016).

© 2022 World Scientific Publishing Company
https://doi.org/10.1142/9789811251948_0003

Anyonic and Fermionic Statistics in a Mesoscopic Collider

H. Bartolomei*, M. Kumar†, M. Ruelle*, and G. Fève*,‡

**Laboratoire de Physique de l'Ecole normale supérieure*
ENS, Université PSL, CNRS, Sorbonne Université
Université de Paris, Paris, France
†*Low Temperature Laboratory, Department of Applied Physics*
Aalto University School of Science
P.O. Box 15100, 00076 Aalto, Finland
‡*gwendal.feve@ens.fr*

We discuss the observations of anyonic statistics in mesoscopic colliders implemented in a two-dimensional electron gas in the quantum Hall regime. By tuning the magnetic field at integer ($\nu = 2$ and $\nu = 3$) or fractional values ($\nu = 1/3$) of the filling factor, we observe clear distinct signatures between electrons (which obey Pauli exclusion principle and antibunch) and anyons (which obey partial exclusion and tend to form larger packets of charge). The anyon behavior in the collision is in perfect agreement with theoretical predictions for the exchange phase $\varphi = \pi/3$ as expected for the fractional filling $\nu = 1/3$ and for different operating regimes of the collider. It establishes anyon colliders as a quantitative probe of the fractional statistics of anyons whose existence was predicted forty years ago in two-dimensional systems.

1. Introduction

In three-dimensional systems, particles are divided into two categories depending on the phase φ acquired by the wavefunction describing an ensemble of identical particles when the positions of two particles are exchanged. On the one hand, bosons satisfy $\varphi = 0$ and tend to bunch together. On the other hand, fermions obey $\varphi = \pi$ and obey Pauli exclusion principle, only a single fermion can occupy a given single-particle state. The existence of only two types of particles is linked to the constraint that, in 3D, performing twice the exchange of the positions of two particles is equivalent to the identity operator. However, it was noticed at the end of the 70s [1, 2] that this constraint is lifted for two-dimensional systems, thus defining new types of particles for which the exchange phase φ can take any value, interpolating between the bosonic and fermionic statistics. This new type of particles that exist only in two-dimensional systems have thus been named "anyons" by Franck Wilczek in 1982 [3]. This arbitrary value of the exchange phase means that, when moving an anyon around another one (which is called a braiding operation) the wavefunction picks a phase 2φ that is not an integer multiple of 2π, such that anyons keep a memory of these braiding operations. Interestingly, this memory is insensitive to small deformations of the anyon trajectories and only depends on the number of loops performed by anyons around each other. This topological protection can be exploited to encode robust quantum information operations that would be protected from local fluctuations of the environment [4, 5]. However, this requires to use other families of anyons, called non-abelian [6], for which the exchange operation cannot be described by a simple phase but rather by a unitary operation acting on the many-body degenerated ground state. The value of the exchange phase φ intermediate between the bosonic and fermionic values also means that anyons obey intermediate exclusion statistics [7]. For fermions, adding a single-particle in the system means that one single-particle state becomes unavailable to other particles. For bosons, adding one particle in the system does not restrain the availability of single-particle states for other particles. Anyons obey partial exclusion, several anyons are necessary to suppress the availability of one single-particle state. It means that anyons have an intermediate bunching behavior, with the possibility to regroup to form packets of a few particles.

Soon after the introduction of anyons in two dimensional systems, it was suggested by Halperin [8] and by Arovas, Schrieffer and Wilczek [9], that the elementary excitations of the fractional quantum Hall effect [10] (FQHE) should both carry a fractional charge and obey anyonic statistics. In particular, for the Laughlin states [11] corresponding to a fractional filling $\nu = 1/m$ (with m an odd integer), the fractional Hall conductance, the fractional charge and statistics are all directly related to the filling factor: $G/(e^2/h) = q/e = \varphi/\pi = 1/m$. For $m = 1$ which corresponds to the integer quantum Hall effect, one recovers electron excitations. However, for fractional filling, one expects anyons of fractional charge and statistics. In particular for the $\nu = 1/3$ state, $q = e/3$ and $\varphi = \pi/3$ which is closer to the bosonic limit than the fermionic one.

A clear signature of the existence of anyons has been obtained in the 90s by extracting their fractional charge q [12–14] from the measurement of the current fluctuations resulting from the random tunneling of anyons between two counterpropagating edge channels brought close to each other by a quantum point contact. However, direct experimental signatures of fractional statistics have remained elusive for a long time. Two different routes have been proposed in order to provide evidence of the fractional statistics of the elementary excitations of FQH phases (for a review, see [15]).

The first one is to measure the braiding phase 2φ in a single particle interferometer such as an electronic Fabry-Perot [16, 17] interferometer. However, the measurement of fractional statistics in these systems are obscured by competing effects of the Coulomb interaction [18] which are dominant in small size interferometers [19–21]. Taking a specific care to screen the effects of the Coulomb interaction [20], Aharonov-Bohm oscillations of the conductance through Fabry-Perot interferometers have been observed but not in the fractional regime until recently. Last year using additional two-dimensional electron gases as screening layers, allowing one to operate the interferometer in the non-interacting regime, jumps of phase $2\pi/3$ were observed [22] at filling factor $\nu = 1/3$ which are consistent with the addition of one anyon within the Fabry-Perot cavity.

The second one is to measure the exchange statistics of particles from two-particle interferometry experiments which have been introduced in the context of optics by Hanbury-Brown and Twiss [23, 24]. Such experiments, where one measures intensity correlations (light intensity in optics, current correlations in electronics) at the output of a beam-splitter scattering elementary particles have demonstrated the bunching of photons (bosons) [25] or the antibunching of electrons [26–28] colliding on the splitter. In the context of anyons, it was predicted in the 2000s that current correlation measurements could provide information on their fractional statistics [29–34]. All the different proposed geometries share in common several quantum point contacts which are used both as anyon emitters and anyon scatterers. We discuss in this work the signatures of anyonic statistics [35] observed in the geometry of the anyon collider [36]. We start in Sec. 2 by presenting the principle of the experiment and the theoretical predictions for electron and anyon collisions. We then discuss in Sec. 3 the random emission of particles at a single quantum point contact used as an electron (in the integer case) or anyon (in the fractional case) source. The results of the collision experiments are presented in Sec. 4 for a symmetric bias of the collider and in Sec. 5 for the asymmetric bias. We finally discuss in Sec. 6 the possible existence of edge reconstruction mechanisms leading to the presence of upstream neutral modes that could affect the results of anyon collisions.

2. Principle of the Experiment

A simple representation of a collision experiment is schematized in Fig. 1a. Two particles are incoming on a beam-splitter (one on each input arm) giving two possible outcomes in the collision process. The two particles may bunch together in the same output of the splitter (e.g. output 4) which occurs with the classical probability $P(2,0) = T(1-T)$ where T is the backscattering probability. In this case, if particles carry a charge, there is an excess of charge in output 4 (compared to the average charge transmitted in output 4) and a deficit of charge in output 3 resulting in negative cross-correlations of the current fluctuations: $S_{34} < 0$. The two particles may also antibunch, leaving in two distinct outputs of the splitter. In this situation, the charge in each output exactly equals the average charge and cross-correlations are suppressed: $S_{34} = 0$. The measurement of cross-correlations is thus a way of measuring the degree of bunching or exclusion of particles in a collision process. The latter is directly related to the statistics of the particles. In order to get an insight into the effect of quantum statistics in the collision, one can take into account bunching or exclusion properties of the colliding particles by weighting the classical bunching probability $P(2,0) = T(1-T)$, where T is the backscattering probability of the splitter, by the exclusion factor $(1-p)$ (see Fig. 1). Positive p corresponds to a fermion-like behavior reducing the probability to observe two particles in the same output (in particular, perfect exclusion expected for fermions is reached for $p = 1$). On the contrary, negative values of p increase the probability to observe two particles in the same output corresponding to a boson-like behavior.

Collisions have been implemented in electrical conductors using a quantum point contact as a beam-splitter for charged particles. Implementing such collisions with anyons in the FQHE requires in addition a source of anyons. Unfortunately, it is not known yet how to deterministically generate anyonic excitation at a given location of the conductor. However, it is known that the backscattering of charge at a quantum point contact tuned in the weak backscattering regime occurs through the random emission of fractionally charged anyons. Using two quantum point contacts as random generators of a diluted beam of anyons at the two inputs of a third quantum point contact (see Fig. 1b and Fig. 1c) used as a collider, one can implement such a collision experiment with anyons as suggested by Rosenow and collaborators [36]. Anyons are randomly emitted at inputs 1 and 2 with probabilities T_1 and T_2 (which are the backscattering probabilities of the input QPCs) with $T_1, T_2 \ll 1$. In this case, effects of quantum statistics on the outcomes of the collision experiments are maximized by choosing a symmetric bias of the collider where the same voltage is applied at the input of QPC1 and QPC2 ($V_1 = V_2$), which are also tuned at equal backscattering probabilities ($T_1 = T_2 = T_S$), resulting in equal incoming anyon currents on both inputs, $I_1 = I_2$, such that the current difference between the inputs vanishes,

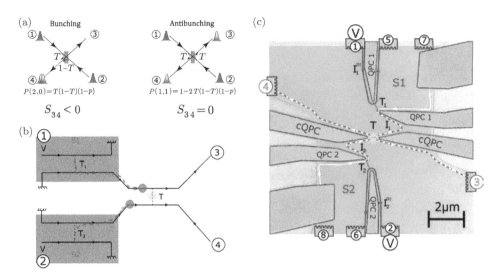

Fig. 1. a) Two particles are incoming at each input of a beam-splitter. They can either bunch together in the same output of the splitter, e.g output 4 (left panel) or antibunch and exit in two different outputs (right panel). In the bunching case, there is an excess of charge (with respect to the average value) in output 4 and a deficit of charge in output 3, bunching thus shows up as negative cross-correlations of the current fluctuations. In the antibunching case, the charge at each output equals the average value and cross-correlations are suppressed. b) Schematic description of the experiment. Each source S_i consists in a quantum point contact with a weak backscattering probability T_i. It is biased by the voltage V generating the diluted anyon current I_i towards the central quantum point contact used as a beam-splitter of backscattering probability T. c) Scanning electron microscope picture of the sample (false colors). The two-dimensional electron gas is represented in green. In the quantum Hall regime, electronic transport occurs along the edge channels represented as red (respectively white) lines if they are connected (respectively not connected) to a voltage source. Metallic split gates (orange) define quantum point contacts used as anyon emitters (for QPC1 and QPC2) or beam-splitter in the collision (for cQPC).

$I_- = I_1 - I_2 = 0$. In this case, the output cross-correlations are proportional to the total input current $I_+ = I_1 + I_2$. In the classical model mentioned above, one has $S_{34} = -2qT(1-T)T_S(1-p)I_+$ showing in this simple example that, through the exclusion factor $(1-p)$, cross-correlations directly probe the tendency of particles to bunch together or on the contrary to exclude each other. In particular, for fermions, the Pauli exclusion principle imposes $p = 1$ such that the cross-correlations vanish. On the contrary, anyons obey generalized exclusion statistics [7] resulting in only partial spatial exclusion which should manifest in the observation of negative cross-correlations.

In order to predict the correct value of the cross-correlations in the anyon case, one has to go beyond the classical model described above and rely on a quantum mechanical description of the anyon collision. This is precisely what Rosenow and collaborators achieved in Ref. [36]. In this description, the propagation of charge along channels 1 and 2 at the input of the collider is described via bosonic fields $\phi_1(x,t)$ and $\phi_2(x,t)$ which commutation relations encode the statistics of anyons: $[\phi_i(x,t),\phi_j(x,t')] = i\pi\delta\delta_{ij}\mathrm{sign}(t-t')$. In the absence of edge reconstruction mechanisms, the statistical parameter δ equals (up to the factor π) the anyon exchange phase in the bulk of the system: $\delta = \varphi/\pi = 1/m$ (for Laughlin states). However, it may be different when edge reconstruction is present [37, 38] (edge reconstruction mechanisms are discussed and investigated in Sec. 6). By tuning the central quantum point contact in the weak backscattering regime, charge tunneling occurs through the transfer of anyons described by the tunneling operator $A(t) = \zeta e^{i\phi_1(0,t)-i\phi_2(0,t)}$ related to the tunneling current by $I_T = iq(A^\dagger - A)$. Finally, the random emission of anyons from the input quantum point contacts with probability $T_S \ll 1$ can be described by a shift of the bosonic field operators $\phi_i = \phi_i^{(0)} + 2\pi\lambda N_i$ where $\phi_i^{(0)}$ describes the equilibrium field and N_i is a random variable with Poisson statistics describing the number of transmitted anyons. The parameter λ describes screening mechanisms that may occur in cases where the edge structure is complex and several co- or counter propagating edge modes are present [37, 39]. In the absence of such mechanisms and for Laughlin states, one simply has $\lambda = 1/m$. In this limit where the input diluted beams of anyons obey Poissonian statistics, and where the collider is biased symmetrically ($I_- = 0$), Rosenow and collaborators expressed the output cross-correlations as a function of the total input current:

$$S_{34} = 2qPTI_+ \tag{1}$$

$$T = \left(\frac{\partial\langle I_T \rangle}{\partial I_-}\right)_{I_-=0} \tag{2}$$

$$P = 1 - \frac{\tan\pi\lambda}{\tan\pi\delta}\frac{1}{1-2\delta} = -2 \quad \text{for } \lambda = \delta = \varphi/\pi = 1/3 \tag{3}$$

Equation (1), as in the classical description, predicts current cross-correlations that are proportional to the total input current I_+, the fractional charge q and the splitter backscattering probability T and to a generalized Fano factor P that encodes the statistics of anyons. As discussed above, for anyons at filling factor 1/3 with an exchange phase $\varphi = \pi/3$, the cross-correlations are strongly negative ($P = -2$), revealing the tendency of anyons to form larger packets of charge in a splitter output in the collision process. Collisions should thus reveal drastic differences between electrons (fermions) at integer filling factors with $P = 0$ (as a consequence of the Pauli exclusion principle), and anyons with $\varphi = \pi/3$ at filling factor 1/3 for which $P = -2$ (as a consequence of the partial exclusion of anyons [7]).

3. Random Electron/Anyon Emission at a Single Quantum Point Contact

Prior to the realization of the collision experiment, it is crucial to check that the three quantum point contacts used in our experiment randomly scatter the correct type of particles: electrons in the quantum Hall regime and anyons in the fractional quantum Hall regime. This can be done by measuring the current noise resulting from the random tunneling of quasiparticles at a single given quantum point contact. When the backscattering probability T is small, the current noise is proportional to both the fractional charge q [12–14] and to the current I_0 incoming on the QPC. For weak non-linearities of the backscattered current, the following expression for the current noise, valid in the non-interacting limit [40], has been extended in the FQHE and used to extract the fractional charge for various fractional quantum Hall states:

$$\Delta S_{33} = \Delta S_{44} = 2qT(1 - T)I_0 \left[\coth\left(\frac{qV}{2k_B T_{el}} \right) - \frac{2k_B T_{el}}{qV} \right] \tag{4}$$

$$\Delta S_{34} = -2qT(1 - T)I_0 \left[\coth\left(\frac{qV}{2k_B T_{el}} \right) - \frac{2k_B T_{el}}{qV} \right] \tag{5}$$

where V is the applied voltage and T_{el} the electronic temperature. ΔS_{33} and ΔS_{44} are the excess auto-correlations of the current fluctuations at the two outputs labeled 3 and 4 of the quantum point contact. By measuring the excess noise, both the thermal noise and the amplifier noises are subtracted. ΔS_{34} is the excess cross-correlation of the current fluctuations between outputs 3 and 4. In this experiment, where a noiseless current I_0 is partitioned by a single quantum point contact, current conservation imposes $I_3(t) + I_4(t) = I_0$, which also imposes the following constraint on the current fluctuations: $\Delta S_{33} + \Delta S_{44} + 2\Delta S_{34} = 0$ as the input current I_0 is noiseless. This explains why ΔS_{33} and ΔS_{34} only differ by a minus sign but otherwise carry the same information. An important advantage of the measurement of cross-correlations, compared to auto-correlations, is that the large noise offset related to thermal fluctuations and the amplifier noise is almost completely suppressed (the small remaining noise offset in the cross-correlations

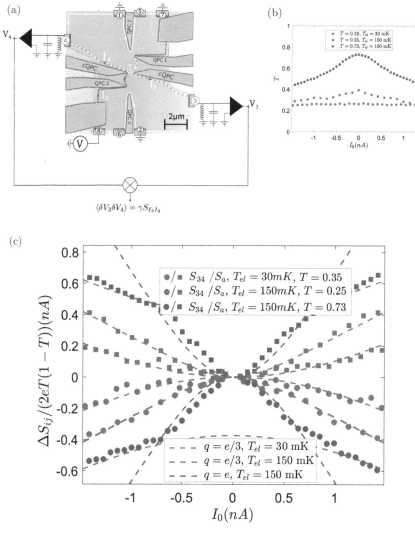

Fig. 2. a) Experimental configuration: the current I_0 is generated at contact 8, input QPC2 is set to fully transmit the current I_0 while cQPC partitions I_0 with backscattering probability T. b) Backscattering probability as a function of I_0. c) Measurements of auto and cross-correlations of the current fluctuations as a function of I_0. c) Dashed lines represent theoretical predictions from Eq. (4) and (5) for various temperatures and charges $q = e/3$ and $q = e$.

is less than 1% of the offset for auto-correlation measurements and is subtracted in the measurement of excess noise). The calibration of the cross and auto-correlation noise measurements is described in Annex A.1.

Figure 2 presents various noise measurements for the fractional filling factor 1/3 in the configuration described in panel 2a. The input quantum point contacts QPC1 and QPC2 are fully open and the current I_0 is partitioned by cQPC only. Figure 2c presents the cross and auto-correlations of the current fluctuations as a function of the incoming current I_0 for various backscattering probabilities T of cQPC (see Fig. 2b) and various electronic temperatures T_{el} in order to test Eqs. (4) and (5) and extract the charge q. As expected, auto-correlations and cross-correlations give identical results except for the sign difference. For rather small values of the backscattering probability $T = 0.35$ and $T = 0.25$, the measurements are perfectly consistent with fractional charge $q = e/3$ expected for the quasiparticles at filling factor 1/3. The dependence on temperature predicted by Eqs. (4) and (5) is also very well observed between $T_{el} = 30$ mK and $T_{el} = 150$ mK. For large values of the backscattering probability, electron emission is expected [12]. This is exactly what is observed for $T \approx 0.75$ where, for $I_0 \leq 0.7$ nA, the noise data follow the prediction $q = e$. As can be seen in Fig. 2b, T decreases with increasing incoming current I_0, eventually restoring the weak backscattering regime where anyons with charge $q = e/3$ should be emitted. Consistently, the charge extracted from the partition noise measurement switches from $q = e$ to $q = e/3$ for $I_0 \geq 0.7$ nA.

The charge of the excitations randomly generated by QPC1 and QPC2 can also be extracted from partition noise measurements. The measurement configurations are presented in Fig. 3a and Fig. 3d. QPC1 and QPC2 are set to partially backscatter the input current I_0 with probabilities T_1 and T_2. In order to measure the partitioning by a single quantum point contact (input QPCs), cQPC is fully closed. As a consequence, only the autocorrelation noises ΔS_{33} and ΔS_{44} can be measured. They are presented in Fig. 3b (for QPC1) and Fig. 3e (for QPC2). Red points correspond to the measurement at the integer filling factor $\nu = 2$. As expected, the noise data are consistent with the transfer of electrons with the charge $q = e$. For the fractional filling factor 1/3, measurements in the weak backscattering regime (blue and cyan points) are consistent with the fractional charge $q = e/3$. In the strong backscattering regime at filling factor $\nu = 1/3$ (blue navy points), the results are similar to the measurements performed on cQPC. For small values of the input current, the electron charge $q = e$ is measured, as expected when the backscattering probability is large. When I_0 is increased, T_1 (or T_2) decrease, restoring the weak backscattering regime which shows up in a change in the slope of the noise data that evolves from $q = e$ towards $q = e/3$.

These experiments, where a single quantum point contact partitions the noiseless current I_0, confirm that electrons (respectively anyons) with charge $q = e$ (resp. $e/3$) can be randomly emitted when the bulk filling factor has an integer value (resp. fractional value $\nu = 1/3$). Interestingly, they

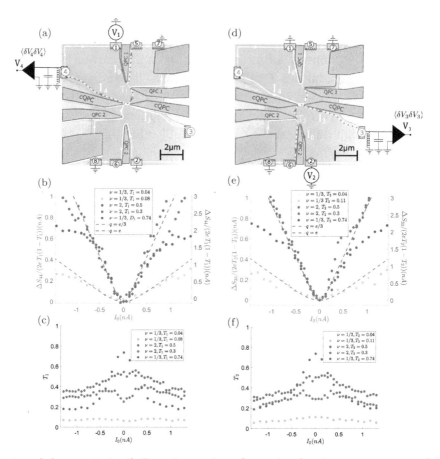

Fig. 3. a) (respectively d) Experimental configuration for the measurement of the partition noise by input QPC1 (respectively QPC2). b) (respectively e) Measurement of the auto-correlations of the current fluctuations as a function of the input current I_0. c) (respectively f) Backscattering probability T_1 (respectively T_2) as a function of I_0.

also show that, even in the fractional case ($\nu = 1/3$), electron collisions can be implemented by setting the input quantum point contacts in the strong backscattering regime, where the tunneling of charge occurs through a standard insulating region such that the strong correlations building the fractional state are absent.

4. Electron and Anyon Collisions

Once the role of the quantum point contacts as random emitters of electrons and anyons has been established, these three basic elements can be combined in the collision experiment. In order to compare the behavior of electrons and anyons, the experiment will be implemented both in the integer and

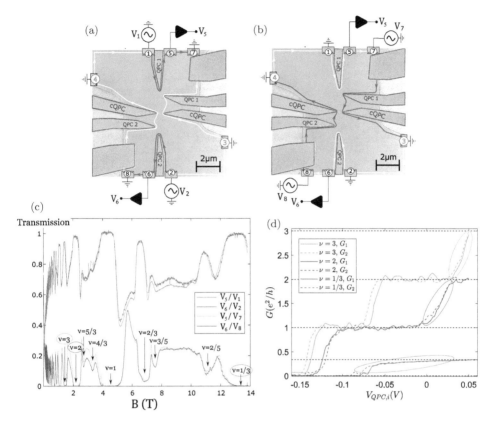

Fig. 4.   a/b) Experimental configuration for the measurement of the total current transmitted/backscattered by QPC1 and QPC2 as a function of the magnetic field, all QPCs are set to be fully transmitted. c) Transmission and backscattering probabilities by QPC1 and QPC2. The transmission is very close to 1 and the backscattering probability fully suppressed for integer and fractional values of the filling factor. d) Conductance as a function of the voltage applied on the gates of QPC1 and QPC2 for filling factor $\nu = 3$, $\nu = 2$ and $\nu = 1/3$. Three (two) steps of conductance e^2/h can be observed for filling factor $\nu = 3$ ($\nu = 2$) (the fluctuations of the conductance on each plateau does not reflect imperfect quantization of the conductance but rather the experimental noise). The collision is implemented by partitioning the outer edge channel (orange and red circles). Only one step of conductance $e^2/(3h)$ is observed at filling $\nu = 1/3$.

the fractional quantum Hall regime. Figure 4c presents the measurements of the transmissions and backscattering probabilities of QPC1 and QPC2 as a function of the magnetic field (see Fig. 4a and Fig. 4b for the measurements configurations). For integer and fractional filling factors, the backscattering probability is fully suppressed (as the bulk of the conductor becomes insulating) which is a necessary condition to implement the collision experiment. We chose filling factors 2 and 3 to implement electron collision, and

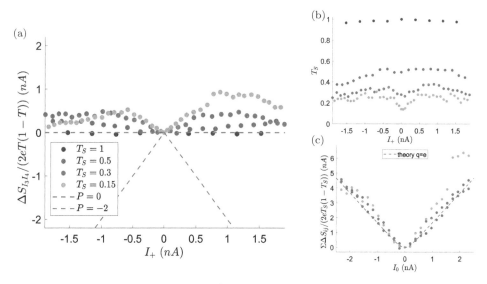

Fig. 5. Electron collisions, $\nu = 2$. a) Normalized excess cross-correlations by the factor $eT(1 - T)$ as a function of the total input current I_+. The red dashed line is the prediction for fermions $P = 0$ and the blue one the predictions for anyons with the phase $\varphi = \pi/3$, $P = -2$. b) Backscattering probability T_S for input QPCs. c) Normalized excess noise incoming on cQPC as a function of the input current I_0. It is computed from the sum of auto and cross-correlations of the current fluctuations at the output of cQPC. The red dashed line is the prediction for the emission of electrons by QPC1 and QPC2 (charge $q = e$).

filling factor $1/3$ for the anyon collision. For $\nu = 3$ (respectively $\nu = 2$), the current is carried by three (respectively two) edge channels. The collision experiment is then implemented by partitioning the outer edge channel (see Fig. 4d) both at QPC1, QPC2 and cQPC. At $\nu = 1/3$ the current is carried by a single edge channel (see Fig. 4d).

In the collision experiment (see the sample in Fig. 1), two diluted currents of electrons (for $\nu = 2$ and $\nu = 3$) and anyons (for $\nu = 1/3$) are generated by the partitioning of the currents I_1^0 and I_2^0 generated simultaneously at the inputs of QPC1 and QPC2. Both backscattering probabilities are set at the same value, $T_1 = T_2 = T_S$ such that the currents incoming on cQPC are equal, $I_1 = I_2$, implementing the collision in the symmetric configuration: $I_- = 0$. We then measure the output current cross-correlations ΔS_{34} as a function of the total current $I_+ = I_1 + I_2$ at the input of cQPC, for different values of the backscattering probabilities T_S. We start by describing electron collisions in the integer case ($\nu = 2$ and $\nu = 3$) where the suppression of cross-correlations is expected as a signature of the Pauli exclusion principle for fermions.

Figure 5a shows our measurements of ΔS_{34} for various values of T_S (plotted in Fig. 5b) at filling factor $\nu = 2$. All measurements show the same characteristic behavior: ΔS_{34} is slightly positive for small values of I_+ then tend to flatten with a slope very close to zero as expected for fermions (the red dotted line is the prediction for fermions, $P = 0$). The slight increase of ΔS_{34} tends to be more important when the backscattering probability T_S is lowered and could be related to residual effects of the Coulomb interaction that would tend to reinforce the exclusion statistics of fermions. Although the measurements presented in the previous section already established that particles emitted by QPC1 and QPC2 carry the electron charge at $\nu = 2$, it is instructive to measure in the collision experiment itself what is the charge of the colliding particles. This can be done from the simultaneous measurement of the auto and cross-correlations of the current fluctuations at the collider output, using the current conservation relation presented above: $\Delta S_{33} + \Delta S_{44} + 2\Delta S_{34} = \Delta S_{11} + \Delta S_{22}$. As discussed in the previous section, the sum of the current noises at the outputs of cQPC equals the sum of the current noises at the inputs. However, contrary to the case where the noiseless input current I_0 was partitioned by a single QPC, the currents I_1 and I_2 at the input of cQPC are noisy, meaning that cross and auto-correlations do not carry the same information in this case and will not be equal up to a minus sign. The sum of the noises at cQPC inputs, $\Delta S_{11} + \Delta S_{22}$ are given by the random partitioning of particles of charge q by QPC1 and QPC2. The charge of the colliding particles can thus be extracted from the sum of the output noises:

$$\Delta S_{33} + \Delta S_{44} + 2\Delta S_{34} = 4qT_S(1 - T_S)I_0 \left[\coth\left(\frac{qV}{2k_BT_{el}} \right) - \frac{2k_BT_{el}}{qV} \right] \quad (6)$$

These measurements, for all the values of T_S, are plotted in Fig. 5c. They confirm, in the same experiment, that the observation of fermionic exclusion ($P = 0$) in the collision experiment is correlated with the emission of electrons with charge $q = e$ by the input QPCs.

Similar measurements can be implemented at the integer filling factor $\nu = 3$ by setting the three quantum point contacts to partition the outer edge channel (see Fig. 4). They are represented in Fig. 6 and lead to the same conclusions as for $\nu = 2$. Cross-correlations are slightly positive for small input current but stay overall very close to the prediction $P = 0$. For larger values of the input current, the slope is very close to 0, reflecting the fermionic statistics of electrons. As in the $\nu = 2$ case, charge measurements performed simultaneously confirm that electrons are colliding on cQPC.

We now turn to the most interesting case which is the anyon collision at filling factor $\nu = 1/3$. Figure 7 presents our measurements when QPC1 and

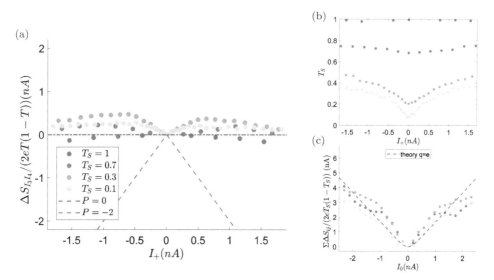

Fig. 6.   Electron collisions, $\nu = 3$. a) Normalized excess cross-correlations as a function of the total input current I_+. b) Backscattering probability T_S for input QPCs. c) Normalized excess noise incoming on cQPC as a function of the input current I_0. The red dashed line is the prediction for the emission of electrons by QPC1 and QPC2 (charge $q = e$).

QPC2 are tuned in the weak backscattering regime $T_S \ll 1$ (see Fig. 7b) that is the relevant regime for the collision of anyons. As can be seen in Fig. 7a, ΔS_{34} shows a completely different behavior compared to the electron case: cross-correlations are strongly negative with a slope $P \approx -2$ which is exactly what is expected for anyons with an exchange phase $\varphi = \pi/3$. These strongly negative cross-correlations demonstrate the reduced exclusion of anyons which tend to form packets of charge in one given output of the splitter, leaving an excess charge in one output correlated to a deficit of charge in the other. The quantitative analysis of the slopes suggests that this behavior is slightly reduced when going away from the Poissonian regime (from $P = -1.9 \pm 0.1$ for $T_S = 0.05$, $P = -1.7 \pm 0.1$ for $T_S = 0.15$, to $P = -1.5 \pm 0.1$ for $T_S = 0.25$). As in the integer case, we can simultaneously extract the charge of the colliding particles by measuring the sum of auto and cross-correlations of the current fluctuations. As can be seen in Fig. 7c, the fractional exclusion statistics of anyons are observed when the charge is fractional, $q \approx e/3$, providing a consistent picture of anyon collisions.

Interestingly, the strong backscattering regime offers the possibility to study electron collision even for fractional filling factor $1/3$. Indeed, the charge measurements performed in the previous section have shown that,

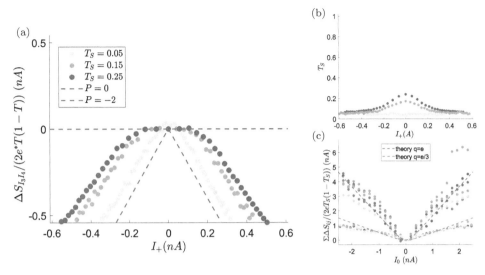

Fig. 7. Anyons collisions, $\nu = 1/3$, weak backscattering regime. a) Normalized excess cross-correlations as a function of the total input current I_+. b) Backscattering probability T_S for input QPCs. c) Normalized excess noise incoming on cQPC (computed from the sum of auto and cross-correlations of the current fluctuations at the output of cQPC). Red and orange data points correspond to integer filling factors, $\nu = 2$ and $\nu = 3$. The blue points correspond to the fractional case, $\nu = 1/3$. The red dashed line is the prediction for the emission of electrons by QPC1 and QPC2 (charge $q = e$). The blue dashed line is the prediction for the emission of anyons with $q = e/3$.

starting with a large value of $T_S \approx 0.8$, the colliding particles should be electrons for small current I_+ and eventually switch to anyons for higher values of I_+, restoring the weak backscattering regime. Our measurements presented in Fig. 8 are perfectly consistent with this picture. The cross-correlations start by being slightly positive, which is reminiscent of the electron case, before switching to a negative slope which is the signature of the anyon collision. The simultaneous measurements of the colliding charge show that the change from the electron to the anyon behavior in the collision precisely occurs when the charge deviates from the electron charge and evolves towards $q = e/3$. This also provides a very consistent picture between the charge measurements and the collision data. Finally, the measured slope in the anyon regime ($P = -1.3$) is smaller (in absolute value) compared to previous measurements (see Fig. 7c) confirming the reduction of the slope when the backscattering probability of QPC1 and QPC2 is increased, moving away from the Poissonian emission of anyons.

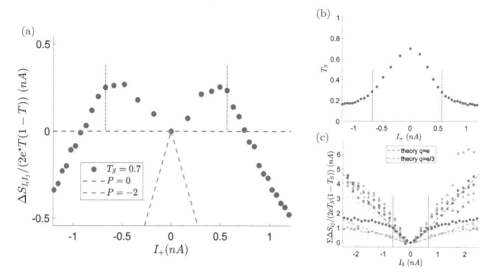

Fig. 8. Collisions, $\nu = 1/3$, strong backscattering regime. a) Normalized excess cross-correlations as a function of the total input current I_+. b) Backscattering probability T_S for input QPCs. c) Normalized excess noise incoming on cQPC (computed from the sum of auto and cross-correlations of the current fluctuations at the output of cQPC). The red dashed line is the prediction for the emission of electrons by QPC1 and QPC2 (charge $q = e$). The blue dashed line is the prediction for the emission of anyons with $q = e/3$. On all the panels, the black dashed line marks the limit between the strong and weak backscattering regimes.

5. Asymmetric Bias of the Collider

We have discussed so far the results of electron and anyon collisions for a symmetric bias of the collider: $V_1 = V_2 = V_S$ and $T_1 = T_2 = T_S$, such that $I_1 = I_2$ and $I_- = 0$. This is the best setting of the collider in order to emphasize the differences between electrons (fermions) and anyons. Indeed, for a symmetric bias, fermionic exclusion (Pauli exclusion principle) shows up as a complete suppression of the cross-correlations of the current fluctuations between the splitter outputs. The observation of strongly negative cross-correlations in this regime can then be seen as a robust signature of fractional statistics. We will now investigate the asymmetric bias ($I_1 \neq I_2$ such that $I_- \neq 0$). In this regime, due to the asymmetry between the two inputs, negative cross-correlations are expected in both cases (electrons and anyons). However, in the anyon case, the quantitative dependence of the Fano factor P as a function of the imbalance I_-/I_+ provides a stringent test of the theoretical predictions of the quantum description of anyon collisions developed in Ref. [36]. In particular, this specific dependence is strongly sensitive to the two parameters of the theory: the screened colliding charge

λ and more importantly the exchange statistics δ:

$$P(x = I_-/I_+) = Re\left[\left(1 - i\frac{x}{\tan(\pi\lambda)}\right)^{2\delta-2}\right]$$

$$- x\tan(\pi\lambda)\,Im\left[\left(1 - i\frac{x}{\tan(\pi\lambda)}\right)^{2\delta-2}\right]$$

$$- \frac{\tan(\pi\lambda)}{\tan(\pi\delta)(1 - 2\delta)}Re\left[\left(1 - i\frac{x}{\tan(\pi\lambda)}\right)^{2\delta-1}\right] \quad (7)$$

Predictions from Eq. (7) are plotted in Fig. 9 for different fractional statistics belonging to the Laughlin sequence ($\nu = \lambda = \delta = 1/m$) for $m = 3$ (blue curve), and $m = 5$ (magenta curve). For comparison similar traces in the fermionic case for $T_S \approx 0.5$ are also shown (red curve). As can be seen in the figure, different statistics are reflected by different values of the Fano factor P for $I_-/I_+ = 0$ but also by specific dependences of P in the imbalance I_-/I_+.

Figure 9 also presents our results for the measurement of $P(I_-/I_+)$ at filling factor $\nu = 1/3$ and $\nu = 2$ for different values of the backscattering

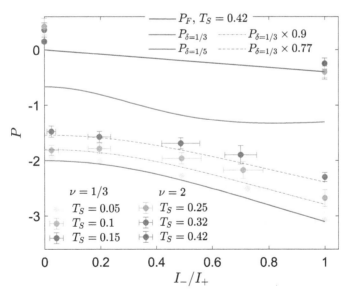

Fig. 9. Predictions from Eq. (7) for $\lambda = \delta = 1/m$ with $m = 3$ (blue line) and $m = 5$ (magenta line) as well as for the fermionic case with $T_S = 0.4$ (red line). Experimental data for $\nu = 1/3$ ($T_S = 0.05$, $T_S = 0.1$ and $T_S = 0.15$) and $\nu = 2$ ($T_S = 0.25$, $T_S = 0.32$, and $T_S = 0.42$). The dash-dot line and the dashed line represent $P_{1/3}$ rescaled by the factor 0.9 and 0.77.

probability of QPC1 and QPC2. The backscattering probabilities are still set to be equal, $T_1 = T_2 = T_S$, and the imbalance is tuned by applying different voltages $V_1 \neq V_2$ at the inputs of QPC1 and QPC2, thereby generating different currents, $I_1 \neq I_2$ towards cQPC. For all values of T_S, P decreases when I_-/I_+ increases. At filling factor 1/3 and for a fixed value of I_-/I_+, P increases when T_S increases, consistently with what was discussed above for $P(0)$. Comparing these data with the predictions, of Eq. (7), the agreement is excellent for $T_S = 0.05$. For increasing values of T_S, one has to take into account the deviations from $P(0) = -2$ which are probably related to corrections to the Poissonian statistics of the emitted anyons. Interestingly, the correct dependence on I_-/I_+ can be obtained for all the data at filling factor 1/3 by rescaling Eq. (7) such that it gives the correct value for $I_-/I_+ = 0$ (see the dashed and dash-dot lines in Fig. 9). However, taking properly into account deviations from the Poissonian regime remains to be done. Finally, we also show for comparison experimental data at filling factor $\nu = 2$ (red points) and $I_-/I_+ = 0$ as well as $I_-/I_+ = 1$. The difference with the $\nu = 1/3$ case is striking, reflecting the fermionic statistics of electrons. Indeed, the data compares well with the prediction for the fermionic statistics (red line, for $T_S = 0.4$) confirming that collision experiments can discriminate clearly fractional statistics from fermionic ones.

6. Edge Reconstruction and Neutral Modes

As presented in the previous section, our results agree remarkably with the predictions from Rosenow *et al.* for an exchange phase $\varphi = \pi/3$. These results are expected for a simple structure of the edge with a single channel of conductance $G = e^2/(3h)$. This corresponds to the simple description of the edge of the $\nu = 1/3$ fractional state but this description may be more complex if edge reconstruction mechanisms are present. These mechanisms, which are more likely to occur for smooth edge confining potentials lead to a reconstruction of the charge density and to the appearance of several counter-propagating modes at the edge. For example, in the integer case $\nu = 1$, it has been predicted [41, 42] that the reconstruction mechanism leads to the appearance of two additional modes (one propagating downstream and the other upstream). Similar mechanisms have also been predicted in the fractional case [43, 44] and in particular for $\nu = 1/3$. Another situation where counter-propagating modes are known to be present is the $\nu = 2/3$ case where the topological order is characterized by two counter-propagating modes [45] at the edge hosting electrons (charge e) and anyons (fractional charge $e/3$). However, inter-edge interaction and tunneling favor the appearance of two new eigenmodes, one downstream mode carrying the charge and an upstream neutral mode [37]. In general edge reconstruction mechanisms should result in the appearance of upstream neutral modes which may be responsible for non-universal modifications [38, 46] of the parameter δ that could differ from φ/π. It is thus very important to check the absence of neutral modes in the anyon collider.

In order to do so, we combine techniques introduced to detect neutral modes from noise measurements at the output of quantum point contacts. In a first experiment [47], an upstream neutral mode was generated by Joule heating at an ohmic contact and detected by measuring the charge noise resulting from the partitioning of the neutral mode at a quantum point contact (labeled N $\rightarrow$ C conversion). It was later shown [48] that the dual process exists (labeled C $\rightarrow$ N conversion): the partitioning of a charge mode at a QPC may generate an upstream neutral mode in case neutral modes are present at the edge. The $\nu = 2/3$ case offers a reference situation where the upstream neutral mode is known to be present. However, by using the techniques described above, upstream neutral modes were also detected for non-hole conjugate states [49] where the existence of neutral modes is not expected but also not forbidden, due to edge reconstruction mechanisms.

In order to probe the existence of neutral modes in anyon collider samples, we combine the C $\rightarrow$ N and N $\rightarrow$ C conversion mechanisms (see Fig. 10c). The neutral mode (if present) is first generated at cQPC by partitioning the current I_0 generated at ohmic contact 8. The neutral mode should then propagate upstream towards QPC1 where it can be converted back into charge by setting $T_1 \neq 0$ and $T_1 \neq 1$ (N $\rightarrow$ C mechanism). As cQPC is tuned in the weak backscattering regime ($T \approx 0.2$ in these experiments), one expects that the noise resulting from the partitioning of the neutral mode at QPC1 should be mostly transmitted towards output 3. One thus expects a modification of ΔS_{33} due to the presence of the neutral modes while ΔS_{34} and ΔS_{44} should exhibit much smaller modifications. In order to check the ability of this experimental scheme to detect the presence of neutral modes, we start by studying filling factor $\nu = 2/3$ where neutral modes are known to be present. Figure 10a presents the measurements of ΔS_{33} as a function of I_0, the incoming charge current at cQPC, and for three different transmissions T_1 of QPC1. For $T_1 = 0$ or $T_1 = 1$, the conversion mechanism N $\rightarrow$ C is absent and the neutral mode cannot be detected at output 3. On the contrary, $T_1 = 0.5$ corresponds to the most efficient N $\rightarrow$ C conversion and one expects an increase of ΔS_{33} if the neutral mode is present. As can be seen in Fig. 10a, one indeed observes a very clear increase in the noise for $T_1 = 0.5$ compared to $T_1 = 0$ and $T_1 = 1$ at filling factor 2/3. This shows that our

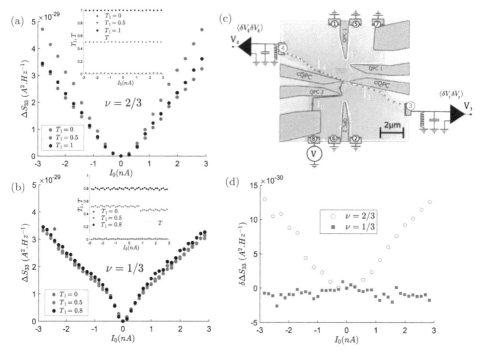

Fig. 10. a) $\nu = 2/3$, ΔS_{33} as a function of I_0 for $T_1 = 0$, $T_1 = 0.5$ and $T_1 = 1$. Inset: transmission of QPC1 and cQPC (green line) as function of I_0. b) $\nu = 1/3$, ΔS_{33} as a function of I_0 for $T_1 = 0$, $T_1 = 0.5$ and $T_1 = 0.8$. Inset: transmission of QPC1 and cQPC. c) Experimental configuration for probing neutral modes. The neutral mode (orange line) is created by partitioning the current I_0 at cQPC (C → N) and propagates upstream towards QPC1 where it is partitioned and converted back to charge noise (N → C). d) $\delta \Delta S_{33}$ for $\nu = 2/3$ and $\nu = 1/3$.

experimental setup can detect neutral modes (if present) in the same sample and experimental conditions as in the collisions experiments. We now move to the $\nu = 1/3$ case by implementing the same experiment for an identical charge current I_0 incoming on cQPC. As can be seen in Fig. 10b, we observe no difference between the different configurations of QPC 1 ($T_1 = 0$, $T_1 = 0.5$ and $T_1 = 1$). This can be seen even more clearly by plotting $\delta \Delta S_{33}$, defined as the difference between ΔS_{33} for $T_1 = 0.5$ and the mean of the open and close configurations of QPC1. Figure 10d represents $\delta \Delta S_{33}$ for $\nu = 1/3$ and $\nu = 2/3$. As discussed above, the data for $\nu = 2/3$ shows a clear increase when I_0 is increased, contrary with the data for $\nu = 1/3$ which is completely flat (it is even slightly below zero which is related to a small variation of the noise offset). This shows that neutral modes are absent at filling factor $1/3$, or that their effect is more than ten times smaller compared to $\nu = 2/3$ (and is only limited by our experimental resolution). The absence of any effect of neutral modes for $\nu = 1/3$ (contrary to $\nu = 2/3$) is consistent with the signatures of fractional statistics with $\delta = \varphi/\pi = 1/3$ in the collision experiments.

7. Conclusion

We have investigated electron and anyon statistics in the geometry of the collider. By measuring the cross-correlations between the output currents, clear differences are observed between fermionic statistics (for which cross-correlations are suppressed as a consequence of the Pauli exclusion principle) and fractional statistics (characterized by strongly negative cross-correlations revealing the partial exclusion of anyons). By comparing quantitatively the dependence of the cross-correlations with the input anyon current we observe an excellent agreement with a quantum mechanical description of anyon collisions for an exchange phase $\varphi = \pi/3$ as expected for filling factor $\nu = 1/3$. By checking the absence of upstream neutral modes within the same experimental geometry, we can assess the absence of edge reconstruction mechanisms that could lead to deviations of the exchange parameter δ with respect to the universal value $\varphi/\pi = 1/3$. These experiments show that anyon colliders can quantitatively probe the fractional statistics of anyons that were predicted more than 40 years ago [1, 2]. This opens new perspectives for probing other abelian statistics, for other Laughlin states but also for more complex states for which the fractional charge of the anyons and the fractional statistics are given by two distinct numbers [31]. Such more complex states are also characterized by a more complex edge structure with several edge channels. Interactions between co-propagating channels are known to be important in the context of electron collisions in the integer regime [50–53]. In the context of fractional statistics, one expects also that anyon collisions may be affected by interactions between edge channels. Additionally, the time-domain or high-frequency regimes have been poorly investigated in the fractional case, although they provide important informations on the characteristic time or frequency scales [54–56] of the dynamics of the propagation of anyons. Combining collision experiments with the triggered emission of fractional quasiparticles [57] would allow one to perform on-demand braiding of single anyons in a quantum conductor. Finally, it would be very interesting to extend such collision experiments for the filling factor $\nu = 5/2$ where non-abelian statistics [6, 58] are predicted and have been confirmed from thermal transport measurements [59]. This non-abelian case raises interesting experimental and theoretical questions as no prediction exists at the moment for anyon collisions in the non-abelian case.

A.1. Calibration of the Noise Measurements

We describe here the calibration of the noise measurements at outputs 3 and 4 of the collider. The current fluctuations are converted into voltage fluctuations via the quantized Hall resistance $R_\nu = h/(\nu e^2)$. The measurement frequency is then shifted in the MHz range using two tank circuits (see Fig. A.1a) using an inductance and a capacitance in parallel with R_ν. The inductance is made of a copper wire inductor ($L \approx 115\ \mu H$), and the capacitance is set by the coaxial cables connecting the sample to the cryogenic amplifiers ($C \simeq 180\ pF$). Due to a small mismatch of the resonance frequencies $f_{0,i}$ of the two tank circuits, a small discrete capacitance is added in parallel at output 4 such that $f_{0,3} \simeq f_{0,4} \simeq f_0$, thereby maximizing the cross-correlation signal. Losses in the inductor can be taken into account by adding a resistance R_L in parallel (see Fig. A.1a), giving a total resistance $R = (R_L^{-1} + R_\nu^{-1})^{-1}$. The equivalent impedance of the circuit at output $i = 3/4$ and frequency f is therefore given by:

$$Z_i(f) = \frac{R_i}{1 + jQ_i\left(\frac{f}{f_{0,i}} - \frac{f_{0,i}}{f}\right)} \tag{A.1}$$

$$Q_i = \sqrt{\frac{C_i}{L_i}}R_i \tag{A.2}$$

Finally, the signal collected by the two tank circuits is amplified by a chain of cryogenic and room temperature amplifiers of total gain G_i. Using a vector signal analyzer at the output of the amplification chain, we record the auto and cross-correlations of the output voltage fluctuations by integrating the noise spectrum in a bandwidth $\Delta f \approx 100$ kHz centered on the frequency f_0. These output voltage fluctuations $\langle \delta V_i \delta V_j \rangle$ are then related to the input white current noise S_{ij} by:

$$\langle \delta V_i \delta V_j \rangle = G_i G_j \int_{f_0 - \frac{\Delta f}{2}}^{f_0 + \frac{\Delta f}{2}} df\, Re(Z_i Z_j^*) S_{ij} = \gamma_{ij} S_{ij}, \tag{A.3}$$

where the γ_{ij} are extracted from a proper calibration of the noise measurement setup. The first step of this procedure is to extract the output impedance Z_i of the noise measurement line. We first apply an uncalibrated ac signal at ohmic contact 8 of the sample. Leaving all QPCs open, this signal is transmitted towards output 4. By varying the frequency of the ac signal and measuring the voltage at output 4 after amplification, one can extract accurately the resonance frequency $f_{0,4}$ and the quality factor Q_4 (see Fig. A.1b). By closing cQPC, the signal is reflected towards output

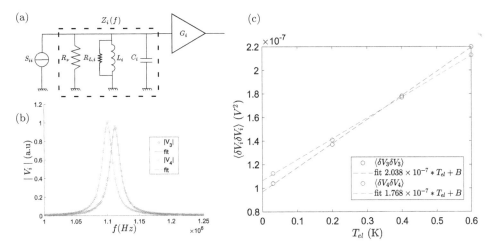

Fig. A.1.   a) The current noise S_{II} is converted to a voltage noise on the Hall resistance of the sample R_{ν} in parallel with a tank circuit of resistance $R_{L,i}$, inductance L_i and capacitance C_i. The cryogenic amplifier is connected at the output of the tank circuit. b) Measurement of $|Z_i(f)|$ (at $\nu = 1/3$) from the transmission of an uncalibrated ac signal at frequency f. The blue and red lines are a fit using Eq.(A.2) providing $f_{0,3} = 1.112 \times 10^6$ Hz and $Q_3 = 56.5$, $f_{0,4} = 1.1 \times 10^6$ and $Q_4 = 56.5$. c) Calibration of the gain $G_3 = 1710$ and $G_4 = 1610$ from the measurement of the thermal noise at outputs 3 and 4 as a function of temperature ($\nu = 1/3$). Measurements are performed in a bandwidth $\Delta f = 200$ kHz.

3, allowing for the determination of $f_{0,3}$ and Q_3 (see Fig. A.1b). Repeating these measurements for different magnetic fields, we can extract the values of f_{0_i} and Q_i for each value of the filling factor. The second step is to calibrate the gain G_i of the amplification chains. For this calibration, we measure the thermal noise generated by the resistance R_i by heating the mixing chamber from the base temperature $T_{\rm el} \approx 30$ mK to a few hundreds of mK. The output auto-correlation of the voltage fluctuations are then given by:

$$\langle \delta V_i \delta V_i \rangle = G_i^2 \int_{f_0 - \frac{\Delta f}{2}}^{f_0 + \frac{\Delta f}{2}} df\, 4k_B T_{\rm el} \mathrm{Re}(Z_i(f)) = \alpha_i \times T_{\rm el} \qquad (\text{A.4})$$

By a linear fitting of the output noise with the temperature $T_{\rm el}$ (see Fig. A.1c), we can extract the fit parameter α_i for each output, and, using the two output impedances extracted in the last paragraph, deduce the gain of the two amplifiers G_i (note that γ_{ii} can be directly extracted from the slope α_i using $\gamma_{ii} = \alpha_i R_i/(4k_B)$). Finally, knowing the impedance $Z_i(f)$ and the gain G_i of each output, the factor γ_{34} for the calibration of the cross-correlations can be extracted from the numerical integration of Eq.(A.3).

References

[1] J. Leinaas and J. Myrheim, *Nuovo Cimento Soc. Ital. Fis. B* **37**, 1 (1977).

[2] F. Wilczek, *Phys. Rev. Lett.* **48**, 1144 (1982).

[3] F. Wilczek, *Phys. Rev. Lett.* **49**, 957 (1982).

[4] A. Y. Kitaev, *Ann. Phys.* **303**, 2 (2003).

[5] C. Nayak, S. H. Simon, A. Stern, M. Freedman, and S. D. Sarma, *Rev. Mod. Phys.* **80**, 1083 (2008).

[6] G. Moore and N. Read, *Nucl. Phys. B* **360**, 362 (1991).

[7] F. Haldane, *Phys. Rev. Lett.* **67**, 937 (1991).

[8] B. Halperin, *Phys. Rev. Lett.* **52**, 1583 (1984).

[9] D. Arovas, J. Schrieffer, and F. Wilczek, *Phys. Rev. Lett.* **53**, 722 (1984).

[10] D. Tsui, H. Stormer, and A. Gossard, *Phys. Rev. Lett.* **48**, 1559 (1982).

[11] R. B. Laughlin, *Phys. Rev. Lett.* **50**, 1395 (1983).

[12] C. Kane and M. Fisher, *Phys. Rev. Lett.* **72**, 724 (1994).

[13] R. de Picciotto, M. Reznikov, M. Heiblum, V. Umansky, G. Bunin, and D. Mahalu, *Nature.* **389**, 162 (1997).

[14] L. Saminadayar, D. Glattli, Y. Jin, , and B. Etienne, *Phys. Rev. Lett.* **79**, 2526 (1997).

[15] D. E. Feldman and B. Halperin, *Rep. Prog. Phys.* **84**, 076501 (2021).

[16] C. de C. Chamon, D. E. Freed, S. A. Kivelson, S. L. Sondhi, and X. G. Wen, *Phys. Rev. B* **55**, 2331 (1997).

[17] K. T. Law, D. E. Feldman, and Y. Gefen, *Phys. Rev. B* **74**, 045319 (2006).

[18] B. I. Halperin, A. Stern, I. Neder, and B. Rosenow, *Phys. Rev. B* **83**, 155440 (2011).

[19] F. E. Camino, W. Zhou, and V. J. Goldman, *Phys. Rev. Lett.* **98**, 076805 (2007).

[20] N. Ofek, A. Bid, M. Heiblum, A. Stern, V. Umansky, and D. Mahalu, *Proc. Nat. Ac. Sci.* **107**, 5276 (2010).

[21] D. T. McClure, W. Chang, C. M. Marcus, L. N. Pfeiffer, and K. W. West, *Phys. Rev. Lett.* **108**, 256804 (2012).

[22] J. Nakamura, S. Liang, G. C. Gardner, and M. J. Manfra, *Nature Physics* **16**, 931 (2020).

[23] R. H. Brown and R. Q. Twiss, *Philos. Mag.* **45**, 663, (1954).

[24] R. H. Brown and R. Q. Twiss, *Nature.* **177**, 27 (1956).

[25] C. K. Hong, Z. Y. Ou, and L. Mandel, *Phys. Rev. Lett.* **59**, 2044 (1987).

[26] R. C. Liu, B. Odom, Y. Yamamoto, and S. Tarucha, *Nature.* **391**, 263 (1998).

[27] S. Ol'khovskaya, J. Splettstoesser, M. Moskalets, and M. Büttiker, *Phys. Rev. Lett.* **101**, 166802 (2008).

[28] E. Bocquillon, V. Freulon, J.-M. Berroir, P. Degiovanni, B. Plaçais, A. Cavanna, Y. Jin, and G. Fève, *Science.* **339**, 1054 (2013).

[29] I. Safi, P. Devillard, and T. Martin, *Phys. Rev. Lett.* **86**, 4628 (2001).

[30] S. Vishveshwara, *Phys. Rev. Lett.* **91**, 196803 (2003).

[31] E. A. Kim, M. Lawler, S. Vishveshwara, and E. Fradkin, *Phys. Rev. Lett.* **95**, 176402 (2005).

[32] G. Campagnano, O. Zilberberg, I. V. Gornyi, D. E. Feldman, A. C. Potter, and Y. Gefen, *Phys. Rev. Lett.* **109**, 106802 (2012).

[33] G. Campagnano, O. Zilberberg, I. V. Gornyi, and Y. Gefen, *Phys. Rev. B* **88**, 235415 (2013).

[34] B. Lee, C. Han, and H.-S. Sim, *Phys. Rev. Lett.* **123**, 016803 (2019).

[35] H. Bartolomei, M. Kumar, R. Bisognin, A. Marguerite, J.-M. Berroir, E. Bocquillon, B. Plaçais, A. Cavanna, Q. Dong, U. Gennser, Y. Jin, and G. Fève, *Science.* **368**, 173 (2020).

[36] B. Rosenow, I. P. Levkivskyi, and B. I. Halperin, *Phys. Rev. Lett.* **116**, 156802 (2016).

[37] C. Kane, M. Fisher, and J. Polchinski, *Phys. Rev. Lett.* **72**, 4129 (1994).

[38] B. Rosenow and B. I. Halperin, *Phys. Rev. Lett.* **88**, 096404 (2002).

[39] I. P. Levkivskyi, *Phys. Rev. B* **93**, 165427 (2016).

[40] D. E. Feldman and M. Heiblum, *Phys. Rev. B* **95**, 115308 (2017).

[41] A. H. MacDonald, S. R. E. Yang, and M. D. Johnson, *Aust. J. Phys.* **46**, 345 (1993).

[42] C. de C.Chamon and X. Wen, *Phys. Rev. B* **49**, 8227 (1994).

[43] X. Wan, K. Yang, and E. H. Rezayi, *Phys. Rev. Lett.* **88**, 056802 (2002).

[44] Y. N. Joglekar, H. K. Nguyen, and G. Murthy, *Physica Review B* **68**, 035332 (2003).

[45] M. Johnson and A. MacDonald, *Phys. Rev. Lett.* **67**, 2060 (1991).

[46] K. Yang, *Phys. Rev. Lett.* **91**, 036802 (2003).

[47] A. Bid, N. Ofek, H. Inoue, M. Heiblum, C. Kane, V. Umansky, and D. Mahalu, *Nature.* **466**, 585 (2010).

[48] Y. Gross, M. Dolev, M. Heiblum, V. Umansky, and D. Mahalu, *Phys. Rev. Lett.* **108**, 226801 (2012).

[49] H. Inoue, A. Grivnin, Y. Ronen, M. Heiblum, V. Umansky, and D. Mahalu, *Nature Communications.* **5**, 4067 (2014).

[50] I. P. Levkivskyi and E. V. Sukhorukov, *Phys. Rev. B* **85**, 075309 (2012).

[51] C. Wahl, J. Rech, T. Jonckheere, and T. Martin, *Phys. Rev. Lett.* **112**, 046802 (2014).

[52] D. Ferraro, B. Roussel, C. Cabart, E. Thibierge, G. Fève, C. Grenier, and P. Degiovanni, *Phys. Rev. Lett.* **113**, 166403 (2014).

[53] A. Marguerite, C. Cabart, C. Wahl, B. Roussel, V. Freulon, D. Ferraro, C. Grenier, J.-M. Berroir, B. Plaçais, T. Jonckheere, J. Rech, T. Martin, P. Degiovanni, A. Cavanna, Y. Jin, and G. Fève, *Physical Review B* **94**, 115311 (2016).

[54] M. Kapfer, P. Roulleau, I. Farrer, D. A. Ritchie, and D. C. Glattli, *Science.* **363**, 846 (2019).

[55] R. Bisognin, H. Bartolomei, M. Kumar, I. Safi, J.-M. Berroir, E. Bocquillon, B. Plaçais, A. Cavanna, U. Gennser, Y. Jin, and G. Fève, *Nature Communications.* **10**, 1708 (2019).

[56] I. Safi, *Physical Review B* **102**, 041113 (2020).

[57] J. Rech, D. Ferraro, T. Jonckheere, L. Vannucci, and M. Sassetti, *Phys. Rev. Lett.* **118**, 076801 (2017).

[58] R. L. Willett, J. Eisenstein, H. Stormer, D. Tsui, A. Gossard, and H. English, *Phys. Rev. Lett.* **59**, 1776 (1987).

[59] M. Banerjee, M. Heiblum, V. Umansky, D. E. Feldman, Y. Oreg, and A. Stern, *Nature.* **559**, 205 (2018).

© 2022 World Scientific Publishing Company
https://doi.org/10.1142/9789811251948_0004

Wilczek's Quantum Connection with USTC

Yu-Ao Chen, Chao-Yang Lu, Qiang Zhang, and Jian-Wei Pan*
University of Science and Technology of China
Hefei 230026, China
*pan@ustc.edu.cn

The four of us, Jian-Wei Pan, Qiang Zhang, Yu-Ao Chen, and Chao-Yang Lu from the University of Science and Technology of China (USTC), send our warmest wishes to Prof. Frank Wilczek on his 70th birthday. Although we come from different backgrounds, we all have been profoundly influenced by Frank during our growth. In the past, we had only learned of Frank's knowledge from books, but then we all had the opportunity to benefit from Frank's teaching face to face, and even achieve some cooperation. Therefore, we take this opportunity to look back on our encounters with Frank over the years, and offer our most sincere regards.

One of us, Jian-Wei Pan, studied theoretical physics for his bachelor and master's degrees at University of Science and Technology of China in the early 1990s. He was the first one who got in touch with Frank's work. By that time, he was so amazed to read about asymptotic freedom. Recalling the time when he was learning quantum chromodynamics and the quark model, "I was shocked by the model, how can the interactions between particles become asymptotically weaker as they get closer to each other?" Jian-Wei said, "however I have never met him in person, so I can only admire him from afar."

The second time when we heard about Frank was in 1999. *Nature* had selected 21 classic works in physics published in the 20th Century in a special edition of *A Celebration of Physics*. Quantum Teleportation by Jian-Wei and his colleagues was one of the 21. Frank wrote an article "Reaching bottom, laying foundations" commenting on the 21 works. We were in awe of both the depth and breadth of his knowledge in all fields of physics.

We became intrigued by the possibility of topological fault-tolerant quantum computing around 2004. Surprisingly, we found that again Frank had been there a long while ago waiting for us. Central to the fantastic idea of topological quantum states and operations is the existence of anyons, exotic quasiparticles living in two-dimensional space, that do not fit into the usual

Fig. 1.   Jian-Wei Pan (left) and Frank Wilczek (right) at Quantum Connections Workshop 2018.

categories of fermions and bosons, but obey a new form of fractional statistics [1, 2]. That is, upon exchange of two such particles, the system wave function will acquire a statistical phase of any arbitrary value—hence its name which was coined by Frank in the early 1980s [3].

In 2006, Jian-Wei sent to Chao-Yang a feasible proposal [4, 5] for observing anyons on a six-photon graph-state experimental platform in Hefei, then the state-of-the-art in multipartite entanglement engineering. The proposal exploited the fact that the statistical properties of anyons are manifested by the underlying ground and excited states. We demonstrated the creation and manipulation of anyons in the Kitaev spin lattice model, and observed the fractional statistics of the Abelian 1/2 anyons [6]. Later, we generated nine-photon graph-state entanglement that allowed us to perform two different braidings, showing the topological robustness of anionic braiding. Similar later experiments have also been extended from the flying qubits to artificial atoms in a solid-state platform, i.e., the superconducting qubits [7],

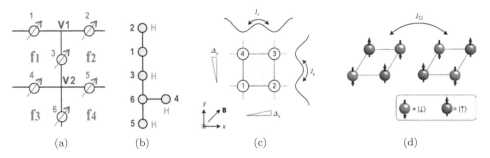

Fig. 2. (a) The small Kitaev spin lattice system with six qubits used for demonstration of anyonic braiding operations. (b) The six-qubit graph state which, after Hadamard (H) transformations on qubits 2, 3, 4, and 5, is equivalent to the ground state of the system in (a). (c) An isolated optical plaquette to mimic four-body interaction, and the sites of each plaquette are enumerated in a counterclockwise. (d) The ring-exchange driven oscillations take place between the two states $| \uparrow, \downarrow, \uparrow, \downarrow \rangle$ and $| \downarrow, \uparrow, \downarrow, \uparrow \rangle$.

and revealing the robustness of anyonic topological braiding by looping the quasiparticles along two distinct but topologically equivalent paths [8].

However, these photonic and superconducting qubit experiments were done without generating the four-body interaction in the Hamiltonian but alternatively, in an easier way, by encoding the underlying anyonic system on corresponding graph states. Thus, the anyons are effective excitations of the ground states that do not cost energy. Ultracold atoms in optical lattices offer the possibility of implementing the background Hamiltonian rather than solving the eigenstates. Yu-Ao had just read Immanuel Bloch's model of simulating Kitaev in the optical lattice [9], and had just learnt that anyon excitation truly existed. Coincidentally an opportunity popped up, and Yu-Ao joined Immanuel's group to study the technology of ultracold atoms in the optical lattice. Later Yu-Ao came back to USTC, and built up our own ultra-cold atoms experiments. Using optical super lattices to study arrays of plaquettes, we were able to manipulate four-body ring-exchange interactions among ultracold atoms, thus creating a minimal toric-code Hamiltonian. Based on this, we studied anyonic statistics by observing fractionalized phase of braiding operations [10].

In 2014, the Wilczek Quantum Center was established in China. As the chief scientist of the center, Frank played an important role by attracting outstanding experts and scholars from at home and abroad, including Peking University, University of Science and Technology of China, Stockholm University, Utrecht University, University of Massachusetts Amherst, and so on to work and promote high-level international cooperation and exchanges between Chinese and foreign researchers, teachers, and students in the quantum frontier field.

Later, under the initiative of Mr. Tsung-Dao Lee, with support from the Ministry of Education, the Ministry of Science and Technology, and the Shanghai Municipal Government, and leaning on Shanghai Jiao Tong University, the Tsung-Dao Lee Institute was established to conduct high-end research in physics, astronomy, and interdisciplinary fields. With his extensive academic influence and outstanding leadership, Frank has served as the founding director of the Institute since 2017, and continues to help the development of scientific research in China.

As the founding director of the Tsung-Dao Lee Institute, Frank has put in enormous efforts in making various contacts, which has allowed the Institute to successively hire 20 top international scientists to form an international advisory committee that focuses on the Institute's team building, research direction, key development research areas, and annual research progress. It conducts academic evaluations, and provides strategic consulting to support the development of the Tsung-Dao Lee Institute. Under his attraction and leadership, numerous leading figures and outstanding young talents from the world's top universities and famous scientific research institutions in the United States, Britain, Germany, France, Japan, South Korea, etc. have joined the institute full-time. With his active promotion, he has pushed and realized joint post-doctoral programs with high-level foreign scientific research institutions, conducted research in frontier fields, built a high-end international exchange platform, and nourished young scientific and technological talents.

Every summer Professor Wilczek organizes the Quantum Frontier Physics Summer School in Stockholm, Sweden, inviting internationally renowned scholars to share academic frontier developments. Through co-organization with the Tsung-Dao Lee Institute, a number of Chinese (including Hong Kong, Macao, and Taiwan) students and scholars were selected and sponsored to participate, which broadens their international views, as well as help advocate the research achievements of the Chinese scientific community. Remarkable results have been achieved.

Later in 2018, Yu-Ao and Jian-Wei were invited to the Quantum Connection Workshop organized by Frank in Stockholm. During the coffee break, together with one of the speakers, Jordan Cotler, Frank introduced us to a fantastic idea: entanglement enabling detection. Generally, measurement devices are usually regarded as objects which destroy quantum correlations, or, crudely speaking, "collapse the wave function." Frank and his colleagues

Fig. 3.   Jian-Wei Pan, Frank Wilczek, Jordan Cotler, and Yu-Ao Chen at Quantum Connections Workshop.

Fig. 4.   Quantum Connections Workshop 2019.

suggested to exploit the quantum nature of our detection devices, and specifically their ability to become entangled with the system they are measuring [11]. This kind of detection can be used to erase wavelength difference of injecting photons. So they also called it as a "color blind" detection.

This interesting detection can find immediate application in optical interferometry. Optical interferometry exploits phase information in light fields in order to reveal properties of the sources, which lies at the heart of both classical and quantum optics. Conventional optical detectors are fundamentally photon counters, whose operation depends upon processes which are sensitive to the photons' energy. Thus, they distinguish between different wavelengths, and therefore optical interference normally involves quasi-monochromatic light. Yet relative phases between photons of different wavelengths potentially provides a rich source of information. With the entanglement enabling "color blind" detection, Frank suggested to achieve the interference between photons with different colors [12].

We were quite excited about this idea and soon aware that the quantum frequency conversion process could serve as a color-blind detection. We immediately called our colleague Qiang Zhang, who was in China at that time. Qiang confirmed that the periodically poled Lithium Niobate waveguide fabricated in our lab can be used for the special purpose [13]. Together we designed an experimental scheme to demonstrate the color-blind detection, and after three months work, we built up a fiber-based color-blind detection setup and observed intensity interferometry between 863 nm light and 1550 nm light [14].

Then, we decided to apply our home-made color-blind detector to imaging. Currently, we, together with Frank and his theoretical group, have been working on super-resolution imaging (see Fig. 5). Utilizing two 10.9 mm-aperture telescopes and a 0.8 m baseline, we measure the distance between a 1063.6 nm source and a 1064.4 nm source separated by 4.2 mm at 1.43 km, which surpasses the diffraction limit of a single telescope by about 40 times [15]. We do hope that this new interferometry, invented by Frank, can find immediate applications in microscopy, astronomy, and remote imaging.

In addition to academics, Frank is also deeply involved in popular science. He has actively participated in various activities and high-end science forums held in Shanghai and USTC. He has also written popular science books, and among them the Chinese translation of *A Beautiful Question: The Great Design of the Universe* was awarded the 14th Wenjin Book Award by the National Library of China. Frank regularly publishes popular science articles, which are translated into Chinese for publication.

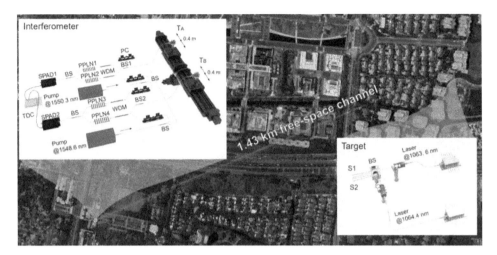

Fig. 5. Experimental setup for the chromatic intensity interferometer in free space.

Fig. 6. Yu-Ao and Frank at a public lecture held at Shanghai Science & Technology Museum.

Fig. 7.   Frank as a guest at the Micius Salon, November 10, 2019.

Fig. 8.   Chao-Yang, Yu-Ao, Biao Wu, Vincent Liu, and Jian-Wei at USTC parallel session of Frank's 70th birthday party.

Frank has a quality that impresses us all. Even though he is such a renowned physicist, he is still very modest, even a bit shy when you talk to him, so one does not feel pressured by his presence. When we were giving talks at MIT, Shanghai Jiao Tong University, and Quantum Connection, as long as he was there, he had always shown up and sat through the entire session with undivided attention. We will follow Frank's vision all the way forward. He has made a lasting impact on USTC, as well as the Chinese physics community, and we anticipate more wonderful works from him in the future.

References

[1] J. M. Leinaas and J. Myrheim, On the theory of identical particles, *Nuovo Cimento B* **37**, 1 (1977).

[2] F. Wilczek, Magnetic Flux, Angular momentum, and statistics, *Phys. Rev. Lett.* **48**, 1144 (1982).

[3] F. Wilczek, From electronics to anyonics, *Physics World* **19**, 22 (2006).

[4] A.Y. Kitaev, Fault-tolerant quantum computation by anyons, *Ann. Phys.* **303**, 2 (2003).

[5] Y.-J. Han, R. Raussendorf, and L.-M. Duan, Scheme for demonstration of fractional statistics of anyons in an exactly solvable model, *Phys. Rev. Lett.* **98**, 150404 (2007).

[6] Chao-Yang Lu, Wei-Bo Gao, Otfried Gühne, Xiao-Qi Zhou, Zeng-Bing Chen, and Jian-Wei Pan, Demonstrating anyonic fractional statistics with a six-qubit quantum simulator, *Phys. Rev. Lett.* **102**, 030502 (2009).

[7] Y.P. Zhong, D. Xu, P. Wang, C. Song, Q.J. Guo, W.X. Liu, K. Xu, B.X. Xia, C.-Y. Lu, S. Han, J.-W. Pan, and H. Wang, Emulating anyonic fractional statistical behavior in a superconducting quantum circuit, *Phys. Rev. Lett.* **117**, 110501 (2016).

[8] C. Song, D. Xu, P. Zhang, J. Wang, Q. Guo, W. Liu, K. Xu, H. Deng, K. Huang, D. Zheng, S.-B. Zheng, H. Wang, X. Zhu, C.-Y. Lu, and J.-W. Pan, Demonstration of topological robustness of anyonic braiding statistics with a superconducting quantum circuit, *Phys. Rev. Lett.* **121**, 030502 (2018).

[9] B. Paredes and I. Bloch, Minimum instances of topological matter in an optical plaquette, *Phys. Rev. A* **77**, 023603 (2008).

[10] H. -N. Dai, B. Yang, A. Reingruber, H. Sun, X.-F. Xu, Y.-A. Chen, Z.-S. Yuan and J.-W. Pan, Four-body ring-exchange interactions and anyonic statistics within a minimal toric-code Hamiltonian, *Nature Physics* **13**, 1195 (2017).

[11] J. Cotler, F. Wilczek, Entanglement enabled intensity interferometry, *arXiv*:1502.02477 (2015).

[12] J. Cotler, F. Wilczek, and V. Borish, Entanglement enabled intensity interferometry of different wavelengths of light, *arXiv*:1607.05719 (2016).

[13] M.-Y. Zheng, G.-L. Shentu, F. Ma, F. Zhou, H.-T. Zhang, Y.-Q. Dai, X. Xie, Q. Zhang, and J.-W. Pan, Integrated four-channel all-fiber up-conversion single-photon-detector with adjustable efficiency and dark count, *Review of Scientific Instruments* **87**, 093115 (2016).

[14] L.-Y. Qu, J. Cotler, F. Ma, J.-Y. Guan, M.-Y. Zheng, X. Xie, Y.-A. Chen, Q. Zhang, F. Wilczek, and J.-W. Pan, Color erasure detectors enable chromatic interferometry, *Phys. Rev. Lett.* **123**, 243601 (2019).

[15] L.-C. Liu, L.-Y. Qu, C. Wu, J. Cotler, F. Ma, M.-Y. Zheng, X. P. Xie, Y. A. Chen, Q. Zhang, F. Wilczek, and J. W. Pan, Improved Spatial Resolution Achieved by Chromatic Intensity Interferometry, *Phys. Rev. Lett.* **127**, 103601 (2021).

https://doi.org/10.1142/9789811251948_0005

Effective Field Theory of Quantum Black Holes

Sangmin Choi[*] and Finn Larsen[†]

Department of Physics and Leinweber Center for Theoretical Physics
University of Michigan, Ann Arbor, MI 48109-1120, USA
[*] *sangminc@umich.edu*
[†] *larsenf@umich.edu*

We review and extend recent progress on the quantum description of near-extremal black holes in the language of effective quantum field theory. With black holes in Einstein-Maxwell theory as the main example, we derive the Schwarzian low energy description of the AdS_2 region from a spacetime point of view. We also give a concise formula for the symmetry breaking scale, we relate rotation to supersymmetry, and we discuss quantum corrections to black hole entropy.

1. Introduction

This article was conceived as a written version of a presentation on original research addressed at physicists who do not necessarily follow current developments closely.[a] To achieve this we have opted to focus on a single research direction, the thermodynamics of a black hole near its ground state. We review progress on the subject over the last few years in a manner that is self-contained and organized as an alternative to the prevailing narrative. In this context we address several gaps in the literature.

Central aspects of black hole physics are captured by focusing on two spacetime dimensions, essentially the radial evolution near the event horizon and its interplay with time. An important recent advance was the understanding that, at low energy, this near-horizon geometry shares its symmetry structure with certain quantum mechanical models in a single dimension [1–4]. Low energy effective field theory is entirely determined in terms of its symmetries so this construction offers an explicit model of holography, a radial direction "emerges" in a model that is formulated entirely in terms of time. The one-dimensional boundary theory obscures the original

---

[a]An extended version of a talk given at *Quantum Connections 2021*, a postpandemic workshop held June 21–25, 2021 in Stockholm, Sweden, honoring the life and science of Frank Wilczek.

black hole interpretation, of course, but it can be recovered by comparing its low energy observables with a gravitational theory in two dimensions that has the same symmetry breaking pattern. For example, Jackiw-Teitelboim gravity (and its relatives) has proven instructive and so it has become a canonical benchmark [5].

The approach we present in this paper is improved, because it is constructive, and is at any rate distinct and complementary. We analyze the symmetry of the near-horizon region *ab initio*, without reference to a specific bulk Lagrangian. In this set-up we are able to explicitly identify the physical degrees of freedom directly in spacetime and, because there are no mysterious divergences, there is no dependence on unknown UV physics. Our strategy is possible because, rather than focusing on the radial mode, we identify the boundary theory as the effective Lagrangian of the complex structure in the bulk geometry. This maneuver, technical as it may appear, is satisfying because it is the natural adaption to two dimensions of the standard AdS/CFT correspondence in higher dimensions, except that in two dimensions we can be much more explicit.

With the Lagrangian in hand, we determine the scale of the low energy theory by comparing with the geometry slightly beyond the near-horizon region. This computation follows the standard UV matching procedure in effective field theory precisely and adapts the nAttractor mechanism established in [6] to the black holes considered as the main examples here. We also show quantitatively that $\mathcal{N} = 2$ supersymmetry, previously developed somewhat formally [7, 8], can be interpreted physically as a relation between rotation of the black hole and thermal excitations away from the supersymmetric limit.

The recent progress we discuss, including the refinements we introduce, rely entirely on low energy effective field theory. Importantly, the underlying principles of nonlinearly realized symmetry, realized by an effective Lagrangian, apply also in the quantum theory. Therefore, the quantum corrections to the low-temperature partition function, determined as $\sim T^{3/2}$ by many researchers, must agree with appropriate complementary descriptions that apply at the highest and lowest energies where the "low temperature" description is justified. We argue that the limitation at high energy is due to Kaluza-Klein modes on the sphere, i.e. higher partial waves of spacetime fields, and at very low energy it is due to finite volume effects. These complementary regimes are themselves described by effective quantum field theories, albeit different ones, that do not depend on the UV completion of quantum gravity. Therefore, at energies where regimes of applicability overlap, quantum corrections must agree. In this presentation, we review results on the quantum corrections to black hole entropy, at zero and generic temperatures, and adapt them to establish the expected agreements. This serves to illustrate the power of effective quantum field theory, as well as its limitations.

This paper is organized as follows. In sec. 2 we introduce the basic thermodynamics of Kerr-Newman black holes in $D = 4$ spacetime dimensions, with focus on their near-extremal behavior. In sec. 3 we discuss the near-horizon geometry of the black hole. Specifically, we determine the space of distinct geometries by analyzing the applicable large diffeomorphisms. In sec. 4 we leverage this data to construct the effective action of low energy excitations of the geometry. In sec. 5 we discuss the scales of the spontaneously broken symmetry which, we show, enjoy some protection due to supersymmetry. Moreover, the two scales in the problem are related to one another by supersymmetry. In sec. 6 we discuss the power and limitations of effective quantum field theory for gravity, by comparing the effective description of the near-horizon geometry with computations of the quantum corrections to black hole entropy in various regimes. We finish, in sec. 7, with a brief summary aimed at further applications of the spacetime wave functions we determine.

2. Black Holes in Einstein-Maxwell Theory

In order to keep the presentation broadly accessible, as our primary setting we consider $D = 4$ Einstein-Maxwell theory. The black holes in this theory are the Kerr-Newman black holes. They are asymptotically flat and depend on just three quantum numbers: mass M, angular momentum J, and electric charge Q.[b]

The Bekenstein-Hawking area law, applied to the Kerr-Newman black holes, gives the entropy[c]:

$$S = \frac{A}{4G_4} = \frac{\pi}{G_4} \left[\frac{J^2}{M^2} + \left(MG_4 + \sqrt{(MG_4)^2 - Q^2 - \frac{J^2}{M^2}} \right)^2 \right]. \quad (1)$$

---

[b]Black holes in $D = 4$ Einstein-Maxwell theory can also have magnetic charge P. Because of classical duality symmetry, their geometries depend only on the combination $\sqrt{Q^2 + P^2}$, and so taking $P = 0$ involves no loss of generality at the classical level. In the quantum theory there are interesting subtleties (including [9]) but they are not closely connected to the main points of this presentation.
[c]In this equation we display G_4, in order to record dimensions once and for all, but henceforth we generally take $G_4 = 1$ and restore it only when needed for clarity.

The argument of the square root is negative if, for given charges J, Q, the mass violates the extremality bound

$$M^2 \geq M_{\text{ext}}^2 = \frac{1}{2}Q^2 + \sqrt{\frac{1}{4}Q^4 + J^2}. \tag{2}$$

The pathology of the entropy formula when the black hole mass is too small is a genuine feature of the underlying black hole solutions: regular geometries exist if and only if $M \geq M_{\text{ext}}$.

The basic $D = 4$ Einstein-Maxwell theory we focus on, a theory that is well-known from elementary textbooks, is identical to the bosonic part of $\mathcal{N} = 2$ minimal supergravity. In the supersymmetric theory there are also two gravitini but fermions can only appear in the action at quadratic (or higher) order so, as far as bosonic solutions to the theory are concerned, it is consistent to set them to zero. From this point of view the significance of supersymmetry is that there are *two* independent supercharges in $\mathcal{N} = 2$ supergravity and, when they act sequentially, they relate gravity and the electromagnetic field.

The inequivalent orderings of the two supersymmetries is controlled by the supersymmetry algebra. In a unitarity representation, it yields the BPS bound:

$$\{\mathcal{Q}, \mathcal{Q}^\dagger\} = 2(M - Q) \geq 0. \tag{3}$$

The notation here is schematic: we suppress the spinor indices on the supersymmetry generators $\mathcal{Q}$ and also suppress their two-fold multiplicity, but the numerical coefficients are accurate. Comparison with the extremality condition (2) shows that the supersymmetry condition is stronger, its saturation corresponds to *two* conditions:

$$M = Q \quad \text{and} \quad J = 0. \tag{4}$$

The broader lesson, applicable in much more general settings, is that supersymmetric black holes are extremal (for the given charges) *and* their charges must satisfy a constraint. In Einstein-Maxwell theory the constraint on charges is very simple, just $J = 0$, but for supersymmetric black holes with asymptotically AdS-geometry it can be much more complicated [10–12].

The supersymmetric black holes (4) form a one parameter family among the general Kerr-Newman black holes with quantum numbers (M, J, Q). *Nearly* supersymmetric black holes depend on the reference BPS black hole and, in addition, on two continuous real parameters that break supersymmetry. Concretely, the mass of a nearly supersymmetric black hole exceeds the supersymmetric bound due to temperature and/or angular velocity:

$$M = Q + \frac{1}{2}Q^3\big((2\pi T)^2 + \Omega^2\big). \tag{5}$$

The temperature must be nonnegative while the angular velocity can have either sign.

The scale of symmetry breaking is [13]

$$\frac{C_T}{T} = 4\pi^2 Q^3. \tag{6}$$

The specific heat C_T is proportional to temperature T in the nearly super-symmetric regime so the ratio C_T/T is useful as a symmetry breaking scale that characterizes the state of black hole matter [13]. For a macroscopic black hole it is much larger than the horizon size $Q^3 G_4 \gg Q$. This hierarchy of scales expresses the collective nature of low-lying black hole excitations by introducing an energy scale that is much lower than for a particle in a box with comparable size. In string theory constructions this "large string scale" is realized by the level of an $\mathcal{N} = 2$ superconformal algebra in two dimensions and is closely related to spectral flow [14–17].

Summarizing so far, there are several important symmetries in Einstein–Maxwell theory, and they have an interesting interplay:

- The supersymmetric ground state is very special and imposes two conditions (4). It realizes superconformal symmetry.
- There are two distinct ways to break superconformal invariance: finite temperature and/or rotational velocity (finite angular momentum).
- The two breaking mechanisms are characterized by a single symmetry breaking scale (6) because the two potentials are related by supersymmetry.

3. Near-Horizon Symmetry

In general relativity gravity is a theory of coordinate transformations (diffeomorphisms) so, to understand all the symmetries of the physical system, we must study the black hole geometry. The near-horizon geometry of an extremal 4D black hole is $\mathrm{AdS}_2 \times S^2$ [18]. At very low energy, excitations on the sphere are suppressed but nontrivial dynamics is encoded in the AdS_2 factor. We introduce complex coordinates and present the metric as

$$ds_2^2 = g_{\mu\nu}dx^\mu dx^\nu = \frac{4}{(1-|z|^2)^2}dz d\bar{z}. \tag{7}$$

Here $z = 0$ is the black hole horizon (in Euclidean signature), the radial evolution along $0 \leq |z| < 1$ represents the throat at finite spatial distance from the horizon, and the apparent singularity at $|z| = 1$ is infinitely far from the horizon, where the black hole "attaches" to the surrounding space.

The geometry (7) is a representative of the black hole ground state but it is not unique, there is an entire manifold of degenerate vacua that can be constructed by acting with symmetries. As candidates for alternative vacua, consider the metric deformations:

$$\delta g_{zz} = z^{n-2}, \quad n = 2, 3, \ldots. \tag{8}$$

These variations are all *normalizable*: their square as complex functions, computed by contracting indices using the metric read off from (7), give a finite result when integrated over the entire conformal disk $|z| < 1$. This happens because the diverging volume factor $\sqrt{g}$ at the boundary $|z| \to 1$ is dominated by index contractions with the factor $g^{z\bar{z}}$ that drops off rapidly as $|z| \to 1$.

Before concluding that the metric deformations (8) represent low-lying excitations of the black hole, recall that metric deformations generated by coordinate transformations are not genuinely different geometries, the configuration space of gravity is the space of geometries up to coordinate transformations. In other words, diffeomorphisms $\delta x^\mu = \xi^\mu$ transform the metric coefficients as

$$\delta g_{zz} = 2\nabla_z \xi_z, \tag{9}$$

but the corresponding geometry is physically identical, it has simply been recast in a new coordinate system.

The redundancy realized by diffeomorphisms is huge, especially in low spacetime dimensions. In particular, the sample deformation of the metric (8) is generated from the original "reference" geometry (7) by the coordinate transformation (9) with

$$\xi^{\bar{z}} = \frac{1}{4}\left(\frac{1}{n-1}z^{n-1} - \frac{2\bar{z}}{n}z^n + \frac{\bar{z}^2}{n+1}z^{n+1}\right) - \frac{1}{2(n-1)n(n+1)}\bar{z}^{n+1}. \tag{10}$$

The last term in this equation is such that the diagonal components $g_{z\bar{z}}$ are invariant. If taken at face value, this shows that the deformations $\delta g_{zz} = z^{n-2}$ are pure diffeomorphisms, i.e. they change the metric but not the geometry. However, the diffeomorphism $|\xi^{\bar{z}}| \sim 1$ near the boundary $|z| = 1$ so it is *not* normalizable: the square of the vector $\xi^{\bar{z}}$ must be computed using the background conformal factor $g_{z\bar{z}}$ which diverges, and then integrated over the volume with divergent measure $\sqrt{g}$. Therefore, the variations (8) are *not* pure diffeomorphisms. In other words, since they are normalizable, and not generated by coordinate transformations, they *are* physical metric deformations [19–22].

The modes (9) are a basis for all configurations that can appear in this way. We can combine them (all integers $n = 2, 3, \ldots$) into a single function $\epsilon(z)$ that is regular at the origin $z = 0$ where $\epsilon = \partial_z \epsilon = \partial_z^2 \epsilon = 0$ and parametrizes the generators of diffeomorphisms through

$$\xi^{\bar{z}} = \bar{\epsilon}(\bar{z}) - \frac{1}{2} \int_0^z (1 - z'\bar{z})^2 \partial_{z'}^3 \epsilon(z') dz'$$

$$= \bar{\epsilon}(\bar{z}) - \frac{1}{2}(1 - z\bar{z})^2 \partial_z^2 \epsilon(z) - \bar{z}(1 - z\bar{z}) \partial_z \epsilon(z) - \bar{z}^2 \epsilon(z), \qquad (11)$$

and its complex conjugate. These transformations all preserve conformal gauge, the diagonal metric displayed in (7) is invariant, and so they act on the geometry only by adding simple off-diagonal components:

$$\delta ds^2 = -2 \left(\partial_z^3 \epsilon(z) dz^2 + \text{c.c.} \right). \qquad (12)$$

Thus the space of distinct geometries is parametrized by

$$ds^2 = h_{zz}(z) dz^2 + \text{c.c.}, \qquad (13)$$

where the function $h_{zz}(z)$ is regular at the origin. The regular metric deformations that are not generated by diffeomorphisms are called quadratic holomorphic differentials (QHD's).

The analysis of AdS$_2$ presented here is reminiscent of string theory in the world-sheet formalism but there are important differences [23]. The reference metric (7) is in conformal gauge, as is custom in string theory. However, the Riemann surfaces considered in string theory are compact and have no analogue of the singularity at $|z| = 1$. For example, the sphere S^2 has a conformal factor $g_{z\bar{z}} = 2(1 + |z|^2)^{-2}$ that is well-behaved for any $|z|$. It is because of this crucial difference that AdS$_2$ can have infinitely many QHDs, while S^2 has none. Conversely, AdS$_2$ has no conformal Killing vectors (CKVs), the normalizable vector fields that leave the metric invariant even after fixing to conformal gauge, while S^2 has 3.

It is also instructive to compare with non-critical string theory (and its closely related matrix model descriptions). Again, it is customary to fix conformal gauge at the outset, but the conformal (Weyl) factor becomes a dynamical degree of freedom which, it turns out, is described by Liouville theory [24–26]. In contrast, in our construction we insist that the conformal factor is fixed (and singular), and this forces coordinate transformations

to act only on the QHD (13) which, accordingly, parametrizes the space
of states.

4. The Effective Theory of the Near-Horizon Geometry

The diffeomorphisms (11) relate vacua by a transformation that is a symmetry, except that it acts on a space of distinct boundary conditions at
$|z| = 1$. In this situation low-lying states can be realized by "moving slowly"
among all these configurations. Nonlinear realization of symmetry offers a
systematic formalism that implements this intuition.

In order to proceed, the algebra of infinitesimal symmetries (11) must be
exponentiated to map out the corresponding group manifold. At first this
seems difficult to carry out, because the algebra has infinitely many generators, but the problem here has special properties that help out. A finite
diffeomorphism transforms the QHD (13) as a tensor, except for an anomalous contribution with the infinitesimal form (12). The finite version of the
latter is determined by the requirement that successive coordinate transformations must compose appropriately, i.e. consistently with the Leibniz rule.
This condition is familiar from conformal field theory in two dimensions
where the finite form of (projectively realized) conformal symmetry is given
by the Schwarzian. We can adapt this result to represent the general QHD
(13) as a finite diffeomorphism $f(z)$ that introduces

$$h_{zz}dz^2 = -2 \left(\frac{\partial_z^3 f(z)}{\partial_z f(z)} - \frac{3}{2} \left(\frac{\partial_z^2 f(z)}{\partial_z f(z)} \right)^2 \right) dz^2. \tag{14}$$

This formula expresses the entire space of non-trivial spacetime geometries
in a closed form.[d]

We have stressed the representation of the group theory in terms of two-
dimensional spacetimes, as befits the interpretation in term of near-horizon
black hole geometry. However, low energy effective quantum field theory
derives its power by exploiting the principles of symmetry, without appealing to a particular realization. We can think of the non-normalizable diffeomorphisms (10) as abstract generators that close on themselves and so form
a symmetry algebra. More precisely, they close on an augmented set that

---

[d]The generator of diffeomorphisms (11) is "exact" in that there is no restriction on
$|z|$ (but it is "infinitesimal") while the exponentiation (14) is "exact" in that the
transformation is finite (but it is at asymptotic order $(1 - |z|^2)^2$). The underlying
truly "exact" mathematical structure is the universal Teichmüller space.

includes the vectors $\epsilon(z) = 1, z, z^2$. However, in the geometrical realization these "additional" modes do not change the metric at all, they generate $SL(2)$, the isometry group of AdS$_2$. Therefore, upon exponentiation the generators of the symmetry algebra do not quite form a group, because of the caveat they define a coset. The algebra identifies the coset generated by the non-normalizable diffeomorphisms as Diff(S^1)$/SL(2)$.

The group Diff(S^1) is defined in terms of its action on the circle. There is a canonical map from the QHDs (13) parametrizing deformations of AdS$_2$ to the periodic functions of a single real variable τ on the circle S^1 "at infinity" via the identifications $z = e^{i\tau}$ and $\bar{z} = e^{-i\tau}$. This map is subtle in that the boundary $|z| = 1$ does not belong to the AdS$_2$ geometry which is non-compact because its conformal factor diverges as $|z| \to 1$. However, it makes sense anyway because the QHDs (12) have no intrinsic scale, they depend only on the complex structure which is perfectly smooth as $z \to 1$. This is the natural generalization to AdS$_2$/CFT$_1$ of the holographic map that applies to the AdS/CFT correspondence in higher dimensions.

Representations of Diff(S^1) have been studied in great detail by mathematicians (for a review see [27]). Proper representations simply keep the length of the circle invariant but, in quantum mechanics, it is sufficient to consider projective representations where the group elements transform state vectors among themselves only up to a phase, as long as the phase is assigned consistently with the group structure. An important aspect of the mathematical classification of projective representations is the stabilizer group, comprised of the group elements that act trivially in the representation at hand. The stabilizer group of most projective representations includes $U(1)$, corresponding to the translations along S^1, but only in the case of the so-called "identity" representation is this $U(1)$ enhanced to the $SL(2)$ subgroup of Diff(S^1). Moreover, in this particular case the group action is proportional to (12), with the understanding that the complex number is a pure phase $z = e^{i\tau}$. Therefore, from the purely formal point of view, there is a unique projective representation of the coset Diff(S^1)$/SL(2)$ that is viable for the description of AdS$_2$ at low energy [28]. The fact that it coincides with the one identified by an explicit analysis of the near-horizon geometry of the black hole illustrates the power of low energy effective field theory.

In general spacetime dimension, the energy-momentum tensor in quantum field theory is related to the action as

$$T^{\mu\nu} = -\frac{2\pi}{\sqrt{g}} \frac{\delta I}{\delta g_{\mu\nu}}, \tag{15}$$

and diffeomorphism invariance ensures that $T^{\mu\nu}$ is conserved. Presently, the time τ is the only dimension in the boundary theory so there is just one component, the energy. Moreover, it is only conserved if it is a constant. Therefore, the formula (15) for the energy-momentum "tensor" — it is a single number in one (space)time dimension — shows that the action must be proportional to the metric coefficient in (14) and so determines the effective Lagrangian

$$I = \frac{C_T}{T} \int \frac{d\tau}{2\pi} \left[\frac{1}{2}(\partial_\tau f)^2 + \frac{\partial_\tau^3 f}{\partial_\tau f} - \frac{3}{2} \left(\frac{\partial_\tau^2 f}{\partial_\tau f} \right)^2 \right]. \tag{16}$$

The overall constant of proportionality C_T/T is arbitrary for now, to be discussed further in the subsequent section.

All black hole states, corresponding to a general finite diffeomorphism $f(\tau)$, is assigned the same energy, so we interpret them as degenerate vacua. We pick the specific reference geometry (7) as "the" vacuum because it "looks" simple but, as usual for a spontaneously broken symmetry, any other reference would be physically equivalent. The invariant physical reality is that the (non-normalizable) symmetry generators act on the (arbitrarily chosen) reference vacuum and create physical states that are Goldstone bosons of the broken symmetry.

At the risk of beating a dead horse, we stress that there are (at least) two distinct perspectives on the computation leading to the Schwarzian action (16):

- It is *quantum gravity* in two dimensions: a theory of excitations in the near-horizon region of black hole.
- It is an effective theory of symmetries that act entirely on the asymptotic boundary S^1. This is a scale invariant theory *without gravity*.

The equivalence of these two descriptions is the content of the modern realization of AdS$_2$/CFT$_1$ holography. The presentation here (and elsewhere) *proves* this duality at the level of effective field theory.

That the arguments motivating (and largely establishing) AdS$_{d+1}$/CFT$_d$ holography in dimensions $d > 1$ fail in $d = 1$ were recognized already in [29] and was frequently interpreted as AdS$_2$/CFT$_1$ holography somehow not being possible [30, 30–33]. The modern understanding developed over the last few years is that much the same arguments apply, after all, but at the level of effective quantum field theory. Thus nearAdS$_2$/nearCFT$_1$ holography is stronger in that it is proven, but it is weaker in that it just identifies IR theories, no full duality is claimed.

5. The Symmetry Breaking Scales

The derivation of the Schwarzian (16) does not determine its overall coefficient, the dimensionful symmetry breaking scale C_T/T. In low energy effective theory it is an arbitrary parameter but, in the context of a specific UV completion, such as the SYK model, it can be derived from microscopic parameters [34, 35]. Alternatively, it can be related to the parameters of a particularly simple 2D gravity model, such as JT-gravity [5]. In the application to black holes, the scale is determined by the complete black hole geometry, going beyond the near-horizon limit. In this setting there is an appealing geometrical interpretation of the symmetry breaking scale.

The near-horizon geometry (7) has a single overall scale, the AdS$_2$ curvature $\ell_2 = Q$ (which we mostly suppress to unclutter formulae), but its metric diverges at $|z| = 1$ where the "throat" attaches to surrounding geometry. The full (not "near-horizon") geometry extends farther, to the region where $|z| > 1$. There the area of the transverse sphere S^2 is slightly larger, and the larger radius of the Euclidean circle implies a non-zero local temperature. The matching with the UV scale amounts to the ratio of these two features, it evaluates the radial derivative of the area element at $|z| = 1$. Thus the black hole interpretation captures the UV data by extending the geometry into the region $|z| > 1$, but only infinitesimally. In contrast, the low energy effective theory, as a theory in itself, regulates the divergence at $|z| = 1$ and focuses on the interior $|z| < 1$.

To make these principles explicit, consider a spherically symmetric black hole in $D = 4$ spacetime dimensions, presented in Schwarzschild-like coordinates as

$$ds^2 = -g(r)dt^2 + g^{-1}(r)dr^2 + r^2 d\Omega_2^2.$$

The function $g(r)$ depends only on the radial coordinate r, as indicated by its argument. It vanishes at the horizon $g|_{r=r_{\text{hor}}} = 0$ and its derivative there gives the black hole temperature $T = (4\pi)^{-1}\partial_r g|_{r=r_{\text{hor}}}$. In the context of this presentation, we focus on the Reissner-Nordström black holes where

$$g(r) = 1 - \frac{2M}{r} + \frac{Q^2}{r^2},$$

and especially the supersymmetric limit where $Q = M$ where $g_{\text{BPS}} = (1 - Q/r)^2$. In this case the derivative $\partial_r g$ vanishes at the horizon $r_{\text{hor}} = Q$ so the temperature vanishes in the BPS limit, as expected.

A straightforward way to analyze near-extremal black holes is to relax the BPS condition $Q = M$ from the outset and then study the limit as $M \to Q_+$.

The alternative procedure we pursue, as outlined above, is conceptually distinct and, especially when rotation is incorporated, much simpler computationally. Starting from the strictly supersymmetric black hole, we simply evaluate the temperature $T = (4\pi)^{-1}\partial_r g$ and the entropy $S = (4G_4)^{-1}4\pi r^2$ just *outside* the horizon:

$$\frac{C_T}{T} = \frac{\Delta S}{\Delta T} = \frac{4\pi}{\Delta(\partial_r g)} \Delta\pi r^2 = \frac{8\pi^2 r}{\partial_r^2 g}, \tag{17}$$

with the final expression evaluated at the horizon. The BPS function has second derivative $g''_{\text{BPS}} = 2/Q^2$ at the horizon and this value returns the correct symmetry breaking scale (6). The equivalence of moving away from the horizon (in a given BPS solution) and deforming the solution away from the BPS limit (but always considering the event horizon) was recognized and developed in [6, 36].

The entire geometry of a BPS black hole preserves supersymmetry, but it is enhanced to superconformal symmetry in the near-horizon region. The construction presented here relies only on the BPS geometry, so it computes the scale associated with the breaking of conformal symmetry without breaking supersymmetry at the same time. Therefore, we expect that the scale associated with the breaking of conformal symmetry enjoys protection by supersymmetry.

There is another aspect of supersymmetry that we have, for simplicity, suppressed in the last several sections: we focus on the gravity sector, as expected for a discussion of black holes, but the Einstein-*Maxwell* theory also features a gauge field. Its symmetry structure is analogous to the one discussed for diffeomorphisms, but much simpler. There are normalizable gauge fields in the AdS$_2$ region:

$$A_z = \partial_z \sigma(z) = z^{n-1}, \quad n = 1, 2, \ldots.$$

They are formally "pure" gauge but the applicable gauge function $\sigma(z)$ is not normalizable in the background metric. Therefore, these modes are in fact physical. The effective action for the $U(1)$ field is a simple free scalar. Combining these modes from the gauge sector with the gravitational modes (17), the effective low energy theory of near-extremal Kerr-Newman black holes becomes

$$I = \frac{C_T}{T} \int \frac{d\tau}{2\pi} \left[\frac{1}{2}(\partial_\tau f)^2 + \frac{\partial_\tau^3 f}{\partial_\tau f} - \frac{3}{2}\left(\frac{\partial_\tau^2 f}{\partial_\tau f}\right)^2 - \frac{1}{2}(\partial_\tau \sigma)^2 \right]. \tag{18}$$

As before, this effective action describes radial excitations of the near-extremal black hole in terms of an "angular" variable, the Euclidean time τ.

However, it also incorporates a more conventional angular feature: a rotating black hole mixes the azimuthal angle of the S^2 horizon, that we have suppressed so far, with "the" time. The reference to τ as a "coordinate" and σ as a "gauge parameter" emphasizes our focus on 2D AdS$_2$ (and its 1D boundary S^1) over its 4D progenitor AdS$_2 \times S^2$, not to mention the supersymmetric extensions of these geometries.

This difference in perspectives notwithstanding, we have taken care that τ and σ both have canonical periodicity 2π. As usual, fermionic wave "functions" are more precisely sections of spin bundles and, as such, they can be antiperiodic. However, this caveat must be consistently applied, in that fermions that are antiperiodic around the Euclidean time τ must also be antiperiodic around the gauge "coordinate" σ. It is in this precise sense that the two terms in the action (18) have the "same" normalization. In the version of the setup that incorporates gravitini, the identity of these coefficients is also required by $\mathcal{N} = 2$ supersymmetry in one (space)time dimension [7].

The generalized Schwarzian (18) encodes the basic thermodynamics of the low-lying excitations above the supersymmetric ground state, as well as much else. The linear functions $f = \tau T$, and $\sigma = \Omega \tau / 2\pi$ are well-defined (with coordinate periodicity $\Delta \tau = 2\pi \beta$) and together give the mass formula

$$M = Q + \frac{1}{2} \left(\frac{C_T}{T} \right) \left[T^2 + \left(\frac{\Omega}{2\pi} \right)^2 \right].$$

As we have stressed previously, the T^2 dependence makes a statement about scaling symmetry. The overall coefficient is arbitrary in the low energy theory, but determined by matching with the UV theory. At this point we stress that the *relative* coefficient between the two terms is determined by $\mathcal{N} = 2$ supersymmetry. At the classical level, this claim applies even for Einstein-Maxwell theory, with no gravitini in the theory, but generally the two conceptually distinct response coefficients may differ at the quantum level.

The interrelation between radial/temporal geometry AdS$_2$ and the horizon S^2 can be illuminated by comparison with asymptotically flat black holes in 5D which, in the circumstances that are best developed, can be understood in terms of limits of a near-horizon AdS$_3 \times S^3$ geometry. In this context the isometries of the AdS$_3$ and S^3 factors are $SL(2)^2$ and $SU(2)^2$, respectively, and rotation is interpreted geometrically through coordinate identifications that fibrate an $SU(2)$ nontrivially over an $SL(2)$ factor [15]. In the dual CFT$_2$ with $\mathcal{N} = (4,4)$ supersymmetry rotation is implemented by the spectral flow automorphism. At the classical level, these interrelations ensure that the levels of the underlying $SL(2)$ and $SU(2)$ current algebras coincide, a precise analogue of the agreement between the prefactors of T^2 and $(\Omega/2\pi)^2$ in the mass formula. Generally, there are nontrivial corrections in the quantum theory and it is interesting that, in the AdS$_3$ × S^3 setup, they may be determined by anomalies [37, 38].

Some instances of AdS$_2$ × S^2 can be realized as limits of AdS$_3$ × S^3 [39–41], but others cannot, and such limits may or may not be consistent with supersymmetry. It is interesting to inquire how quantum corrections to the linear response coefficient C_T/T arise directly in four spacetime dimensions and how such precision information may descend to the simple quantum mechanics of horizon modes we consider from genuine quantum field theory in higher dimensions.

6. Quantum Corrections to Black Hole Entropy

There is a well-defined notion of logarithmic quantum corrections to the Bekenstein-Hawking area law:

$$S = \frac{A}{4G_4} - 2a \log A + \cdots , \tag{19}$$

when all macroscopic lengths are scaled uniformly [21]. The correction is due to virtual loops of massless fields in the near-horizon region of the black hole. Therefore, the coefficient a can be computed unambiguously in effective quantum field theory and doing so adds perspective to the power and limitations of the effective field theory description of black holes.[e]

The explicit computations of quantum corrections to black holes can be quite involved. The most laborious part is to compute functional determinants for fields that are non-vanishing in the classical black hole solution. Other fields must be taken into account as well, because they also contribute to virtual loops, and such spectator fields may couple nontrivially to the background. More conceptually, zero-modes of the entire black hole must be treated correctly and, at the quantum level, statistical ensembles are not all equivalent so care must be taken that the entropy is microcanonical (the energy is fixed but the temperature is not). These various features were known for a long time, but they were greatly developed and refined about a decade ago, especially by A. Sen [20, 42–44]. A highlight of this advance was the case of black holes in string theory (that preserve a sufficient amount of

---

[e]We choose the notation a for the coefficient because, in many $D = 4$ examples, there is a close relation to the corresponding Weyl anomaly coefficient. It is unfortunate that, with this convention, each unit anomalous mass dimension of the entropy $M\partial_M \Delta S = +1$ contributes $\Delta a = 1/4$.

supersymmetry) where the coefficients from loops of massless particles computed in effective field theory were shown to agree precisely with the corresponding expansion of microscopic counting formulae [45, 46]. This result gives confidence that the various contributions to the logarithmic corrections have been correctly understood.

To make this general discussion more concrete, we now return to the $D = 4$ Kerr-Newman black hole and specifically its ground state entropy:

$$S = \frac{A_0}{4G_4} - 2a_0 \log A_0 + \cdots , \qquad (20)$$

where $A_0 = 4\pi Q^2$. As we emphasized in the preceding paragraph, there are several comparable contributions to the coefficient a_0. It is interesting to compare them to the description by Schwarzian action (16). This is possible because unknown physics at very high energy, depending on the Planck scale, string scale, or possible compactification scales, all decouple. It contributes to local operators suppressed by a power of energy, rather than a logarithm. Thus the relevant physics is at low energy, yet care must be taken because, as in most effective descriptions, the range where the Schwarzian description applies is limited at both high and low energy.

In the spherical reduction of Einstein-Maxwell theory the propagating modes of gravity and the gauge field have spherical harmonics $l \geq 2$ and $l \geq 1$, respectively. The scale of all these modes is set by Q, the radius of S^2, so they are too heavy to be dynamical degrees of freedom at the much longer length scale of the Schwarzian theory Q^3. However, the couplings in an effective field theory are determined at the highest energies of its applicability, by matching with the UV theory, so the Kaluza-Klein modes can leave an imprint at low energy. We can interpret such contributions as running of the effective low energy cosmological constant due to virtual effects. Numerically, gravity and vector fields couple to one another and combine to a contribution $\Delta a_0 = 53/45$. The completion to $\mathcal{N} = 2$ supergravity by gravitini yields an additional $\Delta a_0 = -589/360$ for a total of $\Delta a_0 = -11/24$ from all Kaluza-Klein modes. The precise numerical coefficients are unimportant in this presentation, we merely note that they are computable and of order one.

The position and orientation of the black hole break translational and rotational symmetry, respectively. These collective degrees of freedom can produce Goldstone modes that remain in the low energy path integral and then their quantum fluctuations contribute with a weight determined by the scaling limit defining (19). At strictly zero temperature and nonvanishing rotation the integral over 3 translational zero-modes contribute $\Delta a_0 = 3 \times (1/4) = 3/4$.[f] In this case the corresponding addition $-(3/2) \log A = -3 \log(\text{length})$ to the entropy is simply due to a single factor of the three-dimensional spatial volume in the partition function.[g]

In our description, we can understand the dependence on the translational mode as a quantum anomaly. If we expand the quantum geometry as

$$g_{zz} = \sum_n c_n g_n,$$

where the modes

$$g_n = \sqrt{\frac{(n^2 - 1)n}{2\pi \ell_2^2}} z^{n-2},$$

are normalized so $\int d^2 z \sqrt{g} |g_n|^2 = 1$ on AdS_2, the path integral measure

$$\mathcal{D}\phi = \prod_{n=2}^{\infty} dc_n,$$

clearly depends on the AdS_2 scale ℓ_2. This quantum dependence introduces the anomalous scaling $-3 \log(\text{length})$

$$\ell_2 \frac{\partial}{\partial \ell_2} \ln \mathcal{D}\phi = -2\pi \ell_2^2 \sum_{n=2}^{\infty} |g_n|^2 = -2\pi \ell_2^2 (1 - |z|^2)^4 \sum_{n=2}^{\infty} \frac{(n^2 - 1)n}{2\pi \ell_2^2} |z|^{2(n-2)} = -3.$$

The first equality assigned the usual value

$$\int \sqrt{g} d^2 z = \int_0 \frac{2\ell_2^2}{(1 - |z|^2)^2} \cdot 2\pi \cdot \frac{1}{2} d|z|^2 = -2\pi \ell_2^2,$$

as the renormalized volume of AdS_2. At high temperature this quantum dependence on the zero-mode precisely cancels the volume dependence $\sim V_3 T^3$ of the surrounding thermal gas [48].

The quantum correction to the excitations described by the Schwarzian is due to the very same modes as the volume dependence of the vacuum. However, because of the boundary condition that identifies z and $\bar{z}$, it captures

---

[f]The factor of 1/4 was explained in the previous footnote.
[g]The dependence of the zero-mode contribution on the theory and the ensemble is far from trivial. It was discussed by Sen in many interesting situations [21, 46–48]. The results were summarized in an Appendix of [44]. For reference, the completion to a spherically symmetric black hole in $\mathcal{N} = 2$ supergravity gives a total contribution $\Delta a_0 = -1/2$ from zero-modes.

only 1/2 of the anomalous dimension:

$$\frac{\partial}{\partial \log(\text{length})} \ln Z = -\frac{3}{2}.$$

The anomalous scaling $\log Z_{\text{Sch}} \sim (3/2) \log T$ for the thermal partition function of the Schwarzian model was computed by many researchers [23, 28, 34, 49]. It can be understood as the "missing" $SL(2)$ volume that is removed in the $\text{Diff}(S^1)/SL(2)$ coset. Our computation relates this anomalous dimension to explicit physical modes.

The agreement between scaling dimensions hides an important distinction between scales. To explain, we return to the generic form of the logarithmic quantum correction, presented in (19) as dependence on black hole parameters through $\log A$, with the understanding that the dimensionful area A must be evaluated in units that are kept fixed as physical characteristics of the black hole are rescaled. The implicit reference scale that sets units could be the Planck length $\sim G_4^{1/2}$, because it is the same for all black holes. However, according to Wilson's physical picture of renormalization it is more appropriate to apply a reference scale set by the fluctuations themselves. For quantum corrections to the supersymmetric ground state we can pick a "standard" black hole with scale Q_0 as a reference and then estimate quantum corrections to other black holes in the family as $\log Q^2/Q_0^2$ with some coefficient we compute.

For logarithmic corrections computed by the Schwarzian theory we have in mind a different situation. Given a single reference black hole with scale Q_0 we study different temperatures T and find logarithmic corrections $\log T$. In this setup the typical length scale of the thermal fluctuations $C_T/T \sim Q_0^3/G_4$ is much larger than the AdS$_2$ scale $\ell_2 \sim Q_0$. Thus the Kaluza-Klein modes make their imprint on the ground state entropy at energies that are much higher than where the Schwarzian description applies.

However, at *very* low temperatures $T \ll Q^3$ the Schwarzian theory fails because the energies determined by the AdS$_2$ description becomes unreliable, the spectrum incorporates wave lengths that probe beyond the "throat" with scale $\sim Q^3$. The low energy spectrum of an asymptotically flat black hole in equilibrium with its surroundings has no lower limit, there is no gap, so modes at extremely low temperature ultimately dominate the entropy of a black hole in flat space because they contribute $S \sim V_3 T^3$ where the volume V_3 can be taken arbitrarily large. Such modes obviously do not characterize the black hole, they are features of the surrounding flat space, and so they should not be included in the accounting of the black hole entropy. Mathematically, the path integral with black hole boundary conditions must be modulo a factor that diverges as the spatial volume $V_3 \to \infty$ with T fixed [48].

Technical as this point may be, it is important to note that the volume V_3 introduces another scale, an IR regulator. This is significant even for strictly supersymmetric black holes where the scale regulating the contribution of KK-modes to the logarithmic correction (20) is the horizon scale ℓ_2, while the appropriate benchmark for the translational zero-modes is the IR volume V_3. This feature allows a smooth transition between the quantum correction (20) and the quantum correction to the Schwarzian description in the low (but finite) temperature limit.

7. Summary

This presentation discussed black hole thermodynamics with emphasis on near-extremal black holes. This low-temperature regime is described by the Schwarzian theory with Lagrangian (16). In the literature, there has been great interest in this theory, as an IR limit of the SYK-model [1–3, 7, 28, 34, 50–54], and as the low energy effective description of JT-gravity [5, 8, 25, 55–68]. We seek to complement these mainstream points of view by further developing the connection to spacetime black holes.

In this spirit, our main result is to present the explicit wave functions in two spacetime dimensions that dominate the black hole thermodynamics at low temperature. The modes we focus on are zero-modes in the two-dimensional spacetime, in the sense that they can be generated by diffeomorphisms. However, because the required coordinate transformations are not normalizable, these modes are in fact physical and, it turns out, described via the Schwarzian action.

The special modes in AdS$_2$ that we highlight appear prominently in discussions of logarithmic corrections to supersymmetric black hole entropy. In our interpretation these modes can be identified with the translational zero-modes that become normalizable at finite temperature. We support this identification by showing that the contribution to the black hole entropy from zero-modes to the entropy of strictly supersymmetric black holes agrees with the corresponding limit of black holes at finite temperature. This success gives confidence that the modes we focus on dominate at low energy.

The study of black holes at very low temperature is promising for illuminating major issues of current interest, such as the black hole information loss paradox (some recent reviews [69, 70]) and its relation to quantum chaos [71, 72]. Some studies in these research directions focus on specific UV-completions, such as the SYK-model, that depend on many additional details. Others consider properties of the Euclidean quantum path integral which, by its nature, is not constructive.

Our results highlight that the supersymmetric ground state is largely inert, only a limited number of modes contribute to the entropy, and the UV aspects of the theory are decoupled as well. The explicit spacetime wave functions also permit the couplings to the ambient spacetime, beyond the near-horizon region, to be determined precisely. Therefore, this simplified setting may offer a useful toy model that captures the essential parts of the quantum information flow between the black hole and its environment.

Acknowledgements

This research was supported in part by the U.S. Department of Energy under grant DE-SC0007859. SC is supported by the Samsung Scholarship, the Leinweber Graduate Fellowship and the Rackham Predoctoral Fellowship. We thank Luca Iliesiu and Joaquin Turiaci for comments.

References

[1] S. Sachdev and J. Ye, Gapless spin fluid ground state in a random, quantum Heisenberg magnet, *Phys. Rev. Lett.* **70**, 3339 (1993). doi: 10.1103/PhysRevLett.70.3339.

[2] S. Sachdev, Holographic metals and the fractionalized Fermi liquid, *Phys. Rev. Lett.* **105**, 151602 (2010). doi: 10.1103/PhysRevLett.105.151602.

[3] A. Kitaev, A simple model of quantum holography (Feb. 12, April 7, and May 27, 2015). URL http://online.kitp.ucsb.edu/online/entangled15/.

[4] V. Rosenhaus, An introduction to the SYK model, *J. Phys. A* **52**, 323001 (2019). doi: 10.1088/1751-8121/ab2ce1.

[5] J. Maldacena, D. Stanford, and Z. Yang, Conformal symmetry and its breaking in two dimensional nearly Anti-de-Sitter space, *PTEP* **2016**(12), 12C104 (2016). doi: 10.1093/ptep/ptw124.

[6] F. Larsen, A nAttractor mechanism for nAdS$_2$/nCFT$_1$ holography, *JHEP* **04**, 055 (2019). doi: 10.1007/JHEP04(2019)055.

[7] W. Fu, D. Gaiotto, J. Maldacena, and S. Sachdev, Supersymmetric Sachdev-Ye-Kitaev models, *Phys. Rev. D* **95**(2), 026009 (2017). doi: 10.1103/PhysRevD. 95.026009. [Addendum: *Phys. Rev. D* **95**, 069904 (2017)].

[8] S. Förste, J. Kames-King, and M. Wiesner, Towards the holographic dual of $N = 2$ SYK, *JHEP* **03**, 028 (2018). doi: 10.1007/JHEP03(2018)028.

[9] S. R. Coleman, J. Preskill, and F. Wilczek, Quantum hair on black holes, *Nucl. Phys. B* **378**, 175–246 (1992). doi: 10.1016/0550-3213(92)90008-Y.

[10] S. Kim and K.-M. Lee, 1/16-BPS black holes and giant gravitons in the AdS(5) X S**5 space, *JHEP* **12**, 077 (2006). doi: 10.1088/1126-6708/2006/12/077.

[11] S. M. Hosseini, K. Hristov, and A. Zaffaroni, An extremization principle for the entropy of rotating BPS black holes in AdS$_5$, *JHEP* **07**, 106 (2017). doi: 10.1007/JHEP07(2017)106.

[12] S. Choi, J. Kim, S. Kim, and J. Nahmgoong, Large AdS black holes from QFT (10. 2018).

[13] J. Preskill, P. Schwarz, A. D. Shapere, S. Trivedi, and F. Wilczek, Limitations on the statistical description of black holes, *Mod. Phys. Lett.* **A6**, 2353–2362 (1991). doi: 10.1142/S0217732391002773.

[14] J. M. Maldacena and L. Susskind, D-branes and fat black holes, *Nucl. Phys. B.* **475**, 679–690 (1996). doi: 10.1016/0550-3213(96)00323-9.

[15] M. Cvetic and F. Larsen, Near horizon geometry of rotating black holes in five-dimensions, *Nucl. Phys. B* **531**, 239–255 (1998). doi: 10.1016/S0550-3213(98)00604-X.

[16] R. Dijkgraaf, J. M. Maldacena, G. W. Moore, and E. P. Verlinde, A Black hole Farey tail (5. 2000).

[17] P. Kraus and F. Larsen, Partition functions and elliptic genera from super-gravity, *JHEP* **01**, 002 (2007). doi: 10.1088/1126-6708/2007/01/002.

[18] H. K. Kunduri, J. Lucietti, and H. S. Reall, Near-horizon symmetries of extremal black holes, *Class. Quant. Grav.* **24**, 4169–4190 (2007). doi: 10.1088/0264-9381/24/16/012.

[19] R. Camporesi and A. Higuchi, Spectral functions and zeta functions in hyperbolic spaces, *J. Math. Phys.* **35**, 4217–4246 (1994). doi: 10.1063/1.530850.

[20] S. Banerjee, R. K. Gupta, and A. Sen, Logarithmic corrections to extremal black hole entropy from quantum entropy function, *JHEP* **03**, 147 (2011). doi: 10.1007/JHEP03(2011)147.

[21] A. Sen, Logarithmic corrections to $N = 2$ black hole entropy: An infrared window into the microstates, *Gen. Rel. Grav.* **44**(5), 1207–1266 (2012). doi: 10.1007/s10714-012-1336-5.

[22] F. Larsen and P. Lisbao, Quantum corrections to supergravity on AdS$_2 \times S^2$, *Phys. Rev. D* **91**(8), 084056 (2015). doi: 10.1103/PhysRevD.91.084056.

[23] A. M. Charles and F. Larsen, A one-loop test of the near-AdS$_2$/near-CFT$_1$ correspondence, *JHEP* **07** (07), 186 (2020). doi: 10.1007/JHEP07(2020)186.

[24] J. Distler and H. Kawai, Conformal field theory and 2D quantum gravity, *Nucl. Phys. B* **321**, 509–527 (1989). doi: 10.1016/0550-3213(89)90354-4.

[25] J. Engelsöy, T. G. Mertens, and H. Verlinde, An investigation of AdS$_2$ backre-action and holography, *JHEP* **07**, 139 (2016). doi: 10.1007/JHEP07(2016)139.

[26] T. G. Mertens, G. J. Turiaci, and H. L. Verlinde, Solving the Schwarzian via the conformal bootstrap, *JHEP* **08**, 136 (2017). doi: 10.1007/JHEP08(2017)136.

[27] B. Oblak. *BMS Particles in Three Dimensions*. PhD thesis, Brussels U. (2016).

[28] D. Stanford and E. Witten, Fermionic localization of the Schwarzian theory, *JHEP* **10**, 008 (2017). doi: 10.1007/JHEP10(2017)008.

[29] J. M. Maldacena, The large N limit of superconformal field theories and supergravity, *Adv. Theor. Math. Phys.* **2**, 231–252 (1998). doi: 10.1023/A: 1026654312961.

[30] A. Strominger, AdS(2) quantum gravity and string theory, *JHEP* **01**, 007 (1999). doi: 10.1088/1126-6708/1999/01/007.

[31] M. Spradlin and A. Strominger, Vacuum states for AdS(2) black holes, *JHEP* **11**, 021 (1999). doi: 10.1088/1126-6708/1999/11/021.

[32] A. Castro, D. Grumiller, F. Larsen, and R. McNees, Holographic description of AdS(2) black holes, *JHEP* **11**, 052 (2008). doi: 10.1088/1126-6708/2008/11/052.

[33] A. Castro and W. Song, Comments on AdS$_2$ gravity (11. 2014).

[34] J. Maldacena and D. Stanford, Remarks on the Sachdev-Ye-Kitaev model, *Phys. Rev. D* **94**(10), 106002 (2016). doi: 10.1103/PhysRevD.94.106002.

[35] D. Bagrets, A. Altland, and A. Kamenev, Sachdev–Ye–Kitaev model as Liouville quantum mechanics, *Nucl. Phys. B* **911**, 191–205 (2016). doi: 10.1016/j.nuclphysb.2016.08.002.

[36] J. Hong, F. Larsen, and J. T. Liu, The scales of black holes with nAdS$_2$ geometry, *JHEP* **10**, 260 (2019). doi: 10.1007/JHEP10(2019)260.

[37] P. Kraus and F. Larsen, Microscopic black hole entropy in theories with higher derivatives, *JHEP* **09**, 034 (2005). doi: 10.1088/1126-6708/2005/09/034.

[38] P. Kraus and F. Larsen, Holographic gravitational anomalies, *JHEP* **01**, 022 (2006). doi: 10.1088/1126-6708/2006/01/022.

[39] R. K. Gupta and A. Sen, Ads(3)/CFT(2) to Ads(2)/CFT(1), *JHEP* **04**, 034 (2009). doi: 10.1088/1126-6708/2009/04/034.

[40] V. Balasubramanian, J. de Boer, M. M. Sheikh-Jabbari, and J. Simon, What is a chiral 2d CFT? And what does it have to do with extremal black holes? *JHEP* **02**, 017 (2010). doi: 10.1007/JHEP02(2010)017.

[41] A. Castro, C. Keeler, and F. Larsen, Three dimensional origin of AdS$_2$ quantum gravity, *JHEP* **07**, 033 (2010). doi: 10.1007/JHEP07(2010)033.

[42] S. Bhattacharyya, B. Panda, and A. Sen, Heat kernel expansion and extremal Kerr-Newmann black hole entropy in Einstein-Maxwell theory, *JHEP* **08**, 084 (2012). doi: 10.1007/JHEP08(2012)084.

[43] C. Keeler, F. Larsen, and P. Lisbao, Logarithmic corrections to $N \geq 2$ black hole entropy, *Phys. Rev. D* **90**(4), 043011 (2014). doi: 10.1103/PhysRevD.90.043011.

[44] A. M. Charles and F. Larsen, Universal corrections to non-extremal black hole entropy in $\mathcal{N} \geq 2$ supergravity, *JHEP* **06**, 200 (2015). doi: 10.1007/JHEP06(2015)200.

[45] S. Banerjee, R. K. Gupta, I. Mandal, and A. Sen, Logarithmic corrections to $N = 4$ and $N = 8$ black hole entropy: A one loop test of quantum gravity, *JHEP* **11**, 143 (2011). doi: 10.1007/JHEP11(2011)143.

[46] A. Sen, Microscopic and macroscopic entropy of extremal black holes in string theory, *Gen. Rel. Grav.* **46**, 1711 (2014). doi: 10.1007/s10714-014-1711-5.

[47] A. Sen, Quantum entropy function from AdS(2)/CFT(1) correspondence, *Int. J. Mod. Phys. A* **24**, 4225–4244 (2009). doi: 10.1142/S0217751X09045893.

[48] A. Sen, Logarithmic corrections to Schwarzschild and other non-extremal black hole entropy in different dimensions, *JHEP* **04**, 156 (2013). doi: 10.1007/JHEP04(2013)156.

[49] M. Heydeman, L. V. Iliesiu, G. J. Turiaci, and W. Zhao, The statistical mechanics of near-BPS black holes (11. 2020).

[50] A. Jevicki, K. Suzuki, and J. Yoon, Bi-Local holography in the SYK model, *JHEP* **07**, 007 (2016). doi: 10.1007/JHEP07(2016)007.

[51] A. Jevicki and K. Suzuki, Bi-Local holography in the SYK model: Perturbations, *JHEP* **11**, 046 (2016). doi: 10.1007/JHEP11(2016)046.

[52] G. Turiaci and H. Verlinde, Towards a 2d QFT analog of the SYK model, *JHEP* **10**, 167 (2017). doi: 10.1007/JHEP10(2017)167.

[53] J. Liu and Y. Zhou, Note on global symmetry and SYK model, *JHEP* **05**, 099 (2019). doi: 10.1007/JHEP05(2019)099.

[54] J. Maldacena and A. Milekhin, SYK wormhole formation in real time, *JHEP* **04**, 258 (2021). doi: 10.1007/JHEP04(2021)258.

[55] C. Teitelboim, Gravitation and Hamiltonian structure in two space-time dimensions, *Phys. Lett. B* **126**, 41–45 (1983). doi: 10.1016/0370-2693(83)90012-6.

[56] R. Jackiw, Lower dimensional gravity, *Nucl. Phys. B* **252**, 343–356 (1985). doi: 10.1016/0550-3213(85)90448-1.

[57] A. Almheiri and J. Polchinski, Models of AdS$_2$ backreaction and holography, *JHEP* **11**, 014 (2015). doi: 10.1007/JHEP11(2015)014.

[58] K. Jensen, Chaos in AdS$_2$ holography, *Phys. Rev. Lett.* **117**(11), 111601 (2016). doi: 10.1103/PhysRevLett.117.111601.

[59] S. Forste and I. Golla, Nearly AdS$_2$ sugra and the super-Schwarzian, *Phys. Lett. B* **771**, 157–161 (2017). doi: 10.1016/j.physletb.2017.05.039.

[60] M. Cvetič and I. Papadimitriou, AdS$_2$ holographic dictionary, *JHEP* **12**, 008 (2016). doi: 10.1007/JHEP12(2016)008. [Erratum: *JHEP* **01**, 120 (2017)].

[61] P. Nayak, A. Shukla, R. M. Soni, S. P. Trivedi, and V. Vishal, On the dynamics of near-extremal black holes, *JHEP* **09**, 048 (2018). doi: 10.1007/JHEP09(2018)048.

[62] U. Moitra, S. P. Trivedi, and V. Vishal, Extremal and near-extremal black holes and near-CFT$_1$, *JHEP* **07**, 055 (2019). doi: 10.1007/JHEP07(2019)055.

[63] P. Saad, S. H. Shenker, and D. Stanford, JT gravity as a matrix integral (3. 2019).

[64] L. V. Iliesiu, S. S. Pufu, H. Verlinde, and Y. Wang, An exact quantization of Jackiw-Teitelboim gravity, *JHEP* **11**, 091 (2019). doi: 10.1007/JHEP11(2019)091.

[65] T. G. Mertens and G. J. Turiaci, Defects in Jackiw-Teitelboim quantum gravity, *JHEP* **08**, 127 (2019). doi: 10.1007/JHEP08(2019)127.

[66] D. Stanford and E. Witten, JT gravity and the ensembles of random matrix theory, *Adv. Theor. Math. Phys.* **24**(6), 1475–1680 (2020). doi: 10.4310/ATMP.2020.v24.n6.a4.

[67] L. V. Iliesiu, On 2D gauge theories in Jackiw-Teitelboim gravity (9. 2019).

[68] L. V. Iliesiu and G. J. Turiaci, The statistical mechanics of near-extremal black holes, *JHEP* **05**, 145 (2021). doi: 10.1007/JHEP05(2021)145.

[69] A. Almheiri, T. Hartman, J. Maldacena, E. Shaghoulian, and A. Tajdini, The entropy of Hawking radiation, *Rev. Mod. Phys.* **93**(3), 035002 (2021). doi: 10.1103/RevModPhys.93.035002.

[70] S. Raju, Lessons from the Information Paradox (12. 2020).

[71] J. S. Cotler, G. Gur-Ari, M. Hanada, J. Polchinski, P. Saad, S. H. Shenker, D. Stanford, A. Streicher, and M. Tezuka, Black holes and random matrices, *JHEP* **05**, 118 (2017). doi: 10.1007/JHEP05(2017)118. [Erratum: *JHEP* **09**, 002 (2018)].

[72] P. Saad, S. H. Shenker, and D. Stanford, A semiclassical ramp in SYK and in gravity (6. 2018).

What the World Looks Like Upside Down

Jordan Cotler

Society of Fellows
Harvard University
Cambridge, MA 02138, USA
jcotler@fas.harvard.edu

Frank pushed through the turnstile at Gröna Lund, feasting his eyes on the pastel-colored roller coasters before sizing up the drop towers needling the summer sky. "I want to ride them all," he declared to Betsy. Not one for roller coasters myself, I looked out past the rides and ice cream stands to the waterfront, and to Stockholm on the shore beyond. I walked up by Frank as he was mentally planning the quickest route to the ride queues. "I want to ride that one first," he said, pointing towards a purple steel coaster with a vertical hairpin loop. "Why that one?" I asked. He replied, "I want to see what the world looks like upside down."

I first met Frank when I was a sophomore at MIT and he has since had a profound impact on my life. I remember walking through the entrance hall to the Center for Theoretical Physics and on one wall were research statements provided by each Professor listing their subfields of study. Most said something along the lines of:

String theory and black holes
M-theory
Supersymmetry

or

Collider physics
Jet analysis
Effective field theory

Frank's statement stood out as being a single sentence which read:

Interests: The laws of physics, and anything which satisfies them.

This one sentence aptly sums up Frank's unique approach to physics. He has worked on essentially all subfields of theoretical physics and sees everything as part of a connected whole. Further, he has a preternatural intuition for ripe problems, fluidly moving between different subjects to actualize original and fundamental contributions.

When I first started working with Frank, I was struck by his kindness and intellectual generosity. He initially gave me a list of research problems to consider, spanning diverse areas including quantum foundations, quantum optics, and quantum field theory. As we began exploring ideas together, I experienced firsthand how Frank operates. For context, I had talked with other professors about some of my own research ideas and many were quick to point out the flaws and tell me why they wouldn't work. Frank was different. Upon initially hearing an idea, he wouldn't judge or shoot it down, but rather find its virtue and build upon it. This process of ideating with Frank is among my favorite activities — he is improvisational and masterful, but ensures it is not a solo act. These physics jazz sessions could last for hours, until we had filled his chalkboard with lists of ideas and directions spanning wide stretches of physics and the imagination. By taking a broad enough view of physics, any idea could find a home. But how to shape these ideas into concrete calculations? "The work will teach us how to do it," Frank said, citing a fortune cookie prophecy taped to his door.

In physics, there is an almost mystical interplay between discovery and creation. Does one create new laws of physics, or merely discover them? Sidestepping this Platonic conundrum, I can say that I, along with many others, view Frank's physics as *inventive*. Among the more famous examples of this kind are his pioneering work on anyons, his ingenious conjuring of axions, and more recently his vision of time crystals. When you read any of these papers, it's hard not to think: Who else could have thought of *that*? And then you appreciate how incredibly clever it all is. I've sometimes wondered if the reason so many of Frank's creations have been realized in nature is because the universe also thinks they're a good idea.

Even from the early days of our collaboration, Frank instilled in me the importance of *experiments*. Physics research can be imaginative and fanciful, but we need to always have in our minds the connection to reality. He emphasized that this is a form of necessary self-discipline; otherwise we might accidentally channel our efforts to understand a beautiful world in our heads that has little connection to the universe in which we live. Frank would constantly bring up the question of how our ideas might one day be realized in experiments, and he was always scouting out experimental opportunities.

One summer, Frank invited me to visit him and Betsy at their home in New Hampshire. Their house is situated next to a lake and adjacent to picturesque New England woods. Betsy drove me up from Cambridge since Frank was already at the house, and she parked the car right at the edge of the lake. She explained that their house was on a piece of land connected to the woods' edge by a narrow isthmus. When the lake swelled due to rain, the isthmus would become so narrow that it was advised to take off your shoes and socks and walk across the narrow balance beam of land, the water lapping at your toes. So, I took off my shoes and socks and walked across. To work with Frank, you have to get your feet wet.

When I reached the other side, there was Frank — sitting on the porch looking at the water. He was wearing a fishing hat and accompanying vest, his chest pockets filled with pens of all colors and what appeared to be punch cards. I thought we might be going fishing, but in fact we were going on a long walk to fish for ideas.

We hiked through the woods together for a long while — our feet crunching twigs and leaves, our minds churning equations and connections. If a particularly notable thought came up, Frank would pause and slip a punch card out of his pocket, jotting down a key phrase with an appropriately colored pen. There was something profound about pondering nature while being immersed in it, with Frank as my guide.

Betsy and Frank were gracious hosts. Each morning Frank would make me a fantastic parfait-esque concoction containing every superfood known to man. And we would end each evening with a scoop of Cherry Garcia ice cream from their impressive stash in the freezer.

I remember one night sitting on the porch, talking about our long list of projects and the interesting physics that lay ahead of us. Frank turned to me and said, "You know, I think you have good taste in problems. You should trust your instincts, and as you move forward in your career you should consider picking problems for yourself." Those words were most impactful and formative to my development as a physicist. Here was this person who I held in such high esteem, giving me the confidence to grow into an independent scientist. In his gentle way, Frank was encouraging me to trust myself and my own ideas. I consider this to be the highest form of teaching — to help a student become an independent thinker.

That fall began my last year at MIT, and I was applying for graduate school. Frank and Betsy were doing more traveling, and Frank and I continued our collaborations over Skype when he was not in Cambridge. In January I visited Frank and Betsy at Arizona State University where they would escape the harsh winter during MIT's annual Independent Activities Period. I was with Frank in his office when I got a call from Patrick Hayden (who would become my PhD adviser) telling me that I had been admitted to Stanford. Frank and I were both delighted with the news and he suggested we go get a drink to celebrate, though I reminded him I wasn't yet 21. So we went out for Mexican food instead. Frank, Betsy and I toasted my acceptance to graduate school over Cokes.

My leaving MIT for Stanford was also a crossroads in my working relationship with Frank as we would no longer be able to regularly meet in person to engage in long discussions in front of his blackboard. But we overcame distance by continuing our collaborations via Skype throughout my time in graduate school and thereafter. When I would have the opportunity to see Frank in person, I would be so fortunate as to travel the world.

Aside from trips to Arizona and a memorable trip to China, I traveled to Stockholm for several weeks every summer for the "Quantum Connections" workshop at NORDITA. These workshops are a treat — they bring together experts from around the world to speak on a veritable smorgasbord of physics topics that samples exciting developments across many subfields. A consistent core of the participants are Frank's collaborators and former students. After attending for several years, the workshop became like a family reunion, with Frank and Betsy the patriarch and matriarch. There was a palpable feeling that Frank's academic family was an extension of his own. This closeness was reinforced by group outings to museums, delicious Swedish restaurants, and of course the much beloved amusement park Gröna Lund. During the last several years, the workshop and accompanying summer school intersected with the Swedish midsummer celebrations in which we would enjoy a wonderful feast followed by dancing around a maypole singing Swedish folk songs while wearing flower wreaths on our heads.

A highlight of my Swedish travels is the yearly trip to the Nobel Museum, and not just because of the ice cream in the accompanying café. The museum contains artifacts and documents from Alfred Nobel on the founding of his eponymous prize, but also donated objects of significance from Nobel Laureates — a microscope, a radio antenna, a notebook, a Skinner box to name just a few. A notable feature of the museum is the banners — each with an image of a Nobel Laureate — riding on tracks across the ceiling like shirts at a drycleaner. I would gaze upward at the laureates parading across the ceiling and be inspired to dream about timeless physics problems which still elude us.

I've always been struck by Frank's boundless curiosity and sense of wonder. It's perhaps well captured by his Skype tagline: "Tell me something interesting, preferably true (even if not provable)." One example of his curious nature is when he decided to research what it would be like to be able to see an extra color. Not only is Frank masterful at asking good questions, he knows how to operationalize an idea in order to work his way towards an answer. In this case, Frank purchased special cameras and developed an augmented reality interface to create the perception of extended color vision. Along the way, he learned how to code in new programming languages, figured out the necessary background in electronics, and read extensively on the theory of color perception going all the way back to Goethe and Maxwell, true to his fortune cookie maxim that the work would teach him how to do it.

Implicit in Frank's creative process is a large degree of discipline. He lives a structured life which allows him to develop and nurture unstructured thoughts. He has been known, upon waking up in the morning, to factor a randomly generated large integer in his head without putting a pen to paper, and by the end of the day he makes sure to have walked the requisite daily minimum number of steps or stairs as tracked on his Fitbit. When not thinking about physics, he can often be found solving puzzles from a puzzle book or newspaper, or learning Swedish from a language app. Frank has become so comfortable with the Swedish language that once when we were standing in line at a Swedish ice cream shop, he was reading a newspaper article posted on the wall and turned to me to suggest I read it too. I had to remind him that it was written in Swedish! Frank's curiosity goes well beyond physics. He recently taught himself to juggle by watching YouTube videos, and has become proficient in Python and is learning to program artificial neural networks.

Frank has a gentle personality and is known for his spontaneous sense of humor. Once, I witnessed him during a dinner hold up a bread roll and a stone and ask, "Quick Betsy, what's this?" to which without missing a beat she responded, "Rock and roll!" On another occasion I was with Frank in China when he was swarmed by college students who brought copies of his books for him to autograph. One student presented him with a copy of the Feynman Lectures. Not wanting to disappoint, Frank opened up the front cover and signed it "Richard Feynman."

Frank's natural mode is being "at play", whether working on an art project or puzzling about supersymmetry and grand unification. No question is too whimsical to not be taken seriously; no question is too profound to be out of bounds. Frank delights in the joy of discovery and wants to bring us along for the fun.

I am so fortunate that Frank has included me in on the fun for nearly a decade. I feel tremendously grateful for his mentorship and friendship.

Frank and I on the porch in New Hampshire in 2014.

https://doi.org/10.1142/9789811251948_0007

Gravitons in the Strong-Coupling Regime

J. Gamboa[*,‡], R. MacKenzie[†,§], and F. Méndez[*,¶]

Departamento de Física
Universidad de Santiago de Chile
Casilla 307, Santiago, Chile
[†]*Département de physique*
Université de Montréal
Montréal, QC, Canada, H3C 3J7
[‡]*jorge.gamboa@usach.cl*
[§]*richard.mackenzie@umontreal.ca*
[¶]*fernando.mendez@usach.cl*

In the context of gravity in the strong-coupling regime, the propagation amplitude of gravity coupled to relativistic particles undergoing geodesic separation is calculated exactly. Geodesic separation gives rise to boundary terms associated with the $h_\times$ and h_+ graviton components. At low temperatures the propagation amplitude vanishes, implying no graviton propagation in this regime.

1. A Personal Note from One of the Authors

Before launching into gravitational fields, quantum fluctuations and path integrals, I would like to offer a few words about my experiences as a young physicist working with Frank Wilczek. Soon after I had completed the first year of my PhD at UCSB and found myself faced with the prospect of finding a PhD supervisor, the corridors of Broida Hall and the ITP (at the time occupying the top floor of Ellison Hall on the UCSB campus) were abuzz with the exciting news that none other than Frank Wilczek would be joining the ITP as one of its permanent staff. *Frank Wilczek!* I exclaimed, sharing the excitement of those around me, privately wondering who Frank Wilczek was. (I hope I can be forgiven for this lack of awareness; my excuse is that I had studied engineering as an undergraduate.)

A few months later, I found myself in Frank's office, timidly listening to his passionate description of his latest obsession: what was known at the time as new inflation. I left his office more than a little bewildered, with a stack of papers by Albrecht and Steinhardt, Linde and others (photocopied from hot-off-the-press preprints — remember those?! — by one of the ITP staff), with the task of going through them for our next discussion. A few weeks later, the same scenario played out, with inflation replaced by Frank's newest latest obsession, rare K decays. After a few more such experiences (one of which, on grand unified theories, yielded my first paper and cemented the fact that, yes, I would do my PhD under Frank's supervision), I landed on the subject that stuck (probably to Frank's relief!): solitons. I can conjure in my mind the sparkle in Frank's eyes as he explained the basic facts of 't Hooft-Polyakov monopoles, and I was hooked.

While working diligently on my PhD under Frank's tutelage, I of course witnessed Frank in action outside the scope of our work together. I think Frank epitomized the underlying philosophy of the ITP: putting people together from different fields and seeing what would come out of it. Frank would ask penetrating questions at seminars on every subject from Aharonov to Zeeman. He was always working in parallel on several subjects at a time and producing papers at a bewildering rate; it seemed like every week he had a new latest obsession or clever idea that had him brimming with excitement. Some would turn out to not bear fruit, many would, and some would turn out to be foundational.

I recall wondering if he had gone off the rails when one day he told me about how particles can be neither fermions nor bosons in two dimensions; how could someone so brilliant be thinking about something so crazy, I privately thought. That work, of course, falls into the "foundational" category and is certainly among Frank's greatest achievements. It also epitomizes much of Frank's work: very clever and creative, not overly technical, very physical and intuitive.

Doing my PhD under Frank's supervision came about due to many instances of serependipity; it is certainly one of my life's greatest priviledges to have done so. It is therefore an honour to contribute to this 70th birthday festschrift volume. Happy birthday, Frank! — Richard MacKenzie

2. Gravitons in the Strong-Coupling Regime

In a recent article, Parikh, Wilczek and Zahariade [1] have suggested that the geodesic separation [2] of a pair of freely falling masses includes a stochastic component due to quantum fluctuations of the gravitational field. This noise depends on the state of the gravitational field; surprisingly, for certain types of state (such as thermal or squeezed states), the effect is enhanced and potentially detectable. This gives rise to the tantalizing possibility that the growing array of gravitational wave observatories might also provide the first experimental evidence for quantum gravity effects.

In this letter, we would like to focus on a variation of the approach followed in [1] which suggests new aspects of quantum gravity arising as a consequence of the boundary conditions when the effective action of quantum gravity is calculated via the path integral in Euclidean space.

The variation that we will consider is the strong-coupling limit (SCL) that was originally proposed by Klauder in [9] and extended to string theory in [10–13] and to quantum gravity in [15]. The same SCL also underlies (with some variations) work in lattice gauge theory [14], but in this paper we follow [10–13] and [16–21].

Following Klauder's proposal for a scalar field theory [9], in the SCL one makes the replacement $(\partial_\mu \varphi)^2 \to \dot{\varphi}^2$. Thus, instead of

$$\mathcal{L} = \frac{1}{2}(\partial_\mu \varphi)^2 - V(\varphi),$$

the dynamics is governed by

$$\mathcal{L} = \frac{1}{2}\dot{\varphi}^2 - V(\varphi).$$

In other words, different points in space are decoupled from one another and the problem reduces to a quantum mechanical one with an infinite number of uncoupled degrees of freedom.

In order to see the physical content of this approximation, let's consider a Nambu string described by the Lagrangian [22]

$$\mathcal{L} = -T\sqrt{-\sigma_{\mu\nu}\sigma^{\mu\nu}}, \tag{1}$$

where $T = 1/(2\pi\alpha')$ is the string tension, α' is the Regge slope and $\sigma_{\mu\nu} = \dot{X}_\mu X'_\nu - \dot{X}_\nu X'_\mu$ is the area tensor. Here $\dot{X}_\mu$ and X'_μ denote derivatives with respect to the coordinates of the worldsheet, τ and σ respectively. Note that the string tension plays the same role as the mass of a relativistic particle with Lagrangian $L = -m\sqrt{-\dot{x}_\mu \dot{x}^\mu}$.

From (1) one gets the Hamiltonian constraints

$$\mathcal{H}_\perp = \frac{1}{2}\left(\mathcal{P}^2 + T^2 X'^2\right) = 0, \tag{2}$$

$$\mathcal{H}_1 = \mathcal{P} \cdot X' = 0.$$

The limit $T \to 0$ (or equivalently the limit $\alpha' \to \infty$) describes a tensionless string, for which the string spectrum is massless. (With some modifications, this procedure can also be extended to two-dimensional quantum gravity models; see [21].)

The above ideas can be implemented to study the case of gravity in the SCL. Indeed, using the ADM formalism [23], we can write the constraints

$$\mathcal{H}_\perp = G_{ijkl}[g^{(3)}]\pi^{ij}\pi^{kl} + \frac{1}{16\pi G}\sqrt{g^{(3)}}R^{(3)}, \tag{3}$$

$$\mathcal{H}_i = -\pi^j_{i\,;j}, \tag{4}$$

where $g^{(3)}_{ij}$ are the components of the spatial metric, $G_{ijkl}[g^{(3)}]$ is the supermetric and $R^{(3)}$ is the scalar curvature of the three-dimensional spatial section.

Note that the factor $(16\pi G)^{-1}$ plays the same role as the string tension in the previous example while Newton's constant G is the analog of the Regge slope; consequently, the SCL corresponds to the limit

$$G \to \infty. \tag{5}$$

Thus, from the previous point of view, the SCL is a description in which the Lagrangian only contains derivatives with respect to time and each point of spacetime in this limit is causally disconnected. Mathematically, this corresponds to the replacement of the Poincaré group by the so-called Carroll group [24–27].

Linearized gravity in this limit is greatly simplified since the usual Einstein equations $\Box h_{\mu\nu} = -\kappa T_{\mu\nu}$ reduce to

$$\ddot{h}_{\mu\nu} = -\kappa T_{\mu\nu}, \tag{6}$$

to which we must add dynamics for the matter.

Consider a pair of freely falling particles with geodesic separation $\xi_\mu(t)$. Whereas at weak coupling the system would be described by the Einstein-Hilbert action coupled to the two particles (see (2) of [1]), at strong coupling it is described by the following Lagrangian:

$$L = \frac{1}{2}\dot{h}_{\mu\nu}\dot{h}^{\mu\nu} + \frac{m}{2}\dot{\xi}_\mu\dot{\xi}^\mu + \frac{\alpha}{4}\dot{h}_{\mu\nu}(\dot{\xi}^\mu\xi^\nu + \xi^\mu\dot{\xi}^\nu), \tag{7}$$

where m is a mass and α is a positive coupling constant which is proportional to m. In what follows, we will set $m = 1$ for simplicity. The Lagrangian (7) is the starting point of our analysis.

The equations derived from (7) are

$$\ddot{h}_{\mu\nu} = -\frac{\alpha}{4}(\ddot{\xi}_\mu\xi_\nu + \ddot{\xi}_\nu\xi_\mu + 2\dot{\xi}_\mu\dot{\xi}_\nu),$$

$$\ddot{\xi}_\mu = -\frac{\alpha}{2}\ddot{h}_{\mu\nu}\xi^\nu. \tag{8}$$

Note that $h_{\mu\nu}$ is a cyclic coordinate, so the first of these can be integrated.

The quantum theory is defined via the Euclidean path integral; the propagation amplitude is [28, 29]

$$G[\phi', \phi; \beta] = \int \mathcal{D}h \mathcal{D}\xi \, e^{-S}, \tag{9}$$

where, of course, we assume some judicious gauge choice has been made and where

$$S = \int_{-\beta/2}^{+\beta/2} dt \, L.$$

The notation ϕ in (9) collectively denotes $(h_{\mu\nu}, \xi_\mu)$ so $G[\phi', \phi; \beta]$ is the amplitude to go from an initial configuration $\phi = (h, \xi)$ at Euclidean time $-\beta/2$ to a final configuration $\phi' = (h', \xi')$ at Euclidean time $+\beta/2$. The path integral is over all configurations interpolating between the initial and final configurations.

In order to compute the effective action of gravity, we integrate over ξ. Since the action is quadratic in ξ this gives, up to an overall h-independent factor,

$$G[h', h; \beta] = \int \mathcal{D}h \, \det \left[-\delta_{\mu\nu}\partial_t^2 - \frac{\alpha}{2}\ddot{h}_{\mu\nu} \right]^{-1/2} \times \, e^{-\int_{-\beta/2}^{+\beta/2} dt \frac{1}{2}\dot{h}^2}. \tag{10}$$

To simplify the discussion, we define

$$\mathbb{M}_{\mu\nu} = -\delta_{\mu\nu}\partial_t^2 - \frac{\alpha}{2}\ddot{h}_{\mu\nu}. \tag{11}$$

We use the transverse-traceless (TT) gauge in which $h_{\mu\nu}$ is traceless and has the form

$$h_{\mu\nu} = e_{\mu\nu}^+ h_+(t) + e_{\mu\nu}^\times h_\times(t), \tag{12}$$

where $e_{\mu\nu}^{+,\times}$ are polarization tensors which we assume are constant. If the system describes gravitational waves propagating along the z-axis, then the perturbation can be written

$$[h] = \begin{pmatrix} 0 & 0 & 0 & 0 \\ 0 & h_+ & h_\times & 0 \\ 0 & h_\times & -h_+ & 0 \\ 0 & 0 & 0 & 0 \end{pmatrix}. \tag{13}$$

Ignoring an irrelevant constant, the determinant in (10) is

$$\det \mathbb{M} = \det \begin{pmatrix} -\partial_t^2 - \frac{\alpha}{2}\ddot{h}_+ & -\frac{\alpha}{2}\ddot{h}_\times \\ -\frac{\alpha}{2}\ddot{h}_\times & -\partial_t^2 + \frac{\alpha}{2}\ddot{h}_+ \end{pmatrix}. \tag{14}$$

We choose the polarization $h_\times = 0$, giving

$$\det \mathbb{M} = \det \left(-\partial_t^2 + \frac{\alpha}{2}\ddot{h}_+\right) \det \left(-\partial_t^2 - \frac{\alpha}{2}\ddot{h}_+\right).$$
$$\equiv \det \mathbb{M}_1 \det \mathbb{M}_2. \tag{15}$$

For definiteness, we focus on the operator $\mathbb{M}_1$ (the corresponding result for $\mathbb{M}_2$ is given in (24)), which can be factorized as follows

$$-\partial_t^2 + \frac{\alpha}{2}\ddot{h}_+ = \left(-\partial_t + \dot{V}\right)\left(\partial_t + \dot{V}\right), \tag{16}$$

where $V(t)$ is defined through the Riccati equation

$$-\ddot{V} + \dot{V}^2 = \frac{\alpha}{2}\ddot{h}_+. \tag{17}$$

This procedure has become standard in supersymmetric quantum mechanics [30,31] where $V = -\ln \psi_0$ and ψ_0 is the ground state (assumed to be of zero energy in SUSY quantum mechanics) of the associated eigenvalue problem to (16).

Using (16), we can write the first determinant in (14) as

$$\det \mathbb{M}_1 = \det \left(-\partial_t^2 + \frac{\alpha}{2}\ddot{h}_+\right) = \det \left(-\partial_t + \dot{V}\right) \det \left(\partial_t + \dot{V}\right)$$
$$= \prod_{n=-\infty}^{\infty} \lambda_n^+ \prod_{n=-\infty}^{\infty} \lambda_n^- \tag{18}$$

where $\{\lambda_n^+, \lambda_n^-\}$ are the eigenvalues of the corresponding operators:

$$\left(-\partial_t + \dot{V}\right)\psi^+ = \lambda^+ \psi^+, \tag{19a}$$

$$\left(\partial_t + \dot{V}\right)\psi^- = \lambda^- \psi^-. \tag{19b}$$

These equations are easily solved; up to a multiplicative constant, we find

$$\psi^+(t) = e^{+V(t)-\lambda^+ t}, \tag{20a}$$

$$\psi^-(t) = e^{-V(t)+\lambda^- t}. \tag{20b}$$

The eigenvalues are determined by imposing periodic boundary conditions on $\psi^\pm$ on the interval $[-\beta/2, \beta/2]$, giving

$$\lambda_n^\pm = \frac{\Delta V(\beta) \mp 2n\pi i}{\beta}, \tag{21}$$

where $\Delta V(\beta) = V(\beta/2) - V(-\beta/2)$ and $n \in \mathbb{Z}$.

The determinant can be evaluated by substituting (21) into the logarithm of (18), giving

$$\log(\det \mathbb{M}_1) = \sum_{n=-\infty}^{\infty} \log\left[b^2 + a^2 n^2\right] \qquad (22)$$

where to simplify the evaluation of the sum we have written $a = 2\pi/\beta$ and $b = \Delta V(\beta)/\beta$. The sum can be evaluated by differentiating with respect to b [34,35], resulting in an integral representation of $\coth(\pi b/a)$ which can be integrated with respect to b, giving

$$\det \mathbb{M}_1 = \sinh^2 \frac{\Delta V(\beta)}{2}, \qquad (23)$$

where an irrelevant multiplicative constant related to regularization of the summation has been dropped.

The calculation of the determinant of the operator $\mathbb{M}_2$ is similar (although associated with another eigenvalue problem); the result is

$$\det \mathbb{M}_2 = \sinh^2 \frac{\Delta W(\beta)}{2}, \qquad (24)$$

where W is a function analogous to V that satisfies a different Riccati equation (cf. (17))

$$-\ddot{W} + \dot{W}^2 = -\frac{\alpha}{2}\ddot{h}_+, \qquad (25)$$

and $\Delta W(\beta) = W(\beta/2) - W(-\beta/2)$.

The propagation amplitude (10) becomes

$$G[h', h; \beta] = \int \mathcal{D}h_+ \det(\mathbb{M})^{-1/2} \times e^{-\int_{-\beta/2}^{+\beta/2} dt \frac{1}{2}\dot{h}_+^2}$$

$$= \int \mathcal{D}h_+ \frac{e^{-\int_{-\beta/2}^{+\beta/2} dt \frac{1}{2}\dot{h}_+^2}}{\sinh|\Delta V(\beta)|\sinh|\Delta W(\beta)|} \qquad (26)$$

It is interesting to examine the behavior of this expression in the low-temperature limit, that is, when $\beta \to \infty$. The functions $V(t)$ and $W(t)$ depend in a rather complicated manner on $h_+(t)$ through the Riccati equations (17) and (25), respectively. Define χ_V and χ_W by

$$\chi_V(t) = e^{-V(t)}, \qquad \chi_W(t) = e^{-W(t)}.$$

Then (17) and (25) become

$$\ddot{\chi}_V - \frac{\alpha}{2}\ddot{h}_+ \chi_V = 0, \qquad \ddot{\chi}_W + \frac{\alpha}{2}\ddot{h}_+ \chi_W = 0, \qquad (27)$$

while (26) reads

$$G[h', h; \beta] = \int \mathcal{D}h_+ \frac{e^{-\int_{-\beta/2}^{+\beta/2} dt \frac{1}{2}\dot{h}_+^2}}{\sinh\left|\log\frac{\chi_V(+\beta/2)}{\chi_V(-\beta/2)}\right| \sinh\left|\log\frac{\chi_W(+\beta/2)}{\chi_W(-\beta/2)}\right|}. \qquad (28)$$

It can be shown that under very general conditions one of the factors in the denominator of (28) diverges as $\beta \to \infty$ while the other remains finite. For example, for the special class of functions with behavior $\ddot{h}_+ \sim t^k$ ($k > 0$), χ_W remains finite while $\chi_V \to \infty$. More generally, χ_V and χ_W are zero-energy solutions of Schroedinger-like equations with potentials $\pm\ddot{h}_+(t)$, respectively. If $\ddot{h}_+$ is positive as $t \to \pm\infty$, χ_V diverges exponentially while χ_W is oscillatory; if $\ddot{h}_+$ is negative as $t \to \pm\infty$, the roles of χ_V and χ_W are reversed; finally, if $\ddot{h}_+$ changes sign, each of χ_V and χ_W will be oscillatory on one side and divergent on the other. In all cases, the denominator in (28) goes to infinity in the path integral over a large set of functions $\ddot{h}_+$, and the propagation amplitude goes to zero.

In other words, the graviton does not propagate at low temperatures, at least at strong coupling which is an ingredient for graviton condensation.

As a final comment, we would like to point out that classically the strong-coupling regime, at least mathematically in our context, resembles a Kasner universe for each point of spacetime. The decoupling between neighboring points of spacetime can be recognized as an example of a BKL oscillation [36] which is a kind of cosmological singularity. On the other hand, the vanishing of the propagation amplitude suggests that this cosmological singularity is smoothed out by quantum effects.

This work was supported by Dicyt 041831GR (J. G.), the Natural Sciences and Engineering Research Council of Canada (R. M.) and Dicyt 041931MF (F. M.). We thank Rafael Benguria for useful discussions.

References

[1] M. Parikh, F. Wilczek, and G. Zahariade, *Int. J. Mod. Phys. D* **29** (2020), 2042001; *ibid.*, arXiv:2010.08205 [hep-th]; ibid., arXiv:2010.08208 [hep-th].

[2] For a recent reference see for example, H. Culetu, arXiv:1605.05655 [gr-qc].

[3] F. Dyson, *Int. J. Mod. Phys. A* **28** (2013), 1330041.

[4] G. Amelino-Camelia, *Nature* 398, 216 (1999).

[5] G. Amelino-Camelia, *Phys. Rev. D* 62, 024015 (2000).

[6] E. P. Verlinde and K. M. Zurek, arXiv:1902.08207 [gr-qc].

[7] E. Verlinde and K. M. Zurek, *JHEP* 04, 209 (2020).

[8] T. Guerreiro, *Class. Quant. Grav.* 37, 155001 (2020).

[9] J. R. Klauder, *Commun. Math. Phys.* **18** (1970), 307–318.

[10] A. Schild, *Phys. Rev. D* **16** (1977), 1722.

[11] F. Lizzi and G. Sparano, *Phys. Lett. B* **232** (1989), 311–316.

[12] A. Karlhede and U. Lindstrom, *Class. Quant. Grav.* **3** (1986), L73–L75.

[13] J. Gamboa, C. Ramirez, and M. Ruiz-Altaba, *Phys. Lett. B* **225** (1989), 335–339; *ibid.*, *Nucl. Phys. B* **338** (1990), 143–187.

[14] See, for example, J. B. Kogut and L. Susskind, *Phys. Rev. D* **11** (1975), 395–408.

[15] C. J. Isham, *Proc. Roy. Soc. Lond. A* **351**, 209 (1976).

[16] M. Pilati, *Phys. Rev. D* **28**, 729 (1983).

[17] M. Henneaux, M. Pilati, and C. Teitelboim, *Phys. Lett.* **110B**, 123 (1982).

[18] C. Teitelboim, *Phys. Rev. D* **25**, 3159 (1982).

[19] R. A. Isaacson, *Phys. Rev.* **166**, 1272 (1968).

[20] R. A. Isaacson, PhD thesis, University of Maryland (1967).

[21] J. Gamboa, *Phys. Rev. Lett.* **74**, 1900 (1995).

[22] M. Kalb and P. Ramond, *Phys. Rev. D* **9** (1974), 2273–2284.

[23] R. L. Arnowitt, S. Deser, and C. W. Misner, *Gen. Rel. Grav.* **40** (2008), 1997–2027.

[24] J. M. Levy-Leblond, *Ann. Henri Poincaré* **3**, 1 (1965).

[25] C. Duval, G. W. Gibbons, P. A. Horvathy, and P.-M. Zhang, *Class. Quant. Grav.* **34**, no. 17, 175003 (2017).

[26] C. Duval, G. W. Gibbons, and P. A. Horvathy, *J. Phys. A* **47**, no. 33, 335204 (2014).

[27] E. Bergshoeff, J. Gomis, and G. Longhi, *Class. Quant. Grav.* **31**, no. 20, 205009 (2014).

[28] G. W. Gibbons, and S. W. Hawking, *Phys. Rev. D* **15**, 2738 (1977).

[29] G. W. Gibbons, and S. W. Hawking, *Phys. Rev. D* **15**, 2752 (1977).

[30] E. Witten, *Nucl. Phys. B* **188**, 513 (1981).

[31] F. Cooper and B. Freedman, *Ann. Phys.* **146**, 262 (1983).

[32] E. Gozzi, *Phys. Lett.* **129B**, 432 (1983). Erratum: [*Phys. Lett.* **134B**, 477 (1984)]).

[33] J. Gamboa and J. Zanelli, *Phys. Lett.* **165B**, 91 (1985).

[34] G. Dunne and D. Cangemi, *Ann. Phys.* **249**, 582 (1998).

[35] O. Espinosa, J. Gamboa, S. Lepe, and F. Mendez, *Phys. Lett. B* **520**, 421 (2001).

[36] V. Belinsky, I. Khalatnikov, and E. Lifshitz, *Adv. Phys.* **19**, 525 (1970).

© 2022 World Scientific Publishing Company
https://doi.org/10.1142/9789811251948_0008

Adventures in Phase Space: From Non-Commuting Coordinates to Quantum Error Correction

S. M. Girvin

Yale Quantum Institute
PO Box 208 334
New Haven, CT 06520-8263, USA
steven.girvin@yale.edu

Frank Wilczek has made deep contributions to our understanding of geometric phases in quantum mechanics. This paper explores a two examples of such geometric phases from rather different areas of physics, both related to the geometry of phase space and non-commuting coordinates.

1. A Personal Note

Frank Wilczek and I overlapped during our time in graduate school at Princeton, but our experiences were quite different. While he was busy writing his Nobel Prize winning thesis on asymptotic freedom, I was struggling to pass the qualifying exam and then learn how to do even the most basic things in condensed matter theory.

A few years later I was working as a staff scientist (in a surface chemistry group of all things) at the National Bureau of Standards (now NIST) when the integer and fractional quantum Hall effects were discovered and changed my life. In October 1987, Frank was kind enough to invite me to speak at a workshop on "Non-Integrable Phases in Dynamical Systems" that he and Alfred Shapere organized at the Theoretical Physics Institute at the University of Minnesota. My talk was entitled Off-Diagonal Long-Range Order in the Quantum Hall Effect," and was about the Chern-Simons composite boson representation of the FQHE low-energy physics. I discussed how a singular gauge transformation that attached 3 flux quanta to the electrons created geometric phases that turned them into effective bosons that (in a mean-field approximation at Landau level filling factor 1/3) moved in zero effective magnetic field and Bose condensed.

Frank's work with Tony Zee on geometric phases in multi-component field theories containing skyrmions [1] later turned out to influence the work of many of us on skyrmion spin textures in the quantum Hall effect [2, 3] and pseudo-spin textures in bilayer quantum Hall systems [4]. The topological density associated with spin and pseudo-spin textures combined with the quantized Hall conductance cause topological spin defects to acquire quantized charge.

I will not discuss this particular topic in the present chapter, but rather another topic related to collective excitations in the quantum Hall effect, namely non-commuting coordinates in the lowest Landau level. This will provide a nice segue into my current research on bosonic quantum error correction codes based on non-commuting coordinates in the phase space of oscillators.

2. Geometry of Phase Space: Non-Commuting Translations and Boosts

The density distribution $\rho(\vec{r}, \vec{p})$ of a gas in phase space plays an essential role in classical statistical mechanics. Things are trickier in quantum mechanics because the position and momentum operators do not commute. This in turn implies that the geometry of quantum phase space is such that adiabatic transport around a closed loop in phase space induces a geometric phase proportional to the area of the enclosed loop. To see this, consider a one-dimensional system with wave function $\psi(x)$. Translation of the momentum (a "boost") is effected via

$$\mathcal{D}_p(\Delta_p)\psi(x) = e^{i\Delta_p x/\hbar}\psi(x), \tag{1}$$

while translation of the position is effected via

$$\mathcal{D}_x(\Delta_x)\psi(x) = \psi(x - \Delta_x) = e^{-i\Delta_x \hat{p}/\hbar}\psi(x), \tag{2}$$

where $\hat{p} = -i\hbar\frac{d}{dx}$ is the momentum operator (and generator of displacements).

Now consider a set of translations and boosts which moves the system around the closed loop in phase space illustrated in Fig. 1. The first translation by $+\Delta_x$ yields

$$\mathcal{D}_x(+\Delta_x)\psi(x) = \psi(x - \Delta_x). \tag{3}$$

The momentum boost $+\Delta_p$ yields

$$\mathcal{D}_p(+\Delta_p)\mathcal{D}_x(+\Delta_x)\psi(x) = e^{+i\Delta_p x/\hbar}\psi(x - \Delta_x). \tag{4}$$

The second translation by $-\Delta_x$ yields

$$\mathcal{D}_x(-\Delta_x)\mathcal{D}_p(+\Delta_p)\mathcal{D}_x(+\Delta_x)\psi(x) = e^{+i\Delta_p(x+\Delta_x)/\hbar}\psi(x). \tag{5}$$

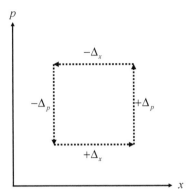

Fig. 1. A closed (right-handed) loop in phase space enclosing area $A = \Delta_x \Delta_p$ which yields a geometric phase $e^{+iA/\hbar}$.

The final momentum boost by $-\Delta_p$ returns the system to its original state except for a geometric phase which depends only on the (oriented) area of the loop

$$\mathcal{D}_p(-\Delta_p)\mathcal{D}_x(-\Delta_x)\mathcal{D}_p(+\Delta_p)\mathcal{D}_x(+\Delta_x)\psi(x) = e^{+i\Delta_p\Delta_x/\hbar}\psi(x). \tag{6}$$

Finally we note that general translations along arbitrary directions defined by the vector $\mathbf{V} = (\Delta_x, \Delta_p)$ are effected via the operator

$$\hat{T}(\mathbf{V}) = e^{+i(\Delta_p\hat{x} - \Delta_x\hat{p})/\hbar} = e^{+i\mathbf{R}^{\mathrm{T}}\Omega\mathbf{V}/\hbar}, \tag{7}$$

where $\mathbf{R} \equiv (\hat{x}, \hat{p})$ is a vector whose components are the position and momentum operators and Ω is the symplectic form

$$\Omega = \begin{pmatrix} 0 & +1 \\ -1 & 0 \end{pmatrix}. \tag{8}$$

Using the Feynman disentangling theorem, this can be decomposed into

$$\hat{T}(\mathbf{V}) = \mathcal{D}_p(\Delta_p)\mathcal{D}_x(\Delta_x)e^{-\frac{i}{2}\Delta_x\Delta_p/\hbar}, \tag{9}$$

from which it follows that if the second half of the square trajectory in Fig. 1 is replaced by a single displacement, $\mathcal{D}_{-\vec{V}} = \mathcal{D}_{\vec{V}}^{\dagger}$, along the diagonal from the upper right to lower left corners of the square, the resulting triangular path has geometric phase $e^{+\frac{1}{2}\Delta_x\Delta_p/\hbar}$, consistent with the fact that it has half the area of the square trajectory.

More generally, a fact which will be useful later is that

$$\hat{T}(\mathbf{U})\hat{T}(\mathbf{V}) = \hat{T}(\mathbf{V})\hat{T}(\mathbf{U})e^{i\frac{2\pi}{\hbar}\mathbf{V}^{\mathrm{T}}\Omega\mathbf{U}} = \hat{T}(\mathbf{U}+\mathbf{V})e^{i\frac{\pi}{\hbar}\mathbf{V}^{\mathrm{T}}\Omega\mathbf{U}}, \tag{10}$$

which implies that two translations commute if and only if their symplectic norm is an integer multiple of Planck's constant, h

$$\frac{1}{h}\mathbf{V}^{\mathrm{T}}\Omega\mathbf{U} \in \mathbb{Z}. \tag{11}$$

Equivalently, the two translations define a parallelogram whose area is an integer multiple of h.

Direct experimental measurement of the geometric phase resulting from closed trajectories can be obtained by coupling a qubit to an oscillator and executing conditional displacements which can be realized in both trapped ions [5–12] and in circuit QED [13]. These conditional displacement operators are a generalization of Eq. (7) that take advantage of the fact that the forces driving the oscillator can be made spin dependent

$$\hat{T}_{\mathrm{c}}(\mathbf{V}) = \hat{T}(Z\mathbf{V}), \tag{12}$$

where Z is the Pauli spin operator of the ancilla qubit. The protocol begins by placing the qubit in a superposition state and the oscillator in its ground state

$$|\psi\rangle = \frac{1}{\sqrt{2}}\left\{|\uparrow\rangle + |\downarrow\rangle\right\}|0\rangle. \tag{13}$$

Then the oscillator is moved around a clockwise (counterclockwise) loop in phase space if the spin is up (down). The spin-dependent "phase kickback" from this unitary rotates the spin around the z axis by an angle given by the difference in geometric phases of the two phase space loops

$$|\psi'\rangle = \frac{1}{\sqrt{2}}\left\{e^{i\theta_{\uparrow}}|\uparrow\rangle + e^{i\theta_{\downarrow}}|\downarrow\rangle\right\}|0\rangle. \tag{14}$$

Observing the "Ramsey interference" fringes caused by this rotation of the ancilla qubit through angle $\theta = \theta_{\downarrow} - \theta_{\uparrow}$ is routinely used by experimentalists to precisely calibrate the relation between applied electromagnetic drive on the oscillator and the resulting displacement amplitude [10–13].

3. Non-Commuting Coordinates and the Fractional Quantum Hall Effect

The fractional quantum Hall effect (FQHE) takes place in a two-dimensional planar electron gas at low temperatures in the presence of a strong magnetic field perpendicular to the plane [14]. It is a curious fact that in this limit, the electrons behave as if their x and y coordinates are non-commuting.

To see this, consider the Lagrangian for a single electron of mass m and charge $-e$ moving under the influence of a vector potential $\vec{A}$

$$\mathcal{L} = \frac{1}{2}m\,\dot{\vec{r}} \cdot \dot{\vec{r}} + (-e)\vec{A}(\vec{r}) \cdot \dot{\vec{r}}. \tag{15}$$

It is convenient to take the specific example of magnetic field $\vec{B} = -B\hat{z}$ using the Landau gauge for the vector potential

$$\vec{A}(\vec{r}) = +By\hat{x}, \tag{16}$$

$$\vec{\nabla} \times \vec{A} = \vec{B} = -B\hat{z}. \tag{17}$$

Taking the limit of strong magnetic field so that the Landau level splitting (cyclotron energy $\hbar\omega_c$) is the largest scale in the problem, is essentially equivlaent to setting the mass to zero. In this limit the Lagrangian becomes

$$\mathcal{L}_0 = -eBy\dot{x}. \tag{18}$$

Curiously, the momentum canonically conjugate to x is proportional to the coordinate y

$$p_x = \frac{\delta\mathcal{L}_0}{\delta\dot{x}} = -eBy = -\frac{\hbar}{\ell^2}y, \tag{19}$$

where $\ell = \sqrt{\frac{\hbar}{eB}}$ is the magnetic length. Thus when quantized, the coordinates are non-commuting and the 2D plane has turned into the phase space of a 1D quantum system. Furthermore, in the approximation we have made, the kinetic part of the Hamiltonian

$$H_0 = p_x\dot{x} - \mathcal{L}_0 = 0 \tag{20}$$

vanishes. (In actuality it is a constant $\frac{1}{2}\hbar\omega_c$ representing the zero-point energy of the cyclotron motion.)

Thus if there is to be any dynamics in the lowest Landau level, it must be generated by the Coulomb interaction energy term

$$V = \frac{1}{2}\sum_{\vec{q}\neq\vec{0}} v(q)\rho_{\vec{q}}^{\dagger}\rho_{\vec{q}}, \tag{21}$$

where $\rho_{\vec{q}}$ is the Fourier transform of the electron density and the Fourier transform of the Coulomb interaction (for a strictly 2D electron gas) is

$$v(q) = \frac{e^2}{4\pi\epsilon_0}\frac{4\pi}{q^2}. \tag{22}$$

The Fourier transform of the electron density in a system of N electrons is given by

$$\rho_{\vec{q}}^{\dagger} = \sum_{j=1}^{N} e^{+i\vec{q}\cdot\vec{r}_j}. \tag{23}$$

Recognizing that the y coordinate is now proportional to the momentum operator we find that, when projected into the lowest Landau level, the Fourier transform of the density $\bar{\rho}_{\vec{q}}^{\dagger}$ acts like the displacement operator in Eq. (7)

$$\bar{\rho}_{\vec{q}}^{\dagger} = \sum_{j=1}^{N} \hat{T}_j(\mathbf{V}), \tag{24}$$

where the displacement is given by

$$\mathbf{V} = (\Delta_x, \Delta_p) = (\ell^2 q_y, \hbar q_x). \tag{25}$$

This novel result tells us that within the lowest Landau level the Fourier components of the density obey the commutator algebra of displacements in phase space [15, 16]. Despite the fact that the kinetic energy is quenched (i.e. a constant) within a Landau level, the charge density has non-trivial dynamics (collective excitations) associated with the fact that it does not commute with the potential energy of interaction. It turns out that for $q\ell \ll 1$, the gapped collective density excitations above the incompressible mth Laughlin ground state at Landau level filling factor $\nu = 1/m$ are well-described by the single-mode approximation expression

$$|\Psi_{\vec{q}}\rangle \propto \bar{\rho}_{\vec{q}}|\Psi_m\rangle, \tag{26}$$

where $|\Psi_m\rangle$ is the Laughlin state. The single-mode approximation for the so-called "magneto-roton" collective excitation spectrum [15, 16] is in excellent agreement with numerical exact diagonalization studies [17] and light scattering experiments [18].

One interpretation of Eq. (26) is that, in a sense monopole excitations (single particles) are unable to move, but dipole excitations (created by the displacement operator $\bar{\rho}_{\vec{q}}$) are able to move — a fact reminiscent of "fracton" models that are currently receiving intense scrutiny [19].

4. Phase Space and Quantum Error Correction

The translation operators defined above can be used to define states living on symplectic lattices in phase. These states in turn can be used to define quantum error correcting codes. We will begin with a brief introduction to quantum error correction (QEC) in general and then see how the machinery of non-commuting translations in phase space can be used to define QEC codes.

4.1. *Introduction to QEC*

Quantum computers are analog devices in the sense that quantum bits can exist in a continuum states. In theory, analog computers are more powerful than digital computers because they can deal with real numbers rather than digital approximations to real numbers. In practice, however, analog computers are not perfect and there is a no-go theorem that error correction is impossible for analog processors. The miracle of quantum error correction arises from the fact that, while quantum errors are continuous, *measured* quantum errors are *discrete*. Here the weirdness of state collapse resulting from measurement is our friend.

The trick is arrange things so that the collapse tells you what error occurred yet tells you nothing about the logical state in which the error occurred — thereby allowing the information to be preserved and the error repaired. All quantum error correcting codes work by having the logical qubit defined as a two-dimensional subspace of a larger Hilbert space. If this logical subspace consists of span $\{|0_\mathrm{L}\rangle, |1_\mathrm{L}\rangle\}$, then the quantum information is stored in the complex coefficients α, β in the logical state

$$|\psi_\mathrm{L}\rangle = \alpha|0_\mathrm{L}\rangle + \beta|1_\mathrm{L}\rangle. \tag{27}$$

We can manipulate this information using the logical Pauli operators

$$Z_\mathrm{L} = |0_\mathrm{L}\rangle\langle 0_\mathrm{L}| - |1_\mathrm{L}\rangle\langle 1_\mathrm{L}| \tag{28}$$

$$X_\mathrm{L} = |0_\mathrm{L}\rangle\langle 1_\mathrm{L}| + |1_\mathrm{L}\rangle\langle 0_\mathrm{L}| \tag{29}$$

$$Y_\mathrm{L} = +iX_\mathrm{L}Z_\mathrm{L}. \tag{30}$$

For example, a logical qubit may be built from N physical qubits. In a stabilizer code, the logical subspace is defined by imposing $N-1$ constraints, namely that the allowed code words are $+1$ eigenstates of $N-1$ different stabilizer operators $S_j; j = 1, \ldots, N-1$. The stabilizers are multi-(physical-) qubit products of Pauli operators which commute both with each other and with the logical qubit Pauli operators, but fail to commute with the various error operators in such a way that errors change the values of some of the stabilizers. Measurements of the stabilizers yield error syndromes whose values uniquely identify which error occurred. Application of the appropriate physical Pauli operator conditioned on the error syndromes then corrects the error without disturbing the logical information stored in the logical state.

Thus quantum error correction is possible in principle. In practice, however, it has proven to be extremely difficult. The main challenge is that the encoding of one logical qubit into N physical qubits immediately raises the error rate by a factor of N. The "Maxwell demon" that monitors the error syndromes and corrects the errors must be extremely fast and make very few errors of its own just to overcome this factor of N to reach the so-called break-even point. One bottleneck has been that rapid highly accurate quantum non-demolition measurements of multi-qubit stabilizer operators is quite challenging. For example, the $N = 9$ qubit Shor code [20] can correct any single physical qubit error. There are three different errors (Pauli X, Y, Z) that could occur on each of the N physical qubits. Thus there are 27 different single-qubit error states that the syndrome measurements must be able to correctly identify and quickly repair before a second error occurs causing the code to fail. To date, this has proven to be a major challenge experimentally.

An alternative approach pioneered by the Yale group has been to store the quantum information in continuous-variable degrees of freedom (harmonic oscillators) in the form of very high Q microwave resonators using the techniques of circuit QED [21–25]. Logical qubit states are linear combinations of photon Fock states that span a two-dimensional subspace of the infinite tower of harmonic oscillator states. There are several benefits to this approach. First, the error model for a weakly damped oscillator is very simple. To a good approximation, the only error is amplitude damping/photon loss and the rate of such errors can be made extremely low in a superconducting resonator. Second, while the available Hilbert space is large, the resonator has only a single mode from which photons are lost, not N different physical locations in which errors can occur (as in the qubit case described above). Thus, for example, it is possible to define logical code words that are eigenstates of photon number parity $\hat{\Pi} = e^{i\pi\hat{n}}$. Photon loss anticommutes with parity

$$a\hat{\Pi} = -\hat{\Pi}a, \tag{31}$$

and thus parity jumps herald photon loss errors. This simplicity (and the fact that in circuit QED, QND measurements of photon number parity are possible) allowed successful quantum error correction (slightly) beyond the break-even point for the first time [26]. This first experiment used bosonic logical code words built from Schrödinger cat states of definite parity [27] in a microwave resonator. Subsequently, a number of different experiments using new bosonic codes such as the binomial code [28, 29] and the 'Truncated 4-component Cat' (T4C) code [30] have also approached the break-even point.

4.2. *Gottesman-Kitaev-Preskill (GKP) Codes*

In 2001, Gottesman, Kitaev and Preskill proposed a novel idea for quantum error correcting codes based on lattice states in phase space [31, 32]. At the time, physical implementation appeared to be nearly impossible, but recent dramatic experimental progress has in fact realized QEC close to the break-even point in both ion traps [12] and circuit QED systems [13].

The GKP code space of the logical qubit is defined to be the $+1$ eigenspace of two translations $\hat{S}_1 = \hat{T}(\mathbf{U})$ and $\hat{S}_2 = \hat{T}(\mathbf{V})$ that obey

$$\frac{1}{h}\mathbf{V}^{\mathrm{T}}\Omega\mathbf{U} = 2, \tag{32}$$

and therefore the code space contains two states. Based on the previous discussion of codes involving N physical qubits, you might think that since the oscillator Hilbert space contains an infinite number of states that you would need an infinite number of stabilizers. This is not the case however. The multi-qubit Pauli operator stabilizers for qubit codes have eigenvalues ± 1 and thus provide only 1 bit of information when measured. The translations used as stabilizers for the bosonic codes have a continuum of eigenvalues lying on the unit circle in the complex plane. The statement that the code space has stabilizer eigenvalues precisely equal to $+1$ therefore represents far more powerful constraints.

To see how the GKP code works, let us specialize to the simplest case of a square lattice in phase space generated by the two stabilizers (displacements)

$$S_p = e^{+i2\sqrt{\pi}\hat{x}}, \tag{33}$$

$$S_x = e^{-i2\sqrt{\pi}\hat{p}}, \tag{34}$$

where from henceforth we are using dimensionless units with $\hbar = 1$. These stabilizers commute

$$S_p S_q = e^{i4\pi} S_q S_p, \tag{35}$$

and they stabilize the code space spanned by the logical code word states

$$\Psi_0(x) = \sum_{n=-\infty}^{+\infty} \delta(x - (2n)\sqrt{\pi}), \tag{36}$$

$$\Psi_1(x) = \sum_{n=-\infty}^{+\infty} \delta(x - (2n+1)\sqrt{\pi}). \tag{37}$$

These "picket fence" states are infinitely squeezed, unnormalizable, and have infinite energy. We will ignore these inconvenient truths for the moment

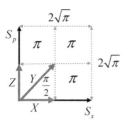

Fig. 2.   Unit cell of the square lattice defined by the stabilizers S_x, S_p. The Pauli operators X_L and Z_L are displacements by half a lattice constant in position and momentum, respectively. The Pauli operator $Y_\mathrm{L} = iX_\mathrm{L}Z_\mathrm{L}$ is displacement by half the diagonal. The factor of i in this relation is consistent with the shaded area being $\pi/2$.

but return to them later. For now, we note that they are also picket fence states in the momentum basis and their Wigner functions have support on a square lattice in phase space. Despite the fact that position and momentum do not commute, the points of the square lattice are sharply defined (infinitely squeezed in both position *and* momentum). This does not violate the Heisenberg principle because both position and momentum remain uncertain modulo the lattice constants.

Remarkably, within this logical subspace, the logical Pauli operators become simple phase space translations as illustrated in Fig. 2 where we see that the "unit cell" has area 4π (or, restoring the units, $4\pi\hbar = 2h$) and therefore holds two quantum states. Within the logical subspace, the Pauli X_L and Z_L operators are displacements by half of the respective lattice constants implying that

$$X_\mathrm{L}^2 = S_x = \hat{I}, \tag{38}$$

$$Z_\mathrm{L}^2 = S_p = \hat{I}, \tag{39}$$

which is consistent with the properties of the Pauli matrices since within the logical space, S_x and S_y are each (effectively) the identity. Similarly

$$X_\mathrm{L} = X_\mathrm{L}^\dagger S_x = X^\dagger, \tag{40}$$

$$Z_\mathrm{L} = Z_\mathrm{L}^\dagger S_p = Z^\dagger, \tag{41}$$

as expected. The area of the four small squares being π implies that

$$Z_\mathrm{L}X_\mathrm{L} = -X_\mathrm{L}Z_\mathrm{L}. \tag{42}$$

Furthermore, the shaded triangle in Fig. 2 has area $\pi/2$ implying that

$$Y_\mathrm{L} = Y_\mathrm{L}^\dagger = e^{i\frac{\pi}{2}} X_\mathrm{L}Z_\mathrm{L} = iX_\mathrm{L}Z_\mathrm{L}. \tag{43}$$

Thus, within the logical space, these translations form a precise representation of the Pauli group.

4.3. *Error Correction with GKP Codes*

The GKP codes were originally designed to correct small (i.e., less than half a lattice constant) displacements of the oscillator in phase space. We have recently shown that they are also remarkably effective against more realistic error modes (e.g., amplitude damping) [33]. However, analytical understanding is easier for the case of small displacement errors. Because both the errors and the stabilizers are displacements, they do not (generically) commute and these errors change the eigenvalues (phases) of the stabilizers. We can measure the error syndromes (changes in the stabilizer eigenvalues) by using conditional displacements. For example, suppose the erroneous cavity state is $|\Psi\rangle$ and we prepare the ancilla qubit in the superposition state $|+x\rangle$. If we perform the conditional stabilizer displacement

$$U_\lambda = \hat{I} \otimes |\uparrow\rangle\langle\uparrow| + S_\lambda \otimes |\downarrow\rangle\langle\downarrow|, \tag{44}$$

(where $\lambda = x, p$) and then measure the ancilla, the phase kickback gives us the real

$$\langle+x|\langle\Psi|U_\lambda^\dagger X U_\lambda|\Psi\rangle|+x\rangle = \mathrm{Re}\,\langle\Psi|S_\lambda|\Psi\rangle \tag{45}$$

and imaginary

$$\langle+x|\langle\Psi|U_\lambda^\dagger Y U_\lambda|\Psi\rangle|+x\rangle = \mathrm{Im}\,\langle\Psi|S_\lambda|\Psi\rangle \tag{46}$$

parts of the error syndrome.

Of course with only a single ancilla, one only obtains one bit of information when measuring X or Y in the conditionally displaced state. Quantum phase estimation protocols that would yield more bits of resolution on the value of the stabilizers [34] are not practical at this point in the hardware development. However, the Devoret group has invented a clever scheme [13] that makes small feedback displacements on the quantum state after each repeated one-bit measurement of each stabilizer. They were able to execute quantum error correction for both the square lattice and the triangular lattice GKP codes, coming very close to the break-even point.

For logical qubits made from multiple physical qubits, we define the break-even point as the logical qubit lifetime reaching the value of the best physical qubit in the set comprising the logical qubit. For bosonic codes we define the break-even point to be where the lifetime of the bosonic code exceeds the lifetime of the longest lived uncorrectable encoding in the oscillator. Superconducting resonators have negligible dephasing errors and are dominated by amplitude damping. In this case, the longest lived encoding uses the smallest possible photon number states, namely the $n = 0, 1$ Fock states. They lose photons at the slowest rate, but of course once a photon is lost the cavity is definitely in $|0\rangle$ and the quantum information stored in the original superpostion state is unrecoverable.

As mentioned previously, the idealized GKP lattice states are unphysical because they are infinitely squeezed and have infinite energy. Real experiments work with lattices of finite extent, typically attempting to create states with a Gaussian envelope of the form

$$|\Phi_\Lambda\rangle \sim e^{-\Lambda\hat{n}}|\Psi\rangle, \tag{47}$$

where Λ is a regularizing constant and $|\Psi\rangle$ is a superposition of the ideal code words in Eqs. (36–37). This state has a Gaussian envelope because $\hat{n} \sim \hat{x}^2 + \hat{p}^2$.

As the measurement feedback loop discussed above drives the value of the stabilizers more and more precisely towards $+1$, the state starts to approach the ideal GKP state and thus the envelope of the state has to expand. To prevent the mean photon number from running away to infinity, the Devoret group used a 'trim' step in their protocol which cuts off the runaway expansion.

Finite energy approximate GKP states are of course not fully translation invariant and the stabilizer value must suffer quantum fluctuations. Inspired by comments from Mazyar Mirrahimi, Baptiste Royer has recently developed a higher-order error correction scheme based on the exact stabilizer for the finite-energy GKP states [35]. These stabilizers are simply similarity transforms of the ideal stabilizers

$$S_x^\Lambda = e^{-\Lambda\hat{n}} S_x e^{+\Lambda\hat{n}} \tag{48}$$

$$S_p^\Lambda = e^{-\Lambda\hat{n}} S_p e^{+\Lambda\hat{n}}. \tag{49}$$

These are neither unitary nor Hermitian and so cannot be measured directly. However, it is possible to cleverly engineer an autonomous (i.e., measurement free) protocol which effectively yields an engineered dissipation that cools the system into the $+1$ eigenstate of each stabilizer. The same idea was independently discovered by the ion trap group of J. Home who put it into practice in experiment [12]. With additional technical improvements in the ion trap and circuit QED experiments, this new protocol may allow us to substantially exceed the break-even point for the first time.

5. Conclusion

It has been a great pleasure for me to interact with Frank Wilczek over the last (nearly) half century and I wish him Happy Birthday and look forward to further illuminating physics conversations in the future!

Acknowledgments

My current research on bosonic quantum error correction described here was supported by ARO W911NF-18-1-0212.

References

[1] F. Wilczek and A. Zee, Linking numbers, spin, and statistics of solitons, *Phys. Rev. Lett.* **51**, 2250–2252 (1983). doi: 10.1103/PhysRevLett.51.2250. URL https://link.aps.org/doi/10.1103/PhysRevLett.51.2250.

[2] S. L. Sondhi, A. Karlhede, S. A. Kivelson, and E. H. Rezayi, Skyrmions and the crossover from the integer to fractional quantum hall effect at small zeeman energies, *Phys. Rev. B.* **47**, 16419–16426 (1993). doi: 10.1103/PhysRevB.47. 16419. URL https://link.aps.org/doi/10.1103/PhysRevB.47.16419.

[3] R. Côté, A. H. MacDonald, L. Brey, H. A. Fertig, S. M. Girvin, and H. T. C. Stoof, Collective excitations, nmr, and phase transitions in skyrme crystals, *Phys. Rev. Lett.* **78**, 4825–4828 (1997). doi: 10.1103/PhysRevLett.78.4825. URL https://link.aps.org/doi/10.1103/PhysRevLett.78.4825.

[4] K. Moon, H. Mori, K. Yang, S. M. Girvin, A. H. MacDonald, L. Zheng, D. Yoshioka, and S.-C. Zhang, Spontaneous interlayer coherence in double-layer quantum hall systems: Charged vortices and kosterlitz-thouless phase transitions, *Phys. Rev. B* **51**, 5138–5170 (1995). doi: 10.1103/PhysRevB.51.5138. URL https://link.aps.org/doi/10.1103/PhysRevB.51.5138.

[5] J. I. Cirac and P. Zoller, Quantum computations with cold trapped ions, *Phys. Rev. Lett.* **74**(20), 4091–4094. doi: 10.1103/PhysRevLett.74.4091. PRL.

[6] A. Srensen and K. Mlmer, Quantum computation with ions in thermal motion, *Phys. Rev. Lett.* **82**(9), 1971–1974. doi: 10.1103/PhysRevLett.82.1971. PRL.

[7] Q. A. Turchette, C. S. Wood, B. E. King, C. J. Myatt, D. Leibfried, W. M. Itano, C. Monroe, and D. J. Wineland, Deterministic entanglement of two trapped ions, *Phys. Rev. Lett.* **81**(17), 3631–3634. doi: 10.1103/PhysRevLett. 81.3631. PRL.

[8] B. E. King, C. S. Wood, C. J. Myatt, Q. A. Turchette, D. Leibfried, W. M. Itano, C. Monroe, and D. J. Wineland, Cooling the collective motion of trapped ions to initialize a quantum register, *Phys. Rev. Lett.* **81**(7), 1525–1528. doi: 10.1103/PhysRevLett.81.1525. PRL.

[9] D. Leibfried, R. Blatt, C. Monroe, and D. Wineland, Quantum dynamics of single trapped ions, *Rev. Mod. Phy.* **75**(1), 281–324. doi: 10.1103/RevModPhys. 75.281. RMP.

[10] D. Leibfried, B. DeMarco, V. Meyer, D. Lucas, M. Barrett, J. Britton, W. M. Itano, B. Jelenkovi, C. Langer, T. Rosenband, and D. J. Wineland, Experimental demonstration of a robust, high-fidelity geometric two ion-qubit phase gate, *Nature* **422**(6930), 412–415. doi: 10.1038/nature01492.

[11] C. Flühmann, T. L. Nguyen, M. Marinelli, V. Negnevitsky, K. Mehta, and J. P. Home, Encoding a qubit in a trapped-ion mechanical oscillator, *Nature* **566**(7745), 513–517. doi: 10.1038/s41586-019-0960-6.

[12] B. de Neeve, T. L. Nguyen, T. Behrle, and J. Home, Error correction of a logical grid state qubit by dissipative pumping, *arXiv:2010.09681.* (2020).

[13] P. Campagne-Ibarcq, A. Eickbusch, S. Touzard, E. Zalys-Geller, N. E. Frattini, V. V. Sivak, P. Reinhold, S. Puri, S. Shankar, R. J. Schoelkopf, L. Frunzio, M. Mirrahimi, and M. H. Devoret, Quantum error correction of a qubit encoded in grid states of an oscillator, *Nature* **584**(7821), 368–372. doi: 10.1038/s41586-020-2603-3.

[14] S. M. Girvin and K. Yang, *Modern Condensed Matter Physics.* (Cambridge University Press, Cambridge). doi: DOI:10.1017/9781316480649.

[15] S. M. Girvin, A. H. MacDonald, and P. M. Platzman, Collective-excitation gap in the fractional quantum hall effect, *Phys. Rev. Lett.* **54**(6), 581–583. doi: 10.1103/PhysRevLett.54.581. PRL.

[16] S. M. Girvin, A. H. MacDonald, and P. M. Platzman, Magneto-roton theory of collective excitations in the fractional quantum hall effect, *Phys. Rev. B* **33**(4), 2481–2494. doi: 10.1103/PhysRevB.33.2481. PRB.

[17] F. D. M. Haldane and E. H. Rezayi, Finite-size studies of the incompressible state of the fractionally quantized hall effect and its excitations, *Phys. Rev. Lett.* **54**(3), 237–240. doi: 10.1103/PhysRevLett.54.237. PRL.

[18] A. Pinczuk, B. S. Dennis, L. N. Pfeiffer, and K. West, Observation of collective excitations in the fractional quantum hall effect, *Phys. Rev. Lett.* **70**(25), 3983–3986. doi: 10.1103/PhysRevLett.70.3983. PRL.

[19] R. M. Nandkishore and M. Hermele, Fractons, *Annual Review of Condensed Matter Physics* **10**(1), 295–313. doi: 10.1146/annurev-conmatphys-031218-013604.

[20] M. A. Nielsen and I. L. Chuang, *Quantum Computation and Quantum Information: 10th Anniversary Edition.* (Cambridge University Press, Cambridge). doi: DOI:10.1017/CBO9780511976667.

[21] A. Blais, R.-S. Huang, A. Wallraff, S. M. Girvin, and R. J. Schoelkopf, Cavity quantum electrodynamics for superconducting electrical circuits: An architecture for quantum computation, *Phys Rev A* **69**(6), 062320, (2004). doi: 10.1103/PhysRevA.69.062320. URL https://link.aps.org/doi/10.1103/PhysRevA.69.062320. PRA.

[22] A. Wallraff, D. I. Schuster, A. Blais, L. Frunzio, R. S. Huang, J. Majer, S. Kumar, S. M. Girvin, and R. J. Schoelkopf, Strong coupling of a single photon to a superconducting qubit using circuit quantum electrodynamics, *Nature* **431**(7005), 162–167. ISSN 1476-4687. doi: 10.1038/nature02851.

[23] P. Krantz, M. Kjaergaard, F. Yan, T. P. Orlando, S. Gustavsson, and W. D. Oliver, A quantum engineer's guide to superconducting qubits, *Appl. Phys. Rev.* **6**(2), 021318, (2019). doi: 10.1063/1.5089550.

[24] A. Blais, S. M. Girvin, and W. D. Oliver, Quantum information processing and quantum optics with circuit quantum electrodynamics, *Nature Physics* **16**(3), 247–256. ISSN 1745-2481. doi: 10.1038/s41567-020-0806-z.

[25] A. Blais, A. L. Grimsmo, S. M. Girvin, and A. Wallraff, Circuit quantum electrodynamics, *Rev. Mod. Phys.* **93**, 025005 (May, 2021). doi: 10.1103/RevModPhys.93.025005.

[26] N. Ofek, A. Petrenko, R. Heeres, P. Reinhold, Z. Leghtas, B. Vlastakis, Y. Liu, L. Frunzio, S. M. Girvin, L. Jiang, M. Mirrahimi, M. H. Devoret, and R. J. Schoelkopf, Extending the lifetime of a quantum bit with error correction in superconducting circuits, *Nature* **536**(7617), 441–445. doi: 10.1038/nature18949.

[27] M. Mirrahimi, Z. Leghtas, V. V. Albert, S. Touzard, R. J. Schoelkopf, L. Jiang, and M. H. Devoret, Dynamically protected cat-qubits: A new paradigm for universal quantum computation, *New J. Phys.* **16**(4), 045014. doi: 10.1088/1367-2630/16/4/045014.

[28] M. H. Michael, M. Silveri, R. T. Brierley, V. V. Albert, J. Salmilehto, L. Jiang, and S. M. Girvin, New class of quantum error-correcting codes for a bosonic mode, *Phys. Rev. X* **6**(3), 031006. doi: 10.1103/PhysRevX.6.031006. PRX.

[29] L. Hu, Y. Ma, W. Cai, X. Mu, Y. Xu, W. Wang, Y. Wu, H. Wang, Y. P. Song, C. L. Zou, S. M. Girvin, L. M. Duan, and L. Sun, Quantum error correction and universal gate set operation on a binomial bosonic logical qubit, *Nature Physics* **15**(5), 503–508. doi: 10.1038/s41567-018-0414-3.

[30] J. M. Gertler, B. Baker, J. Li, S. Shirol, J. Koch, and C. Wang, Protecting a bosonic qubit with autonomous quantum error correction, *Nature* **590**(7845), 243–248. ISSN 1476-4687. doi: 10.1038/s41586-021-03257-0.

[31] D. Gottesman, A. Kitaev, and J. Preskill, Encoding a qubit in an oscillator, *Phys. Rev. A* **64**(1), 012310. doi: 10.1103/PhysRevA.64.012310. PRA.

[32] A. L. Grimsmo and S. Puri, Quantum error correction with the gottesman-kitaev-preskill code, *PRX Quantum* **2**(2), 020101. doi: 10.1103/PRXQuantum.2.020101. PRXQUANTUM.

[33] V. V. Albert, K. Noh, K. Duivenvoorden, D. J. Young, R. T. Brierley, P. Reinhold, C. Vuillot, L. Li, C. Shen, S. M. Girvin, B. M. Terhal, and L. Jiang, Performance and structure of single-mode bosonic codes, *Phys. Rev. A.* **97**(3), 032346. doi: 10.1103/PhysRevA.97.032346. PRA.

[34] B. M. Terhal and D. Weigand, Encoding a qubit into a cavity mode in circuit qed using phase estimation, *Phys. Rev. A.* **93**(1), 012315. doi: 10.1103/ PhysRevA.93.012315. PRA.

[35] B. Royer, S. Singh, and S. M. Girvin, Stabilization of finite-energy gottesman-kitaev-preskill states, *Phys. Rev. Lett.* **125**(26), 260509. doi: 10.1103/ PhysRevLett.125.260509. PRL.

© 2022 World Scientific Publishing Company

https://doi.org/10.1142/9789811251948_0009

Mean Field Theories of Quantum Hall Liquids Justified: Variations on the Greiter–Wilczek Theme

T. H. Hansson* and S. A. Kivelson†

*Fysikum, Stockholm University, Stockholm, Sweden
hansson@fysik.su.se
†Department of Physics, Stanford University, Stanford, CA, USA
kivelson@stanford.edu

We present a field theoretic variant of the Wilczek–Greiter adiabatic approach to Quantum Hall liquids. Specifically, we define a Chern–Simons–Maxwell theory such that the flux-attachment mean field theory is exact in a certain limit. This permits a systematic way to justify a variety of useful approximate approaches to these problems as constituting the first term in a (still to be developed) systematic expansion about a solvable limit.

1. Introduction

In an article from 1990 Greiter and Wilczek (GW) argued [1] that by an adiabatic evolution one can move from a number of filled Landau levels of electrons, to quantum Hall states in the Jain hierarchy. The idea is to slowly concentrate part of the magnetic flux in thin tubes located at the position of the particles. During this process the constant background magnetic field is diminished (or increased if the flux tubes are directed opposite to the background field), and the intermediate states are naturally interpreted as a system of anyons in an effective B field. Clearly this can be thought of as a concrete way to construct Jain's composite fermions. In a later paper, GW gave a more formal argument for their construction using special Hamiltonians with singular interactions for the Laughlin states, and also generalized the idea to include the nonabelian Moore–Read Pfaffian state [2]. In a very recent paper, they have also constructed an interpolating Hamiltonian for the $\nu = 2/5$ Jain state using a technique that might generalize to the other states in the positive Jain series [3].

We now give a field theoretic version of a distinct but strategically similar construction based on an adiabatic evolution of states of composite particles. As in the GW case, one limit is an exact rewriting of the Quantum Hall problem, while the other limit is a solvable point. The difference is that the intermediate states in the GW formulation are states of anyons in a constant magnetic field, while in our approach the intermediate states are for bosons or fermions interacting with a mildly fluctuating dynamical gauge field.

Our composite particles are described by the following Ginzburg–Landau–Chern–Simons–Maxwell (GLCSM) Lagrangian density[a]

$$\mathcal{L}_{\mathrm{GLCSM}} = \mathcal{L}_{\mathrm{mat}} + \mathcal{L}_g$$

$$\mathcal{L}_{\mathrm{mat}} = \psi^\star(i\partial_0 - a_0 + eA_0)\psi - \frac{1}{2m^\star}|(\vec{p} - e\vec{A} + \vec{a})\psi|^2 - V[\rho] \qquad (1)$$

$$\mathcal{L}_g = \frac{1}{2\pi q}\epsilon^{\mu\nu\sigma}a_\mu\partial_\nu a_\sigma + \frac{\varepsilon}{2g^2}\vec{e}\cdot\vec{e} - \frac{1}{2g^2}b^2,$$

where V is a repulsive potential which is a functional of the density, $\rho = \psi^\dagger\psi$ (i.e. it may be non-local in space), $e_i = -\dot{a}_i - \partial_i a_0$ and $b = \epsilon^{ij}\partial_i a_j$ are, respectively, dynamically fluctuating electric and magnetic fields, and A_μ is the background electromagnetic gauge potential where $\vec{\nabla}\times\vec{A} = B$ and $eA_0(\vec{r})$ is a one-body potential that may reflect the presence of disorder, controlled gate potentials, etc.[b] Except when explicitly mentioned we shall put $\hbar = c = 1$. For $q = $ odd we take ψ to be a complex scalar (bosonic) field corresponding to the composite bosons of MacDonald and Girvin [4] in the form introduced by Zhang and us [5], while for $q = $ even, we take ψ to be a Grassman field representing Jain's composite fermions [6] in the form introduced by Lopez and Fradkin [7,8].

In the $g \to \infty$ limit, a_0 is a Lagrange multiplier that enforces the "flux attachment" constraint $2\pi q\rho = b = \epsilon^{ij}\partial_i a_j$ that attaches q flux quanta to each composite particle. In this limit, with $m^\star$ set equal to the bare effective mass of the electron, Eq. (1) is nominally an exact rewriting of the original problem in terms of new composite particles.

However, for finite ε and g, the flux tubes attached to each particle have finite extent, and so have dynamical consequences beyond encoding the particle statistics. This action no longer corresponds precisely to the problem of physical interest. However, we shall see that the approximate mean-field

---

[a]The same effective action was considered in Ref. [42] some time ago in the context of a study of a clean system close to a putative quantum critical point at the transition between an isotropic and a nematic quantum Hall fluid. The topologically massive gauge theory was introduced by Templeton in Ref. [9], and discussed in the context or fractional statistics in Refs. [43] and [44].

[b]More properly, $\mathcal{L}_g$ should be written in terms of two coupled Chern–Simons gauge fields [45] to avoid difficulties associated with the fractional $1/q$ Chern–Simons level numbers [46]. Without downplaying the importance of this subtlety, we will finesse it here in the interest of clarity of presentation.

treatment of flux attachment, which has been so successfully used to analyze various aspects of this problem, is exact in the limit $g \to 0$. Thus, this construction allows for an explicit field theoretic rendering of an adiabatic evolution, in the spirit of the GW thought experiment, from the soluble small g limit to the physical limit, $g \to \infty$.

2. Expression in Terms of Effective Interactions

There are several ways to look at the problem defined by the Langrangian in Eq. (1). We can integrate out the fluctuating statistical gauge field perturbatively resulting in a renormalization of the chemical potential (which we leave implicit) and an effective interaction between particles represented by a contribution to the effective action of the form

$$\delta S = -\frac{1}{2} \int d\vec{r}_1 d\vec{r}_2 d\tau_1 d\tau_2 j_\mu(\vec{r}_1, \tau_1) \hat{D}_{\mu,\nu}(\vec{r}_1 - \vec{r}_2, \tau_1 - \tau_2) j_\nu(\vec{r}_2, \tau_2) + \cdots \tag{2}$$

where $\hat{D}$ is the bare photon propagator, and ... represents higher order terms. The photon in question is massive (gapped) corresponding to the poles in $D(\vec{k}, \omega)$, the Fourier transform of $\hat{D}$, with

$$\omega^2 = \Omega^2 + \varepsilon k^2 \tag{3}$$

where $k \equiv |\vec{k}|$, $\Omega = \mu/\varepsilon$ is the energy gap, and $\mu = g^2/2\pi q$ is the familiar topological mass [9]. Note that in the $\varepsilon \to 0$ limit, where the gauge field has no independent dynamics, the gap tends to infinity.

Despite the fact that the photon is massive, it induces long-range statistical interactions between the composite particles that come from the off-diagonal part that couples current and charge,

$$D^{i0}(\vec{k}, \omega) = 2\pi q \frac{i\epsilon^{ij} k_j}{k^2} G(\vec{k}, \omega), \tag{4}$$

with

$$G(\vec{k}, \omega) = \frac{\mu^2}{\mu^2 + \varepsilon k^2 - (\varepsilon \omega)^2}, \tag{5}$$

and, needless to say, it is this very interaction that endows the quasipartiles, i.e. the vortices, with fractional statistics as explained in the classic paper Ref. [10] by Arovas, Wilczek and Schrieffer. (The full expression for $D_{\mu\nu}$ is given in Appendix A.) In the limit $g \to \infty$, where $G(\vec{k}, \omega) \to 1$, this simply corresponds to attaching q flux quanta to each composite particle, turning them back into the original electrons.

For our discussion, the most important consequence of including the Maxwell terms in $\mathcal{L}_g$ is that they give a size to the flux tubes bound to the charges. The profile of the statistical magnetic field associated with a static composite particle at the origin is

$$b(r) = \frac{q}{\lambda^2} K_0(r/\lambda) \tag{6}$$

where K_0 is a modified Bessel function and the scale is given by $\lambda = \sqrt{\varepsilon}/\mu = 2\pi q \sqrt{\varepsilon}/g^2$. At an intuitive level, in the limit that λ is large compared to the mean spacing between electrons, i.e. when $\pi\lambda^2 \bar\rho \gg 1$ where $\bar\rho$ is the mean electron density, it should become increasingly possible to replace the fluctuating statistical magnetic field by its mean, $b(\vec{r}) \to \bar{b} = 2\pi q \bar\rho$. The actual relation between flux and charge is, of course, retarded, but for small ε, so long as the frequencies characterizing the electron dynamics satisfy the inequality, $\omega \ll \Omega$, this should be negligible as well. Typically, the energies of most interest are set by the scale of the Coulomb interaction, $V_c \sim e^2 \sqrt{\bar\rho} \sim e^2/\ell$, where $\ell \equiv \sqrt{\phi_0/2\pi B}$ is the magnetic length, and the second estimate is valid when the filling factor, $\nu \equiv \bar\rho \phi_0/B \sim 1$.

For completeness, a derivation of Eqs. (3) to (6) are given in Appendix A. We have not attempted to renormalize the full coupled GLCSM theory (1) but we do not envision that would qualitatively change our results.

3. Effective Gauge Theory

An alternative approach is to integrate out the matter fields, leaving us with a description fully in terms of the fluctuating gauge fields. This can be done perturbatively in powers of the amplitude of the fluctuations of the gauge fields about their saddle point values, with the leading order approximation being a version of RPA theory. The first step is to integrate the ψ-field to get an effective action for the gauge field a:

$$S^{\text{eff}}[a] = S_{\text{mat}}[a - eA] + S_g[a] \tag{7}$$

and then identify the static saddle point configurations, $\bar{a}$ for $S^{\text{eff}}[a]$ by solving the classical equations of motion. Correspondingly, the mean fields, $\tilde{B}$ and $\tilde{E}_i$, felt by the composite particles, can be computed from $\tilde{A} \equiv eA - \bar{a}$. The resulting background gauge fields, are related to the expectation values of charges and currents by (see Appendix A)

$$\bar{b}(\vec{k}) = \epsilon^{ij} i k_i \bar{a}_j = 2\pi q\, G(k,0) \left(\langle \rho(\vec{k}) \rangle + \frac{\varepsilon}{\mu} \epsilon^{ik} i k_i \langle j_k(\vec{k}) \rangle \right)$$

$$\bar{e}_i(\vec{k}) = i k_i \bar{a}_0 - i\omega \bar{a}_i = 2\pi q\, G(k,0) \left(\epsilon^{ik} \langle j_k \rangle + \frac{i k_i}{\mu} \langle \rho(\vec{k}) \rangle \right). \tag{8}$$

For example, in the composite fermion representation of an ideal quantum Hall state, $\tilde{B}$ is such that the composite fermion filling factor, $\tilde{\nu} \equiv \bar{\rho}\phi_0/\tilde{B}$ is an integer, while in the composite boson representation, $\tilde{B} = 0$. Conversely, for electron filling $\nu = 1/2$, the composite fermions with $q = 2$ so $\tilde{B} = 0$, while the composite bosons with $q = 1$ experience a field corresponding to $\tilde{\nu} = 1$. In the $g \to \infty$ limit, where $G \to 1$ and $\lambda \to 0$, we regain the usual Chern–Simons expressions, $\bar{b}(\vec{k}) = (2\pi q) \langle \rho(\vec{k}) \rangle$ and $\bar{e}_i(\vec{k}) = (2\pi q)\epsilon^{ik} \langle j_k(\vec{k}) \rangle$; on the other hand, in the $g \to 0$ limit, since $G(k, 0) \sim (k\lambda)^{-2}$ for $k\lambda \gg 1$, even in the presence of disorder where $\langle \rho(\vec{k}) \rangle$ and $\langle \vec{j}(\vec{k}) \rangle$ are non-zero for non-zero k, $\bar{b}(\vec{k})$ and $\bar{e}(\vec{k}) \to 0$ for $k \neq 0$, while $\bar{b}(\vec{0}) = 2\pi q \, \bar{\rho}$ and $\bar{e}_i(\vec{0}) = 2\pi q\epsilon^{ik} \langle j_k(\vec{0}) \rangle$.

The next step is to expand in the fluctuations δa around the saddle point $\tilde{A}$, where for later convenience we also introduce a probe field, $eA \to eA + e\delta A$, in order to identify appropriate response functions. With this, and by a shift $\delta a \to e\delta A + \delta a$, we get

$$S^{\text{eff}}[a] = \int d\vec{r}d\tau \, \mathcal{L}_g(\bar{a}) + S_{\text{mat}}[\tilde{A}] + \int d\vec{r}d\tau \, \mathcal{L}_g(\delta a + e\delta A) \tag{9}$$

$$- \frac{1}{2} \int d\vec{r}_1 d\vec{r}_2 d\tau_1 d\tau_2 \delta a_\mu(\vec{r}_1, \tau_1) \, \hat{\Pi}^{\mu\nu}(\vec{r}_1, \vec{r}_2; \tau_1 - \tau_2)\delta a_\nu(\vec{r}_2, \tau_2) + \cdots$$

where we use the notation $\mu = (i, 0)$ but make no distinction between upper and lower indices. We have used a real time formulation where $S_{\text{mat}} = E_{\text{mat}}t$ with E_{mat} the ground-state energy of the matter fields in the presence of a static background gauge field, $\tilde{A}$. In the Euclidean formulation $S_{\text{mat}} = F_{\text{mat}}/T$ where F_{mat} is the free energy. $\hat{\Pi}(\vec{r}_1, \vec{r}_2, \tau_1 - \tau_2)$ encodes the linear response of the matter fields to an external gauge field, and ... represents the non-linear response of the same matter fields.

In the translationally invariant case, the Fourier transform of $\hat{\Pi}$, $\Pi^{\mu\nu}(\vec{k}, \omega)$, can be expressed [11] in terms of more familiar response functions as

$$\Pi^{ij}(\vec{k}, \omega) = i\omega\tilde{\sigma}_{ij}(\vec{k}, \omega)$$

$$\Pi^{i0}(\vec{k}, \omega) = -\Pi^{0,i}(\vec{k}, \omega) = -ik_j\tilde{\sigma}_{ij}(\vec{k}, \omega) \tag{10}$$

$$\Pi^{00}(\vec{k}, \omega) = \tilde{\kappa}(\vec{k}, \omega),$$

where $\tilde{\sigma}_{ij}$ is the composite particle conductivity tensor and $\tilde{\kappa}$ is the density-density response function that we refer to as the composite particle compressibility since it is equal to the thermodynamic compressibility as $\vec{k}$ and ω tend to zero.

Needless to say, the state of the matter fields depends not only on their statistics and their interactions, but also on the values of the static mean-fields, $\tilde{B}$ and $\tilde{E}_i$. However, even in this case, the spatial variations should be less and less pronounced the larger λ.

Finally, to the extent that the higher order terms in δa can be ignored, it is possible to integrate over the statistical gauge fluctuations exactly. Taking appropriate derivates of the resulting expression with respect to the probe fields, δA, allows us to express the final results for the electron response functions, in particular the resistivity tensor, ρ_{ij}, in terms of the composite particle response functions as

$$\rho_{xx}(\vec{k}, \omega) = \tilde{\rho}_{xx}(\vec{k}, \omega) + i\omega\varepsilon \left(\frac{q}{\mu}\right) G(k, \omega) + \cdots$$

$$\rho_{xy}(\vec{k}, \omega) = \tilde{\rho}_{xy}(\vec{k}, \omega) + qG(k, \omega) + \cdots \qquad (11)$$

$$\kappa(\vec{k}, 0) = \tilde{\kappa}(\vec{k}, 0) \left[1 + \tilde{\kappa}(\vec{k}) \left(\frac{q}{\mu}\right) G(k, 0)\right]^{-1} + \cdots$$

where we restored $\hbar$ and expressed the results in units of the Klitzing constant h/e^2. The ... is to remind us that we neglected the effects of higher order terms in δa.

The self-consistency of this approach — i.e. ignoring the higher order terms, ... — can be justified only if the the gauge field fluctuations are small, i.e. so long as

$$\langle [b(\vec{k}) - \bar{b}(\vec{k})]^2 \rangle \ll (\phi_0)^2. \qquad (12)$$

A more detailed discussion of this condition is given in Appendix B.

4. Application to Gapped States

The basic idea in the GW approach is to adiabatically connect the difficult FQH problem to a simple solvable one without closing the gap. For Abelian states there are two ways of doing this. In the composite boson approach the large g limit corresponds to hard core composite bosons in zero effective magnetic field, i.e. $\tilde{B} = 0$. Here, so long as the disorder is not too strong, the composite bosons can be expected to condense into a superconducting state. Because of the charge flux connection inherited from the Chern-Simons term, the Meißner effect in the superconductor translates into incompressibility of the Hall liquid, the zero resistance of the superconductor into the quantized Hall conductance, and flux quantization into the existence of quasi-particles with fractional charge and statistics [5,12]. In the composite fermion picture, the solvable limit is when the effective magnetic field, $\tilde{B} = \tilde{\nu}^{-1}\bar{\rho}\phi_0$ with $\tilde{\nu}^{-1}$ an integer, n, so that (provided the disorder and the interaction strengths are not too large) the composite fermions fill n Landau levels. This state [6] is incompressible with a gap that is adiabatically connected to the cyclotron gap, and the other properties of the fractional quantum Hall state can be inferred by applying versions of the arguments that have been applied in the integer case.

In order to connect to the analysis of fluctuations in the previous section, we shall here use the composite boson approach, but also comment on the composite fermion picture.

4.1. Abelian states

The Laughlin states provide the simplest case where an adiabatic evolution from $\lambda \gg \ell$ to $\lambda \to 0$ takes us from a system in which the mean-field approximation is justified to the physical problem of interest. If this can done without closing the gap, all the "essential" properties derived from the mean field theory should also hold for the exact theory. We have no proof, but we believe that it is a very likely scenario. Moreover, because we are dealing with incompressible states, we expect the mean-field treatment to be self consistent, and highly accurate at least for the range of g where $\pi\lambda^2\bar{\rho} > 1$. In Fig. 1 we show the field, $b(\vec{r})$, corresponding to a typical configuration of particles (chosen using the square of a $\nu = 1$ Quantum Hall wave-function as a Boltzman weight) for a few values of λ; one can see that $b(\vec{r})$ rapidly approaches a configuration independent constant with increasing λ.

This argument for the Laughlin states also applies, *mutatis mutandis*, to the Halperin (n, n, m) bilayer states [13, 14] if we properly take into account that in this case we need two statistical gauge fields [15]. This will affect details of our estimates of the fluctuations, but will not alter them qualitatively.

The Laughlin states can be viewed as the subset of the Jain states with one filled Landau level. "Hierarchy" states with more than one filled Landau level of composite fermions are most easily understood in the Fradkin–Lopez [7] field theory of composite fermion: by attaching $\pm 2p$ flux quanta to each particle and again decreasing g until the mean field approximation is valid. In this case, one finds incompressible states corresponding to n filled Landau levels at filling factors $\nu = n/(2np\pm1)$. The bosonic picture for these hierarchy states is more subtle. Superficially they look very similar to multi-component states. For example, the Halperin (3,3,2) has $\nu = 2/5$ just as the leading Jain state. The difference is that in the Jain states there is only one

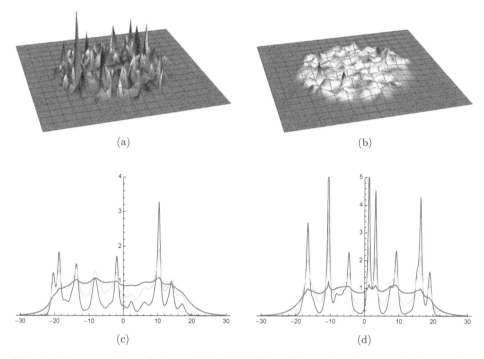

Fig. 1. Contour plots of the statistical b-field configurations for a typical snapshot of 200 electrons in a circular $\nu = 1$ QH state for (a) $\lambda = \ell/2$ and (b) $\lambda = \ell$, where ℓ is the magnetic length. (c) and (d) show the b field along two perpendicular diameters of the droplet. The blue, green and red curves correspond to $\lambda/\ell = 0.5$, 1, and 2 respectively.

type of composite fermion, so the state has to be fully anti-symmetric. In the composite fermion approach this is possible because the electrons reside in two different "effective Landau levels." The physical meaning of this is that the electrons carry different orbital spins [16], and this must be incorporated in the composite boson picture. How to do this was shown in a recent paper [17], which however also relied on a mean filed approximation. Combining those methods with the adiabatic approach of this paper provides a field theoretic understanding not only of the Jain states, but of a larger class of hierarchy states.

From (8) we can also obtain the resistivity tensor at finite $\vec{k}$. Specifically, when composite bosons are condensed in a superfluid state, the screening of the magnetic and electric fields persists to finite $\vec{k}$, so that in equilibrium, and with a λ large enough to justify the mean-field approximation, $\tilde{B}(\vec{k}) = 0$ and $\tilde{E}_i(\vec{k}) = \vec{0}$. At finite $\vec{k}$, $\tilde{B} = \tilde{b} = 0$, which allows us to compute $\vec{E}$ in terms of $\vec{j}$ from (8), and thus to extract (see Appendix A.3) the conductivity tensor which we express as

$$\frac{\sigma_{xy}(\vec{k})}{\sigma_{xy}(\vec{0})} = 1 + \frac{(1-\varepsilon)}{\varepsilon}(k\lambda)^2 + O(k^4). \tag{13}$$

This can be compared whith the expression derived by Hoyos and Son using Galilean invarianace [18]

$$\frac{\sigma_{xy}(\vec{k})}{\sigma_{xy}(\vec{0})} = 1 + \frac{s}{2}(k\ell)^2 + O(1/\omega_c) \tag{14}$$

where s is the orbital spin of the composite particles. At a phenomenological level we can match these expressions by adjusting ϵ and λ, but within our framework there is no reason for doing so.

In this context we note that the flux tubes associated with the electrons do carry angular momentum. The field angular momentum is

$$L_g = \frac{1}{g^2} \int d\vec{r}\, b\,(\vec{r}\cdot\vec{e}) \tag{15}$$

and using $\vec{e} = (1/\mu)\vec{\nabla}b$ that follows form (8) combined with the expression (6) for the b-field associated to a point charge, the integration can be done analytically and gives,

$$L_g = \frac{1}{\varepsilon}\frac{q}{2} \tag{16}$$

independent of λ. This means that the total angular momentum is not changed as we interpolate between a thin and a thick flux tube. In the Lorentz invariant case, $\varepsilon = 1$, we reproduce the expected value for the orbital spin (the thin vortex limit was given in Ref. [19]). We note that in this case the $\vec{k}$ dependence of σ^{xx} vanish, but this might be purely accidental.

4.2. Nonabelian Pfaffian states

In their second paper [2], GW also applied their adiabatic approach to a state with a filled Landau level of bosons,

$$\Psi_{MR} = \mathrm{Pf}\left(\frac{1}{z_i - z_j}\right)\prod_{i<j}(z_i - z_j), \tag{17}$$

a state that requires a strong repulsion to be stabilized. By adiabatically concentrating half of the flux to the particles they ended up with a state at $\nu = 1/2$, and a wave function only differing from (17) by an extra Jastrow factor $\prod_{i<j}(z_i - z_j)$ which is precisely the nonabelian Moore–Read Pfaffian state [20].

In two later papers [21,22] with Wen, GW instead started from fermions in zero magnetic field, and argued that adding a small CS-term would trigger a superconducting instability giving rise to a $p_x + ip_y$ paired state. The connection between the QH system and p-wave paired (spinless) superconductors was later discussed in detail by Read and Green [23].

We shall connect to this latter approach, i.e. we consider the adiabatic continuation from an *assumed* superconducting state of spinless fermions in zero magnetic field, to the MR Pfaffian states of composite fermions in a background field at $\nu = 1/2$. Clearly the existence of such a superconducting state is contingent upon the details of the interaction. Also, superconductivity is not the only possible state in the small λ limit, and in the next section we shall discuss the other obvious candidate, namely the Fermi liquid.

Much of the interest in the Pfaffian state derives from its nonabelian quasiparticles. The paired superconductor hosts vortices that binds Majorana states which are at the origin of the nonabelian statistics [24]. If one could verify that these vortices are present also in the full GLCSM theory, our construction would give a strong argument for having a nonabelian QH state at $\nu = 1/2$ that is not based on an explicit wave function, but rather on a well justified mean field theory.

5. Compressible States

There are at least two circumstances in which compressible states are thought to arise in quantum Hall systems: 1) The first is a composite fermion metal that occurs when the net statistical flux exactly cancels the total magnetic flux, i.e. when $\tilde{B}$ for the composite fermions vanishes. Such a state might exist either in the absence of disorder or in the presence of weak disorder. 2) The other is the critical state that occurs at a continuous transition between two quantum Hall plateaus or at the transition between a quantum Hall state and an insulator. Since, in the absence of disorder [25], these transitions are generically first order, this state presumably exists only in the presence of suitable disorder. Clearly, for either of these states, the notion of adiabatic continuity is more subtle than for inccompressible states. Specifically, even though the mean field treatment is exact in the limit $\lambda \to \infty$, it is a nontrivial issue to what extent the results continue smoothly to the case of large but finite λ.

5.1. *The Composite Fermion Metal*

The effect of dynamically fluctuating gauge fields on the composite fermion metal is a complex problem [26,27]. Typically, the Fermi liquid state is found to be perturbatively unstable, so various clever tricks — including an early and highly influential approach by Nayak and Wilczek [28] — have been adopted to address it. It is a potentially rewarding challenge to devise a systematic approach that exploits the twin small parameters, λ^{-1} and ε.

However, in the presence of disorder, there is an interesting piece of physics that can be extracted for large but finite λ. To be explicit, consider the case of most direct experimental relevance, that is $\nu = 1/2$, which for composite fermions implies $q = 2$. Now, for $\lambda = \infty$, $\tilde{B} = 0$, which is to say that the composite fermions see no trace of the external magnetic field. Consequently, the composite fermion Hall response vanishes, $\tilde{\sigma}_{xy} = 0$. However, this result cannot be generically correct since the electrons are coupled to the magnetic field, and indeed it is possible to prove [29, 30] that, in the special case where the electronic problem is particle-hole symmetric, the composite fermion $\sigma_{xy} = -1/2$. This apparent contradiction can be resolved in an elegant fashion as was shown in Ref. [31]. Clearly, in the presence of disorder, the electron density is expected to be inhomogeneous, and for weak disorder, U, and small k, this can be captured in linear response:

$$\langle \rho(\vec{k}) \rangle = \kappa(k, 0) U(\vec{k}). \tag{18}$$

Correspondingly, there will be a spatially varying effective magnetic field, as in (8). It is still the case that the average field vanishes, but because the average field is correlated with the particle density, the average of the cross-correlation between field and density is finite,

$$\overline{\langle \rho^\star(\vec{k}) \tilde{B}(\vec{k}) \rangle} = -2\pi q\, G(k, 0)\, |\kappa(k, 0)|^2\, \overline{\left|U(\vec{k})\right|^2} \tag{19}$$

where $\overline{O}$ is the average over disorder configurations of O.

Indeed, in Ref. [31], evidence was presented that this correlation results in an emergent particle-hole symmetry, i.e. it implies $\sigma_{xy} = -1/2$, a conclusion that was reached earlier in Ref. [32] using a complementary approach. To this we add the control of mean-field theory and the suppression of large k fluctuations of $\tilde{B}$ that sharpens the analysis.

5.2. Critical States

A QH state near a plateau transition becomes compressible. In the composite boson language, this corresponds to a superconductor to insulator transition (SIT), as originally discussed by Lee, Zhang and one of us [33]. In experiments this transition is always studied as a function of magnetic field at fixed disorder, which in composite boson language corresponds to studying the SIT as a function of increasing $\tilde{B}$. Here the critical value $\tilde{B}_c$ is related to the critical magnetic field, B_c as $B_c = q\phi_0\bar{\rho} + \tilde{B}_c$.

The important point is that — to the extent that the RPA description is valid, i.e. that higher order terms in δa can be ignored — all the critical properties of the system are those of bosons undergoing a field-driven SIT, regardless of the value of q. The implication is that the critical properties of the system are fundamentally the same for a system undergoing a field driven SIT, a $\nu = 1$ to insulator transition (which corresponds to the case $q = 1$), i.e. an integer plateau transition, or a $\nu = 1/3$ to insulator transition (which corresponds to the case $q = 3$), i.e. a fractional quantum Hall transition. The authors of Ref. [33] referred to this as a "law of corresponding states," which has since [34] been referred to as "superuniversality."

To be more explicit, consider what we know of the properties of bosons undergoing a field-driven SIT. For $\tilde{B} < \tilde{B}_c$, the system is superconducting, which means that the composite boson response functions at small ω and $T = 0$ are $\tilde{\rho}_{xx}(\vec{0}, \omega) = (m^\star/e^2\tilde{n}_s)i\omega$ and $\tilde{\rho}_{xy}(\vec{0}, \omega) = 0$ where $\tilde{n}_s$ is the superfluid density.[c] This holds even in the state near the transition so long as all field-induced vortices (quasi-particles) are localized. Because these vortices can always diffuse at finite T by variable-range-hopping, there can be no finite temperature transition. However, we expect there to be a characteristic temperature scale, $T^\star$, below which $\tilde{\rho}_{xx}(\vec{0}, 0)$ decreases in some exponential manner with decreasing T. On the basis of general scaling considerations [35], one expects that both $T^\star$ and $\tilde{n}_s$ vanish upon approach to the critical field in proportion to $(\tilde{B}_c - \tilde{B})^{\nu z}$ where ν and z are, respectively, the correlation length and dynamical exponent of the field driven SIT.

As can be seen from Eqs. (11), this behavior of the composite bosons can be directly translated into statements concerning the electron response functions. At $T \to 0$ (ignoring terms of order ω^2 and higher)

$$\rho_{xx}(\vec{0}, \omega) = i\omega \left(m^\star/e^2 n_s\right)$$
$$\rho_{xy}(\vec{0}, \omega) = q, \tag{20}$$

i.e. no matter how weakly superconducting the composite bosons, the corresponding Hall resistance is quantized and $\rho_{xx} \to 0$ as $\omega \to 0$. Interestingly, the scaling relations imply that the reactive portion of ρ_{xx}, which is proportional to $1/n_s \equiv 1/\tilde{n}_s + q\varepsilon e^2/m^\star\mu$, should diverge in proportion to $(\tilde{B} - \tilde{B}_c)^{-\nu z}$ — a prediction that, as far as we know, has never been tested.

---

[c]A more appropriate description is that $\tilde{n}_s/m^\star$ is the superfluid stiffness.

There are general scaling arguments [33, 36] that suggest that at the critical point of the SIT, the resistivity tensor takes on a universal value, $\tilde{\rho}_{ij}^{(c)}$. Again from Eq. (11), this implies universal values for the resistivity tensor at the point of a quantum Hall transition,

$$\rho_{xx}^{(c)}(\vec{0}, 0) = \tilde{\rho}_{xx}^{(c)}$$
$$\rho_{xy}^{(c)}(\vec{0}, 0) = q + \tilde{\rho}_{xy}^{(c)}. \tag{21}$$

Arguments based on a speculated self-duality at the transition [33, 36–38], suggest that $\tilde{\rho}_{xx}^{(c)} = 1$ and $\tilde{\rho}_{xy}^{(c)} = 0$. This is consistent with a distinct set of theoretical expectations in the context of the $\nu = 1$ to insulator transition where by particle-hole symmetry one expects $\sigma_{xy}^{(c)} = 1/2$ and where various arguments [39, 40] suggest that $\sigma_{xx}^{(c)} = 1/2$ as well — i.e. that $\rho_{xx}^{(c)} = \rho_{xy}^{(c)} = 1$.

A similar analysis can be carried out on the insulating side of the SIT. The results are analogous to the above.

More generally, much of this analysis parallels that of Ref. [33]. What the present work adds is to identify a limit, $\lambda \gg \ell$, in which the neglect of the higher order terms in δa is justified. Of course, there is no *a priori* reason to think that no corrections to the critical properties arise at order $1/\lambda$, and these could well depend on q — thus spoiling the superuniversal aspects of the results. However, it may give some way to understand that — in several experimental circumstances [37, 40, 41] — superuniversality seems to be approximately realized, both with regards to measured critical exponents and the value of the resistivity tensor at criticality. Indeed, inverting the logic of superuniversality, it is possible to translate known results for the quantum Hall plateau transition into predictions for the properties of the SIT. Interestingly, recent experiments [38] on the SIT in superconducting films have found results — including apparent particle-vortex self-duality — that are consistent with the corresponding observations in quantum Hall systems.

6. Future Directions

Until now, we have used the Maxwell terms as a tool to adiabatically connect QH states to other known states such as superconductors or Fermi liquids. Alternatively we could imagine using $\mathcal{L}_{\text{GLCSM}}$ as a phenomenological theory, where the parameters g and ε could be adjusted to fit, e.g., the collective Girvin–Platzman and Kohn modes. At a much more ambitious level, it is also possible to imagine that $\mathcal{L}_{\text{GLCSM}}$ could emerge as an effective field theory once some high-energy degrees of freedom have been integrated out. It is certainly plausible that an effective size for the flux attachment, $\lambda \sim \ell$, would emerge when states in higher Landau levels are integrated out.

It is plausible, but not inevitable, that the resulting low energy effective theory will still have the same $U(1)$ gauge structure. It is, after all, the natural theoretical framework for topological effects like fractional charge and statistics (and possibly also Hall viscosity or shift) which should not be affected by short distance cutoffs, and we would thus expect the crucial current-charge propagator D_{i0} in (4) to remain the same albeit with a renormalized pole position. Just as in the case with massless photons, where a momentum cutoff typically introduces a mass and thus a new (longitudinal) degree of freedom, this could happen also in our case but such a mode is expected to be massive and thus not destroy the infrared behavior. So, without being explicit, we may assume that we can integrate out high energy modes in a way that preserves gauge invariance with respect to the statistical gauge fields. In this sense, L_{GLCSM} with finite g (or a generalized version of it) can be considered to be a course grained version of the "microscopic" problem.

If we accept L_{GLCSM} as physical — i.e. not just a useful prop in a thought experiment — we can use some of the above results to make statements of relevance to the real world. Since, in the limit $\lambda \gg \ell$, the line of analysis provides a justification for a law of corresponding states relating the behavior of integer and fractional quantum Hall plateau transitions to each other and to the magnetic field driven SIT, it is reasonable to conclude that it should apply in an approximate sense so long as $\lambda \gtrsim \ell$. Possibly this rationalizes the considerable emperical support for the notion of corresponding states. One new result of the analysis in this paper that warrants experimental consideration is the relation given in Eq. (20) that relates the reactive portion of ρ_{xx} at low frequencies to the superfluid density of the composite bosons. Recall that for a Gallilean invariant system, Kohn's theorem implies that $n_s = \bar{\rho}$ in this relation. Exploring whether, and in what way, n_s vanishes upon approach to a quantum Hall to insulator transition could reveal a central feature of the SIT of the composite bosons.

We have not touched upon the nature of the quasiparticles. In the bosonic description they are vortex solutions, while in the composite fermionic description they are holes in the various effective Landau levels. In the latter picture the quasiparticles are naturally endowed with an orbital spin, but it remains to understand this in the bosonic version. As hinted at earlier, we might speculate that for the extended flux tubes there might be a more general flux attachment procedure that allows for different orbital spins.

7. Tribute

Since this paper is dedicated to Frank Wilczek on his 70th birthday, we end with two personal notes.

SK: I met Frank when he took up his position at the ITP at UCSB in 1980. I was a freshly minted "solid state physicist" for whom encountering the notion of a unified field of "theoretical physics" — a notion embodied by the breadth of Frank's interests and contributions — was exhilarating and formative. I remember telling Frank about work I was completing in collaboration with my mentor, J. R. Schrieffer, showing that fractional charge (in this case of 1D solitons) can be a sharp quantum observable — something that was much disputed at the time by theorists with frightening credentials. That Frank found the line of reasoning convincing (although, admittedly, he also thought the answer to be so obvious that it was not worth disputing) was one of those little things that had a great impact on my scientific life. Years later, in less happy circumstances, a famous quote of Frank's was a source of some comfort: "If you don't make mistakes, you're not working on hard enough problems." At least I have made mistakes. In recent years — through the catalyst of the friendship between my wife, Pamela Davis, and Frank's charismatic partner, Betsy Devine — I have experienced the joy of inclusion in the Wilczek circle of friends.

THH: I also first met Frank at the ITP in the the fall of 1981, when he and my mentor, Ken Johnson from MIT, co-organized a QCD workshop, but it was only when Frank took up a position in Stockholm in 2016 that I got to know him more closely. I have since witnessed his great impact on the theoretical physics environment at Stockholm University and at Nordita, where he has built a thriving research group. He has also been instrumental in attracting large grants to expand the activities at Nordita in new and exciting directions. Personally I have had the great privilege to work and discuss with Frank both on physics projects, and on environment building activities at Nordita and at the TDLI. As a regular participant in his group meetings, I have also seen how he mentors and encourages young physicists by creating a challenging and critical, but always kind and supportive atmosphere. Work aside, I have fond memories of the many joyful moments I have spent with Frank and Betsy, in the gardens of Högberga, in the rollercoasters of Gröna Lund, and at dinners in Stockholm and Shanghai.

Acknowledgments

We have got very helpful feedback on this work from several colleagues, and we especially want to thank Srinivas Raghu for numerous discussions, and Mikael Fremling for providing input data for the figures. S.A.K. was supported, in part, by NSF Grant No. DMR-2000987 at Stanford.

Appendix A. Details on the CSM Theory

A.1. *Dispersion relation and fluxtube profile*

Using the Coloumb gauge $\vec{\nabla} \cdot \vec{a} = 0$ to write $a_i = \epsilon^{ij}\partial_i \chi$, and with a polar representation of the bosonic field, $\psi = \sqrt{\rho}e^{i\theta}$, we can write the gauge Lagrangian to quadratic order as

$$
\begin{aligned}
\mathcal{L}_g &= \frac{1}{2\pi q}a_0 k^2 \chi + \frac{\varepsilon}{4\pi q\mu}a_0 k^2 a_0 - \frac{1}{4\pi q\mu}\chi[(k^2)^2 - \varepsilon k^2\omega^2]\chi \\
&= \frac{1}{4\pi q\mu}\left(\chi,\ a_0\right)\begin{pmatrix} \varepsilon k^2\omega^2 - k^4 & \mu k^2 \\ \mu k^2 & \varepsilon k^2 \end{pmatrix}\begin{pmatrix} \chi \\ a_0 \end{pmatrix},
\end{aligned}
\tag{A.1}
$$

where $k^2 = -\nabla^2$, $\omega^2 = -\partial_t^2$ and we recall that $\mu = g^2/2\pi q$. Here and in the following we use the simplified notation $\xi(-\vec{k})f(\vec{k})\xi(\vec{k}) = \xi f(\vec{k})\xi$ etc.

To extract correlation functions and response, we introduce a source term

$$
\mathcal{L}_{\text{source}} = -a_0\rho + \vec{a} \cdot \vec{j} = -a_0\rho + \chi j_\chi
\tag{A.2}
$$

where $j_\chi = i\epsilon^{ij}k_i j_j$. Integrating the gauge field gives the response action

$$
S(\rho, \chi) = \frac{1}{2}\left(j_\chi,\ \rho\right)\begin{pmatrix} \varepsilon & -\mu \\ -\mu & \varepsilon\omega^2 - k^2 \end{pmatrix}\begin{pmatrix} j_\chi \\ \rho \end{pmatrix}\frac{2\pi q}{\mu k^2}G(\vec{k},\omega)
\tag{A.3}
$$

where

$$
G(\vec{k},\omega) = \frac{\mu^2}{(\varepsilon\omega)^2 - \mu^2 - \varepsilon k^2}.
\tag{A.4}
$$

Using $b = \nabla^2\rho$ the fluxtube profile is directly extracted from the (χ,ρ) component of the response action,

$$
b(k) = k^2\chi = \frac{2\pi q\mu^2/\varepsilon}{k^2 + \mu^2/\varepsilon}\rho = \frac{2\pi q}{(k\lambda)^2 + 1}\rho
\tag{A.5}
$$

which after Fourier transformation gives (6) in the main text.

A.2. *Response functions*

In the translationally invariant case the part of (10) relevant for calculating linear response can be written as

$$S^{\mathrm{resp}}[\delta a, \delta A] = \int \frac{d\vec{k}d\omega}{(2\pi)^4} \left(\frac{1}{2} (\delta a_\mu + e\delta A_\mu) \Pi_g^{\mu\nu} (\delta a_\nu + e\delta A_\nu) \right.$$
$$\left. - \frac{1}{2} \delta a_\mu \Pi_{\mathrm{mat}}^{\mu\nu} \delta a_\nu \right) \tag{A.6}$$

and after integrating over the fluctuation δa of the statistical field the electronic response function becomes

$$S_{el}^{\mathrm{resp}}[\delta A] = \int \frac{d\vec{k}d\omega}{(2\pi)^4} \, \delta A_\mu \Pi_{\mathrm{mat}}^{\mu\nu} \delta A_\nu \,. \tag{A.7}$$

where Π_{el} is expressed in terms of Π_g and Π_{mat}. This relation is simpler when written in terms of the inverse matrices $D_{el} = \Pi_{el}^{-1}$ etc. (which differ from the standard Minkowski propagator by a factor i)

$$D_{el}^{\mu\nu} = D_{\mathrm{mat}}^{\mu\nu} - D_g^{\mu\nu} \tag{A.8}$$

which are related to the resistivities.

The most direct way to get the explicit expressions for $D_g^{\mu\nu}$, is to write (A.1) in the (a_x, a_y, a_0) basis

$$\mathcal{L}_g = \frac{1}{2} \begin{pmatrix} a_x, a_y, a_0 \end{pmatrix} \frac{1}{2\pi q\mu} \begin{pmatrix} \varepsilon\omega^2 - k^2 & 0 & -i\mu k_y \\ 0 & \varepsilon\omega^2 - k^2 & i\mu k_x \\ i\mu k_y & -i\mu k_x & \varepsilon k^2 \end{pmatrix} \begin{pmatrix} a_x \\ a_y \\ a_0 \end{pmatrix},$$

and then diagonalize this matrix to get

$$D^{ij} = -2\pi q \frac{\varepsilon}{\mu} G(\vec{k}, \omega) \, \delta^{ij}$$

$$D^{i0} = -D^{i0} = -2\pi q \, G(\vec{k}, \omega) \epsilon^{ij} \frac{ik_j}{k^2} \tag{A.9}$$

$$D^{00} = -2\pi q \frac{\varepsilon\omega^2 - k^2}{\mu k^2} G(\vec{k}, \omega).$$

The compressibility can directly be read from D^{00} or equivalently from (A.3). To extract the resistivity tensor $\rho^{ij} = \rho_{xx}\delta^{ij} + \rho_{xy}\epsilon^{ij}$, we write the electric field as

$$e_i = i\omega a_i - ik_i a_0 = i\omega(D^{ij}j_j + D^{i0}\rho) - ik_i D^{0l}j_l \tag{A.10}$$

and then substitute the expressions (A.9) and use current conservation, $\dot{\rho} = \vec{\nabla} \cdot \vec{j}$ to get (11) in the main text. Note that the term $i\omega a_i$ must be included to get the correct $\omega = 0$ result, since there is a term $i\omega\rho = -i\vec{k} \cdot \vec{j}$.

A.3. Derivation of Eq. (13)

Putting the first line in (8) to zero yields

$$\langle\rho\rangle = \frac{\varepsilon}{\mu}\epsilon^{ik}ik_i\langle j_k\rangle \tag{A.11}$$

and substituting this in the second line of (8) we get

$$eE_i = \bar{e}_i = 2\pi q\frac{1}{1+\left(\frac{k}{\mu}^2\right)}\left[1 + \varepsilon\left(\frac{k}{\mu}\right)^2\right]\epsilon^{ik}\langle j_k\rangle. \tag{A.12}$$

From this we can extract the conductivity,

$$\frac{1}{2\pi q}\sigma_{xy}(\vec{k}) = 1 + (1 - \varepsilon)\left(\frac{k}{\mu}\right)^2 + O(k^4). \tag{A.13}$$

Expressing μ in λ we get (13) in the text.

Appendix B. What Does it Mean for Gauge Field Fluctuations to be Small?

In order for the mean-field treatment to be accurate, the fluctuations of the statistical gauge fields must be small. What this means is most readily addressed from the composite boson perspective.

To begin with, let us examine what this means for the static fields produced as a response to the (assumed weak) disorder in the system. If the flux of $\bar{b}$ through any area of a superconductor exceeds a flux quantum, the energy can be lowered by nucleating a vortex, which constitutes a strong and highly non-linear response. Conversely, if the magnetic fields are sufficiently small that the flux through any area is small compared to ϕ_0, the response of the composite bosons is correspondingly small and linear. In Fourier space, this leads to a condition of the form of Eq. (12).

Given a particular realization of the disorder potential $U_{\vec{k}}$, the variations in the composite particle density and current density can be computed in linear response as

$$\langle \rho(\vec{k}) \rangle = \tilde{\kappa}(\vec{k}, 0) U(\vec{k}) + \cdots ,$$

$$\langle j_i(\vec{k}) \rangle = -i\tilde{\sigma}_{ij}(\vec{k}, 0) k_j U(\vec{k}) + \cdots . \tag{B.1}$$

so, when averaged over impurity configurations, the mean-squared variation of $\bar{b}$ follows from (8),

$$\Delta(\vec{k}) \equiv \overline{|\langle b_{\vec{k}} \rangle|^2} = \left| 2\pi q G(k,0) \tilde{K}(k,0) \right|^2 \overline{\left| U_{\vec{k}} \right|^2} \tag{B.2}$$

where $\overline{X}$ is the configuration average of X and

$$\tilde{K}(k,\omega) = \tilde{\kappa}(k,\omega) - \sqrt{\varepsilon}\lambda k_i \epsilon_{ij} \tilde{\sigma}_{jk}(\vec{k},\omega) k_k . \tag{B.3}$$

In the same way, we can compute the mean squared magnitude of the fluctuations of the statistical magnetic field,

$$\delta(\vec{k},\omega) \equiv \langle \, |b_{\vec{k},\omega} - \langle b_{\vec{k},\omega} \rangle|^2 \rangle = |2\pi q G(k,\omega)|^2 \tilde{K}(k,\omega). \tag{B.4}$$

It is not clear that the mean field approximation imposes an equally strong condition on $\delta(\vec{k},\omega)$ as on $\Delta(\vec{k})$, but we believe that a conservative estimate for it being a good approximation to treat $\tilde{B}$ as nearly uniform and weakly fluctuating is to require

$$\Delta(\vec{k}) \quad \& \quad \delta(\vec{k}) \quad \ll (\phi_0)^2 . \tag{B.5}$$

The important feature is that $G(\vec{k},0) \sim (\lambda k)^{-2}$ for $k\lambda \gg 1$. Thus for large λ (small g) all large k fluctuations are effectively quenched. The only remaining issues concern small k fluctuations with $k\lambda \lesssim 1$.

For an incompressible state, $\tilde{\kappa}(k,0) \sim k^2$, so again the fluctuations are automatically small. In other words, for large but finite λ, the mean field theory should be accurate for all incompressible states, and only be questionable for compressible states at values of $k \lesssim 1/\lambda$.

References

[1] M. Greiter and F. Wilczek, *Mod. Phys. Lett. B* **04**, 1063 (1990).

[2] M. Greiter and F. Wilczek, *Nucl. Physics B* **370**, 577 (1992).

[3] M. Greiter and F. Wilczek Adiabatic construction of hierarchical quantum hall states, 2021, arXiv:2105.05625 [cond-mat.mes-hall].

[4] S. M. Girvin and A. H. MacDonald, *Phys. Rev. Lett.* **58**, 1252 (1987).

[5] S. C. Zhang, T. H. Hansson, and S. Kivelson, *Phys. Rev. Lett.* **62**, 82 (1989).

[6] J. K. Jain, *Composite Fermions* (Cambridge University Press, 2007).

[7] A. Lopez and E. Fradkin, *Phys. Rev. B* **44**, 5246 (1991).

[8] A. Lopez and E. Fradkin, *Phys. Rev. B* **69**, 155322 (2004).

[9] S. Deser, R. Jackiw, and S. Templeton, *Ann. Phys.* **281**, 409 (2000).

[10] D. Arovas, J. R. Schrieffer, and F. Wilczek, *Phys. Rev. Lett.* **53**, 722 (1984).

[11] D.-H. Lee, S. Kivelson, and S.-C. Zhang, *Phys. Rev. Lett.* **67**, 3302 (1991).

[12] S. C. Zhang, International *J. Mod. Phys. B* **06**, 25 (1992).

[13] B. I. Halperin, *Helv. Phys. Acta* **56**, 75 (1983).

[14] S. M. Girvin and A. H. MacDonald, Multicomponent quantum hall systems: The sum of their parts and more, in *Perspectives in Quantum Hall Effects* (John Wiley & Sons 1996), Chap. 5, pp. 161–224, https://onlinelibrary.wiley. com/doi/pdf/10.1002/9783527617258.ch5.

[15] B. Blok and X. G. Wen, *Phys. Rev. B* **42**, 8145 (1990).

[16] X.-G. Wen, *Adv. Phys.* **44**, 405 (1995).

[17] Y. Tournois, M. Hermanns, and T. H. Hansson, *SciPost Phys.* **8**, 79 (2020).

[18] C. Hoyos and D. T. Son, *Phys. Rev. Lett.* **108**, 066805 (2012).

[19] C. R. Hagen, *Phys. Rev. D* **31**, 2135 (1985).

[20] G. Moore and N. Read, *Nucl. Phys. B* **360**, 362 (19991).

[21] M. Greiter, X.-G. Wen, and F. Wilczek, *Phys. Rev. Lett.* **66**, 3205 (1991).

[22] M. Greiter, X. Wen, and F. Wilczek, *Nucl. Phys. B* **374**, 567 (1992).

[23] N. Read and D. Green, *Phys. Rev. B* **61**, 10267 (200).

[24] D. A. Ivanov, *Phys. Rev. Lett.* **86**, 268 (2001).

[25] K.-S. Kim and S. A. Kivelson, *npj Quantum Materials* **6** (2021).

[26] S. H. Simon and B. I. Halperin, *Phys. Rev. B.* **48**, 17368 (1993).

[27] G. Murthy and R. Shankar, *Rev. Mod. Phys.* **75**, 1101 (2003).

[28] C. Nayak and F. Wilczek, *Nucl. Phys. B* **417**, 359 (1994).

[29] S. A. Kivelson, D.-H. Lee, Y. Krotov, wrong and J. Gan, *Phys. Rev. B* **55**, 15552 (1997).

[30] G. Murthy and R. Shankar, *Phys. Rev. B* **93**, 085405 (2016).

[31] P. Kumar, S. Raghu, and M. Mulligan, *Phys. Rev. B* **98**, 115105 (2018); *Phys. Rev. B* **99**, 235114 (2019).

[32] C. Wang, N. R. Cooper, B. I. Halperin, and A. Stern, *Phys. Rev. X* **7**, 031029 (2017).

[33] S. Kivelson, D.-H. Lee and S.-C. Zhang, *Phys. Rev. B.* **46**, 2223 (1992).

[34] C. P. Burgess and B. P. Dolan, *Phys. Rev. B* **63**, 155309 (2001).

[35] S. L. Sondhi, S. M. Girvin, J. P. Carini and D. Shahar, *Rev. Mod. Phys.* **69**, 315 (1997).

[36] M. P. A. Fisher, *Phys. Rev. Lett.* **65**, 923 (1990).

[37] E. Shimshoni, S. L. Sondhi, and D. Shahar, *Phys. Rev. B.* **55**, 13730 (1997).

[38] N. P. Breznay, M. A. Steiner, S. A. Kivelson, and A. Kapitulnik, *Proc. Nat. Acad. Sci.* **113**, 280 (2016).

[39] Y. Huo, R. E. Hetzel, and R. N. Bhatt, *Phys. Rev. Lett.* **70**, 481 (1993).

[40] D. Shahar, D. C. Tsui, M. Shayegan, R. N. Bhatt, and J. E. Cunningham, *Phys. Rev. Lett.* **74**, 4511 (1995).

[41] L. W. Wong, H. W. Jiang, N. Trivedi and E. Palm, *Phys. Rev. B* **51**, 18033 (1995).

[42] M. Mulligan, C. Nayak, and S. Kachru, *Phys. Rev. B* **82**, 085102 (2010).

[43] T. H. Hansson and A. Karlhede, *Mod. Phys. Lett. A* **4**, 1973 (1989).

[44] T. H. Hansson, A. Karlhede, and M. Roček, *Phys. Lett. B* **225**, 92 (1989).

[45] E. Frandin, C. Nayak, A. Tsvelik, and F. Wilczek, *Nucl. Phys. B* **516**, 704 (1998).

[46] N. Seiberg, T. Senthil, C. Wang, and E. Witten, *Ann. Phys.* **374**, 395 (2016).

Homage to Frank Wilczek

Roman Jackiw

MIT, Cambridge, MA
jackiw@mit.edu

Shortly after we were confirmed that Frank will be joining our physics department, he and I stepped out for a celebratory lunch. As our conversation wondered about, it occurred to me to ask Frank why he selected MIT among the several offers to him. As I recall, his response was immediate: "I love MIT." This sincere enthusiasm found strong resonance, especially when Frank received Nobel prize for his co-discovery of asymptotic freedom, which suggested anomalous violation of scale symmetry breaking. In this way Frank is firmly placed in the pantheon of discoverers of fundamental physical laws.

© 2022 World Scientific Publishing Company
https://doi.org/10.1142/9789811251948_0011

Ambiguities in the Definition of Local Spatial Densities in Light Hadrons*

R. L. Jaffe

*Department of Physics, Center for Theoretical Physics
and Laboratory for Nuclear Science
Massachusetts Institute of Technology
Cambridge, MA 02139, USA
jaffe@mit.edu*

The relationship between the matrix element of a local operator and the Fourier transform of the associated form factor fails for systems such as the nucleon where its intrinsic size is of order its Compton wavelength. Although one can conceive of an intrinsic charge density distribution in the proton, there does not seem to be an unambiguous way to define, compute, or measure it precisely.

1. Introduction

This note explores and quantifies an impediment to defining local densities in ordinary 3-space in systems whose size is of the same order as their Compton wavelength. A classic example is the electric charge density distribution in the nucleon $\rho_N(r)$. It is widely, but erroneously, believed that $\rho_N(r)$ is given by the Fourier transform of the nucleon's electric form factor. This identification was proposed long ago [1–3] as an extension of the well-known relation that holds for non-relativistic systems like atoms. The "derivation" for the nucleon case is usually credited to Sachs [3]. More recently, analogous relations have been proposed between Fourier transforms of the form factors of components of the energy momentum tensor and other local densities such as the pressure and shear force within nucleons [4–6].

This identification is certainly valid for non-relativistic systems such as atoms and also, with relatively small ambiguities, for nuclei. It fails badly, however, for a system like the nucleon whose Compton wavelength (0.21 fm) is comparable to its size (0.85 fm). Furthermore the problem is more general than the charge density distribution. Indeed, it does not seem to be possible

---

*Reprinted from *Phys. Rev. D* **103**, 016017 (2021). DOI: https://doi.org/10.1103/Phys.Rev.D.103.016017.

to unambiguously define, compute, or measure the spatial dependence of
the nucleon matrix element of any local operator independent of the specific
form of the wave packet state in which the nucleon was prepared. The same
conclusion applies to other light hadrons or, in fact, any system for which
the Compton wavelength and intrinsic size are comparable.

This problem has been known, but not widely known, for many years
in [7][a]. Miller, in particular, has stressed the problem of identifying the
nucleon charge distribution $\rho_N(r)$ with the Fourier transform of the electric
form factor in [8]. Recent lattice calculations of the quark and gluon pressure
and other distributions in hadrons reminded me of the problem and stimu-
lated this note. In a recent paper [9] Miller has again called attention to the
problem and in particular to the failure of the widely accepted connection
between the nucleon's charge radius and the derivative of its electric form
factor at zero momentum transfer, $r_p^2 = -6G'_E(0)$.[b] Miller demonstrates that
this relation is not valid when sufficient care is taken to localize the nucleon
and keep track of relativistic effects. In a sense, this note can be considered a further exploration of the arguments put forward in Refs. [7] and [9],
emphasizing that the problem can be appreciated with only an elementary
knowledge of relativistic quantum mechanics and illustrating it in a simple
model.[c]

The basic problem is that to measure the matrix element of a local oper-
ator like the charge density $\hat{\rho}(\mathbf{r})$ in any quantum system, the coordinate $\mathbf{r}$
that appears in the operator has to be defined relative to the location of
the system. Thus the system must be localized somewhere. It is necessary to
construct a localized wave packet whose center defines the coordinate origin
with respect to which $\mathbf{r}$ is defined. The more tightly one tries to localize the
system in order to give a precise meaning to $\mathbf{r}$, the higher the momentum
components one introduces into its wave function and the larger the relativistic effects that make the matrix element of the operator dependent on
the form of the wave packet. At the other extreme, if one chooses a wave
packet that is large compared to the intrinsic size of the system, then the

---

[a]I first became aware of this problem through discussions with M. Burkardt, see
Ref. [7].
[b]For further references see [9].
[c]Incidentally, the problem does not apply to the matrix elements of *bilocal* operators
like those that define (ordinary, generalized, and transverse momentum dependent)
parton distribution functions. As first recognized by Soper [10] and emphasized by
Burkardt [7] (see also Refs. [8,9]) these correlation functions can be manipulated to
define local distribution functions in the plane transverse to the direction defined
by the infinite momentum frame of the parton model [11].

calculated or measured charge distribution is dominated by the width of the wave packet, not by the intrinsic charge distribution of the system.

A detailed analysis in a simple model (see below) shows that troubles arise if one attempts to localize a system within its Compton wavelength. For an atom, the Compton wavelength is of order $0.2/A$ fm while the charge is distributed over several Angstroms, so there is no problem. For a nucleus, the Compton wavelength (again $0.2/A$ fm) is relatively small compared to its size ($R_A \sim 1.3A^{1/3}$ fm), and the ambiguities in the definition of the charge density and other local distributions are not large, except perhaps for the deuteron. For the nucleon the ambiguities are significant and for the pion they are overwhelming. The condition for the validity of the traditional Fourier transform connection between the form factor and charge density distribution of an object is

$$\Delta \gg R \gg 1/m, \tag{1}$$

where $1/m$ is the Compton wavelength of the object, R is a measure of the localization provided by the wave packet, and Δ is a measure of the intrinsic size of the system, for example $-6G'_E(0)$. Only when $\Delta \ggg 1/m$ can the R dependence be dismissed.

The textbook analysis of the charge distribution of atoms and nuclei finesses this problem by transforming the Schrödinger wave function to center of mass and relative coordinates, thereby defining $\mathbf{r}$ relative to the center of mass. A Schrödinger wave function description of a relativistic bound state like the nucleon does not exist and the transformation to relative and center of mass coordinates is not possible.

The matrix elements of local operators in the nucleon have been calculated for many years. When these calculations are performed directly in coordinate space, as for example in the MIT bag model, their physical significance is unclear for the reasons just explained. On the other hand, the calculation of the form factors of local operators in momentum space is unambiguous — they are in principle measurable in scattering experiments — as, for example in recent lattice calculations of the pressure and shear force in the nucleon [12]. The Fourier transform of such a form factor cannot, however, be interpreted as the coordinate space matrix element of the operator of interest.

Note that this ambiguity has no consequences for the currently interesting discrepancy between different measurements of the nucleon "charge radius" since, as Miller and others have pointed out, what is actually measured and disagrees among experiments is the derivative of the nucleon's charge form factor at zero momentum transfer, $G'_E(0)$. It is the association of $G'_E(0)$ with the nucleon's charge radius that is unwarranted and is further explored in this note.

2. Defining the Charge Density Distribution for a Quantum Particle

2.1. Basic definitions

Spin plays no special role in this analysis, so nothing is lost by considering a spin-0 system. I have in mind a spinless "nucleon", but the analysis applies to any localizable quantum system. It also does not matter what are the constituents of this system. Consider the electric charge density operator $\hat{\rho}(\mathbf{r}, 0)$ at $t = 0$ in the Heisenberg picture. Suppose the system is an eigenstate of $\hat{Q} = \int d^3 r \hat{\rho}(\mathbf{r})$, with eigenvalue Q,

$$\hat{Q}|p\rangle = Q|p\rangle. \tag{2}$$

For definiteness, choose $Q = 1$. Here $|p\rangle$ is a covariantly normalized momentum eigenstate,

$$\langle p'|p\rangle = 2E(2\pi)^3 \delta^3(\mathbf{p}' - \mathbf{p}), \tag{3}$$

where $p = (E, \mathbf{p})$ and $E = \sqrt{m^2 + \mathbf{p}^2}$.

The $\mathbf{r}$ dependence of the matrix element of $\hat{\rho}(\mathbf{r}, 0)$ between momentum eigenstates is determined by the translation invariance of momentum eigenstates,

$$\langle p'|\hat{\rho}(\mathbf{r}, 0)|p\rangle = e^{i(\mathbf{p}'-\mathbf{p})\cdot\mathbf{r}} \langle p'|\hat{\rho}(0)|p\rangle. \tag{4}$$

Having chosen a spin-0 system, the matrix element in the previous equation is determined by a single charge form factor, $F(q^2)$,

$$\langle p'|\hat{\rho}(0)|p\rangle = (E + E')F(q^2) \text{ where} \tag{5}$$

$$q^2 = (p' - p)^2 = (E' - E)^2 - (\mathbf{p}' - \mathbf{p})^2. \tag{6}$$

Combining these equations we have

$$\langle p'|\hat{\rho}(\mathbf{r}, 0)|p\rangle = e^{i(\mathbf{p}'-\mathbf{p})\cdot\mathbf{r}}(E + E')F(q^2). \tag{7}$$

Nothing further can be done without constructing a wave packet state localized at some position with respect to which the coordinate $\mathbf{r}$ is defined.

2.2. *The charge density distribution in a wave packet state*

Let us superpose energy-momentum eigenstates to define a localized, Heisenberg picture state for the particle of interest,

$$|\Psi, \mathbf{x}\rangle = \int \frac{d^3p}{\sqrt{2E(2\pi)^3}} \phi(\mathbf{p}) e^{-i\mathbf{p}\cdot\mathbf{x}} |p\rangle, \tag{8}$$

which is normalized to one by requiring

$$\int d^3p |\phi(\mathbf{p})|^2 = 1. \tag{9}$$

To localize the particle at the origin, set $\mathbf{x} = 0$ and define $|\Psi, 0\rangle \equiv |\Psi\rangle$.

Although any localized wave packet would do, I choose a spherically symmetric gaussian packet to simplify subsequent calculations,

$$\phi(\mathbf{p}) \equiv \phi(p) = \left(\frac{2R^2}{3\pi}\right)^{3/4} e^{-\mathbf{p}^2 R^2/3}, \tag{10}$$

where I have defined the length scale R equal to the RMS radius of the wave packet.

Then the object of interest is the charge density distribution in the localized state,

$$\rho(r) \equiv \langle \Psi | \rho(\mathbf{r}, 0) | \Psi \rangle. \tag{11}$$

It is obtained by substituting from Eq. (10) for $\phi(p)$ and from Eq. (7) for the matrix element between momentum eigenstates,

$$\rho(r) = \int \frac{d^3p\, d^3p'}{(2\pi)^3 \sqrt{4EE'}} (E + E') F(q^2) \phi(p') \phi(p) e^{i\mathbf{q}\cdot\mathbf{r}}. \tag{12}$$

Here $\mathbf{q} = \mathbf{p}' - \mathbf{p}$ and $q^2 = (E' - E)^2 - \mathbf{q}^2$, and $q^2 \leq 0$.

To further simplify computations I assume that the form factor, $F(q^2)$ is also a gaussian parameterized by a length scale Δ,

$$F(q^2) = e^{\frac{1}{6}q^2\Delta^2}. \tag{13}$$

The normalization, $F(0) = 1$, is chosen so that $\langle \Psi | \hat{Q} | \Psi \rangle = 1$. The size of the system is parameterized by the naive mean-square charge radius, $r^2_{\text{naive}} = 6(dF/dq^2|_{q^2=0}) = \Delta^2$, which for the nucleon is approximately $(0.85\,\text{fm})^2$.

To proceed, change to relative and total center-of-momentum variables,

$$\mathbf{p} = \mathbf{P} + \mathbf{q}/2$$
$$\mathbf{p}' = \mathbf{P} - \mathbf{q}/2, \tag{14}$$

giving

$$\rho(r) = \left(\frac{2R^2}{3\pi}\right)^{3/2} \int \frac{d^3P\, d^3q}{(2\pi)^3 \sqrt{4EE'}} (E + E')$$
$$\times \exp\left(\tfrac{1}{6}q^2\Delta^2 - \tfrac{2}{3}\mathbf{P}^2 R^2 - \tfrac{1}{6}\mathbf{q}^2 R^2 + i\mathbf{q} \cdot \mathbf{r}\right), \tag{15}$$

where I have substituted from Eq. (10) for $\phi(p)$.

2.3. Evaluating $\rho(r)$ when $\Delta \gg 1/m$

The integral of Eq. (15) must be evaluated numerically for systems like the nucleon for which Eq. (1) is not satisfied. On the other hand, for systems like atoms and nuclei, where Eq. (1) holds, it is useful to expand the terms in $\rho(r)$ in inverse powers of m. In particular, we expand the kinematic factor $(E' + E)/\sqrt{4EE'}$ and the form factor $F(q^2)$ keeping the first significant term in each. Expansion of the kinematic factor $(E' + E)/\sqrt{4EE'}$ yields,

$$\frac{E' + E}{\sqrt{4EE'}} = 1 + \frac{1}{2m^4}(\mathbf{P} \cdot \mathbf{q})^2 + \mathcal{O}(1/m^6). \tag{16}$$

The nucleon mass enters the form factor through the energy difference,

$$q^2 = (E' - E)^2 - \mathbf{q}^2$$
$$= \left(\sqrt{m^2 + (\mathbf{P} - \mathbf{q}/2)^2} - \sqrt{m^2 + (\mathbf{P} + \mathbf{q}/2)^2}\right)^2 - \mathbf{q}^2$$
$$= -\mathbf{q}^2 + \left(\frac{\mathbf{P} \cdot \mathbf{q}}{m}\right)^2 + \mathcal{O}(1/m^4), \tag{17}$$

so

$$F(q^2) = e^{-\frac{1}{6}\mathbf{q}^2\Delta^2}\left(1 + \frac{\Delta^2(\mathbf{P} \cdot \mathbf{q})^2}{6m^2} + \mathcal{O}(1/m^4)\right). \tag{18}$$

Substituting Eq. (18) and (17) into $\rho(r)$, we obtain

$$\rho(r) \cong \left(\frac{2R^2}{3\pi}\right)^{3/2} \int \frac{d^3P\, d^3q}{(2\pi)^3}\left(1 + \left(\tfrac{1}{2m^4} + \tfrac{\Delta^2}{6m^2}\right)(\mathbf{P} \cdot \mathbf{q})^2\right)$$
$$\times \exp\left(-\tfrac{1}{6}\mathbf{q}^2\Delta^2 - \tfrac{2}{3}\mathbf{P}^2 R^2 - \tfrac{1}{6}\mathbf{q}^2 R^2 + i\mathbf{q} \cdot \mathbf{r}\right). \tag{19}$$

All of these integrals can be performed analytically yielding

$$\rho(r) = \left(1 + \frac{27}{8}\left(\frac{1}{m^4} + \frac{\Delta^2}{3m^2}\right)\left(\frac{R^2 + \Delta^2 - r^2}{R^2(R^2 + \Delta^2)^2}\right)\right)\rho_0(r)$$

where

$$\rho_0(r) = \left(\frac{3}{2\pi(R^2 + \Delta^2)}\right)^{3/2} e^{-3r^2/2(R^2+\Delta^2)}. \tag{20}$$

The expansion in inverse powers of m that made it possible to perform the integrals of Eq. (19) limits the validity of this formula to parameter ranges where $m^2 R^2$ and $m^2 \Delta^2$ are large compared to one.

The traditional identification of the charge density distribution with the Fourier transform of the form factor is obtained by first taking the mass m to infinity and then taking the target wave packet radius to zero. The result for the gaussian model is the "naive" charge distribution,

$$\rho_{\text{naive}}(r) = \left(\frac{3}{2\pi\Delta^2}\right)^{3/2} e^{-3r^2/2\Delta^2} \tag{21}$$

with $r_{\text{RMS}} = \Delta$, which is indeed the Fourier transform of the form factor, Eq. (13). This is the sequence of limits implicitly assumed by Sachs [3]. To get a feel for the dependence of Eq. (20) on the various parameters, it is useful to compute the mean-squared charge radius given by Eq. (20),

$$\langle r^2 \rangle = 4\pi \int_0^\infty dr r^4 \rho(r)$$

$$= \Delta^2 \left(1 - \frac{3}{4m^2 R^2}\right) + R^2 \left(1 - \frac{9}{4m^4 R^4}\right). \tag{22}$$

When the wave packet is large, the mean-squared charge radius is approximately R^2, the radius of the wave packet. To obtain the traditional result, $< r^2_{\text{naive}} >= \Delta^2$, it is necessary to choose $m^2 R^2 \gg 1$ in order to minimize the relativistic corrections in Eq. (22) and to choose $R^2 \ll \Delta^2$ so that the wave packet dependent second term in Eq. (22) is negligible compared to the first. Altogether the condition for a localization independent charge density is

$$\Delta^2 \gg R^2 \gg 1/m^2, \tag{23}$$

as quoted in Eq. (1). If Δ^2 is not much larger than $1/m^2$, then the charge density distribution in the system depends unavoidably on the wave packet used to localize it and Eq. (15) must be evaluated numerically.

Equation (23) is easily satisfied for atoms and large nuclei, so before going on to the most interesting case of the nucleon, we examine the uncontroversial cases of atoms and heavy nuclei.

3. Charge Density Distributions for Atoms and Nuclei

3.1. *Atoms*

The intrinsic size of atoms is roughly a_0, the Bohr radius, while their masses grow with A. So atomic hydrogen is the worst case example among atoms. For atomic hydrogen, we take $\Delta = a_0 \cong 5 \times 10^{-11}$ m, and $m = m_p = 1/(2.1 \times 10^{-16}$ m). Since $\Delta \cong 2.5 \times 10^5/m$ the inequalities of Eq. (1) can be satisfied for a large range of R. Explicit calculation shows that $\rho(r)$ is virtually indistinguishable from $\rho_{\text{naive}}(r)$ for R between 10 fm and $a_0/10$. If we choose, for example, $R = 10$ fm (corresponding to $mR \cong 50$, so the expansion of the previous section should be valid), Fig. 1(a) shows the deviation of the radial charge density $(4\pi r^2 \rho(r))$ of the localized atom from the naive result of Eq. (21) is less than ~ 0.0002 over whole range of r. Thus we can conclude that to an accuracy of roughly 0.02%, the Fourier transform of the form factor $F(-\mathbf{q}^2)$ can be interpreted as a localization independent charge density distribution for the atom with a "resolution" of order 10^{-14} m, a distance that is of order 0.02% of the intrinsic size of the system. If, on the other hand, we take R to be an appreciable fraction of the size of the atom, then the charge density distribution gets broader, reflecting the spread in the quantum wave packet. Figure 1(b) illustrates this effect by comparing the naive charge density distribution with the localized distribution for $R = a_0/4$.

We conclude that the naive charge density distribution obtained by Fourier transform of the form factor provides an excellent representation of the charge density distribution of a localized atom.

3.2. *Nuclei*

For a typical nucleus we take $\Delta = 1.3A^{1/3}$ fm and $m \cong Am_p \cong A/(.21$ fm$)$. The constraint on R becomes progressively easier to satisfy with increasing A. Take carbon $(A = 12)$ for example (see below for the case of a very light nucleus such as deuterium) with $\Delta \cong 3$ fm. Figure 2 shows the difference between the charge density distribution for carbon localized within $R = 0.2$ fm and the Fourier transform of the charge form factor. The difference is less than 0.0005 over the entire range of r indicating that the association of the charge distribution with the Fourier transform of the form factor is valid to this accuracy with a resolution of order the nucleon's Compton

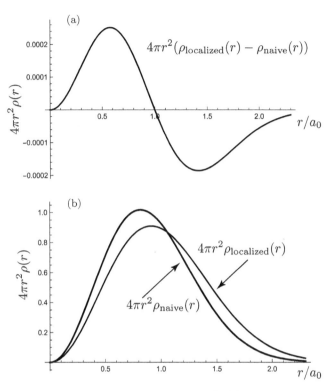

Fig. 1.   Radial charge density distributions, $4\pi r^2 \rho(r)$, in a gaussian model for a hydrogen atom. (a) The difference between the charge density distribution for a hydrogen atom localized within $10\,\text{fm}$ and the naive charge density distribution obtained by Fourier transform of its charge form factor. (b) The radial charge distribution of a gaussian hydrogen atom localized within $0.25\,a_0$ compared to the naive charge distribution.

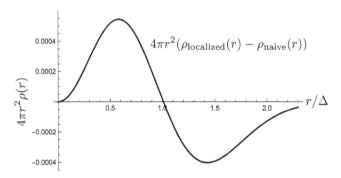

Fig. 2.   The difference between the radial charge density distribution for a carbon nucleus localized within $0.2\,\text{fm}$ and the naive radial charge density distribution obtained by Fourier transform of its charge form factor.

wavelength, 0.2 fm. Clearly the large mass of even a light nucleus such as carbon makes it possible to localize its center of mass to a region small compared to its intrinsic size.

To apply this analysis to hadrons and to the deuteron we must evaluate the integral of Eq. (15) numerically.

4. The Charge Density Distribution in the Nucleon and Deuteron

For the nucleon with $1/m \cong 0.2$ fm and $\Delta \cong 0.85$ fm the expansion $1/mR$ used in the previous section is not valid and Eq. (15) must be evaluated numerically. Figure 3 shows the results of trying of localize the model proton (with a gaussian form factor) at various distance scales. In Fig. 3(a) we show the charge density for the proton localized with $R = 0.5, 0.2$, and 0.05 fm from Eq. (15) compared with the naive charge density distribution

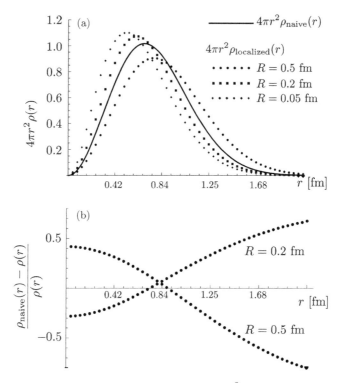

Fig. 3. (a) Radial charge density distributions, $4\pi r^2 \rho(r)$, in a gaussian model for the proton. The solid curve is the naive radial charge density distribution of Eq. (21). The dotted curves are the radial charge density distributions for a proton localized with $R = 0.05, 0.2$ and 0.5 fm; (b) The fractional difference between the naive and localized charge density distributions for $R = 0.2$ fm and $R = 0.5$ fm.

of Eq. (21). The fact that for all values of R the charge density distribution has the same qualitative shape as the naive charge density distribution should not be surprising: $4\pi r^2 \rho(r)$ is positive definite, normalized to one, grows like r^2 at small r and falls like a Gaussian at large r. Thus the overall shape of $4\pi r^2 \rho(r)$ is highly constrained. Within those constraints the R dependence is significant. To display the dependence more clearly we plot the fractional deviation,

$$\frac{\rho_{\text{naive}}(r) - \rho(r)}{\rho(r)},$$

for $R = 0.2$ and 0.5 fm. The fractional differences are of order one, and change dramatically between the two values of R, indicating that the concept of a *localization independent charge density distribution for the proton is not well-defined.*

The deuteron presents an intermediate case. Its intrinsic size is of order $\Delta \cong 2.15$ fm as determined by the slope of its charged form factor at $q^2 = 0$. The deuteron Compton wavelength is $1/m \cong 0.1$ fm, so we expect that the naive charge density distribution should approximate the charge density distribution of a deuteron with values of between these two. Explicit calculation shows that this is the case for values of R near 0.5 fm, roughly the geometric mean of m and Δ. This is illustrated in Fig. 4. In particular, Fig. 4(b) shows that the naive charge density agrees with the localized distribution to $\sim 20\%$ between $r = 0$ and $\sim 1.5\Delta$ for a range of values of R around 0.5 fm. The fractional difference increases at large r where the charge density itself is small. We conclude that the Fourier transform of the deuteron charge form factor gives a charge density distribution that provides a fair approximation to that of a deuteron localized at distances small compared to its intrinsic size.

The pion, an extreme example with an intrinsic size of order $\Delta \sim .5$ fm and a Compton wavelength of $1/m \cong 1.4$ fm, cannot be localized to distances of order its intrinsic size without generating relativistic effects that destroy the relationship between the Fourier transform of its form factor and its charge distribution.

5. Discussion and Conclusions

A simple, Fourier transform relationship between form factors and spatial distributions of the expectation values of local operators was developed during the study of non-relativistic systems like atoms in the early days of quantum mechanics. Although Burkardt [7] and Miller [8] pointed out that this relationship fails in the case of the nucleon, the relationship seems to have entered the folklore of particle physics without careful consideration of

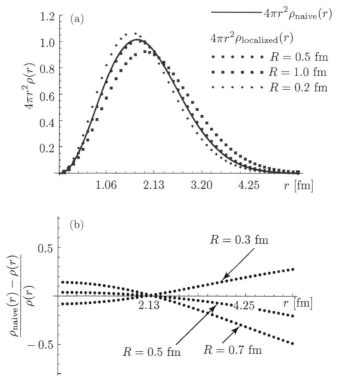

Fig. 4.   (a) Radial charge density distributions, $4\pi r^2 \rho(r)$, in a gaussian model for the deuteron. The solid curve is the naive radial charge density distribution of Eq. (21). The dotted curves are the radial charge density distributions for a deuteron localized with $R = 0.2, 0.5$ and 1.0 fm; (b) The fractional difference between the naive and localized charge density distributions for $R = 0.3$ fm and $R = 0.5$ fm and $R = 0.7$ fm.

whether it is accurate for systems whose size is of the same order as their Compton wavelength. Miller, in particular, has emphasized that the connection fails for the nucleon [8] and has recently re-emphasized that it fails for the famous assertion that the mean squared charge radius of the proton is given by $-6G'_E(0)$ [9]. Defining a quantity such as $\langle \hat{\rho}(r) \rangle_N$ requires one to localize the nucleon and doing so generates localization dependent contributions that invalidate the Fourier transform relation between form factors and local density distributions. I have explored this effect in the simple case for the charge density distribution of a spinless system with a Gaussian form factor. The problem is not special to the charge density operator nor to a spinless hadron nor to the assumption of a Gaussian form factor. Instead this is a general problem that afflicts attempts to extract spatial distributions of local properties of any system that is not much larger than its Compton wavelength. The problem is quite fundamental, since it originates in the interplay between the uncertainty principle and relativity.

One can, of course, construct a function of $\mathbf{r}$ by Fourier transforming the form factor of a local operator, but in the case of the nucleon or other light hadrons, this is of uncertain value and should not be considered an accurate representation of the "actual" spatial distribution of the operator matrix element, which cannot be defined independent of the way in which the hadronic system was localized.

Acknowledgments

I am grateful to Matthias Burkardt for conversations many years ago as well as more recently, to Dimitra Pefkou for recent conversations on this subject and for informing me of Jerry Miller's recent paper [9], and to Jerry Miller for very helpful comments on the manuscript. I also appreciate comments and suggestions from Phiala Shanahan and Will Detmold.

References

[1] R. Hofstadter, F. Bumiller, and M. R. Yearian, *Rev. Mod. Phys.* **30** (1958) 482.

[2] F. J. Ernst, R. G. Sachs, and K. C. Wali, *Phys. Rev.* **119** (1960) 1105.

[3] R. G. Sachs, *Phys. Rev.* **126** (1962) 2256.

[4] M. V. Polyakov and A. G. Shuvaev, [e-Print: hep-ph/0207153].

[5] M. V. Polyakov, *Phys. Lett. B* **555**, 57–62 (2003) [ePrint: hep-ph/0210165].

[6] M. V. Polyakov and P. Schweitzer, *Int. J. Mod. Phys. A* **33** no. 26, 1830025 (2018) [e-Print: 1805.06596].

[7] M. Burkardt, *Phys. Rev. D* **62** 071503 (2000) [ePrint: hep-ph/0005108] [erratum: *Phys. Rev. D* **66**, 119903 (2002)] .

[8] G. A. Miller, *Phys. Rev. Lett.* **99** 112001 (2007); *Phys. Rev. C* **79** 055204 (2009); *Ann. Rev. Nucl. Part. Sci.* **60** 1 (2010).

[9] G. A. Miller, *Phys. Rev. C* **99**, no. 3, 035202 (2019) [arXiv:1812.02714 [nucl-th]].

[10] D. E. Soper, *Phys. Rev. D* **15**, 1141 (1977).

[11] For further work along these lines, see C. Lorcé, L. Mantovani and B. Pasquini, *Phys. Lett. B* **776**, 38–47 (2018) [arXiv:1704.08557 [hep-ph]]; C. Lorcé, [arXiv:2007.05318 [hep-ph]].

[12] P. E. Shanahan and W. Detmold, *Phys. Rev. Lett.* **122**, no. 7, 072003 (2019) [arXiv:1810.07589 [nucl-th]].

© 2022 World Scientific Publishing Company
https://doi.org/10.1142/9789811251948_0012

Fermi Liquids and Fractional Statistics in One Dimension

Jon Magne Leinaas

Department of Physics, University of Oslo
P.O. Box 1048 Blindern, N-0316 Oslo, Norway
j.m.leinaas@fys.uio.no

Interacting fermion systems in one dimension, which in the low energy approximation are described by Luttinger liquid theory, can be reformulated as systems of weakly interacting particles with fractional exchange statistics. This is shown by use of Landau's Fermi liquid theory, with quasiparticles interpreted as adiabatically dressed fermions. An application of this method is included, where boundary excitations of a two-dimensional quantum Hall electron system are studied.

1. Introduction

Ideas of quantum particles with unconventional statistics have over the years been met with much interest, both with respect to theory and to experimental verifications. In three dimensions elementary particles are restricted to the two main types, fermions and bosons. However, in condensed matter systems, where the number of dimensions is effectively reduced to two or one, the elementary (particle-like) excitations can, under certain conditions, satisfy statistics that is different from the two elementary types. In particular, in the fractional quantum Hall effect, the electrons form collective states with new (quasi)particles that are characterized both by fractional statistics and fractional charges.

There are more than one type of unconventional statistics that has theoretically been introduced. The type of statistics seen in the quantum Hall effect, often referred to as fractional *exchange* statistics, describes identical particles where the quantum wave function picks up a complex phase factor when the position of two particles are interchanged [1]. Bosons and fermions are then only special cases, where the phase factor is respectively $+1$ and -1. Particles with other values of the phase factor are generally called *anyons* [2].

Anyons are restricted to systems which effectively are two-dimensional. However, other types of generalized statistics are possible in one dimension. One possibility is based on the assumption that for systems of identical particles only symmetric combinations of particle operators should be regarded as observables [3]. This restriction opens for new types of quantum many-particle states, and in one dimension the new possibilities form a one-parameter set of particle representations, which also here includes bosons and fermions as special cases.

A third suggestion of generalizing quantum statistics is different from the other two by introducing a generalization of the Pauli exclusion principle in many-particle systems, rather than modifying the definition of exchange symmetry of the particles [4]. Also this gives rise to possible generalizations of quantum statistics in one-dimensional systems. This type of statistics is often referred to as fractional *exclusion* statistics.

Here I will show how fermion systems in one dimension, quite generally can be described in terms of particles with fractional exclusion statistics. The starting point is a general fermion system with a fermi sea as ground state. A short description of the Luttinger liquid description of the system is introduced [5], and a Fermi liquid description is derived with 'dressed' fermions as Landau quasiparticles [6]. The Landau (interaction) parameters are identified, and by use of a functional transformation of the variables it is shown that the Landau parameters can be nullified, and that the new variables satisfy fractional exclusion statistics [7]. A concrete realization is then discussed, where a quantum Hall system with boundary excitations effectively forms a one-dimensional system. The results concerning interactions between the two boundaries are discussed and compared with earlier evaluations of the effect.

Much of the first part of this paper is a review of results from an earlier publication [7], however with less details in the derivation of the fractional statistics. Relations between exclusion statistics and Luttinger liquid [8, 9], and between exclusion statistics and Fermi liquid theory [10], have been discussed before, but the approach that is discussed here is different. The convention $\hbar = 1$ is used throughout the paper.

2. The Luttinger Liquid Formulation

The starting point is the following general expression for the Hamiltonian of a one-dimensional system of spinless fermions,

$$H = \sum_{k} \epsilon_0(k) c_k^\dagger c_k + \frac{1}{4L} \sum_{q,k_1,k_2} V(k_1 - k_2, q) c_{k_1}^\dagger c_{k_2}^\dagger c_{k_2-q} c_{k_1+q}. \qquad (1)$$

The dependence of V on the momentum variable $k_1 - k_2$, in addition to q, opens for the possibility of a non-locality of the interaction (see Sec. 7). However, the assumption is that the dependence on this variable is weak. This implies that the effect of the k-dependence for low energy particles close to the same Fermi point can be disregarded, while for the interaction between particles at opposite Fermi points the effect may be significant. The one-dimensional fermion system is assumed to have a ground state in the form of a filled Fermi sea, with well-defined boundaries at the two Fermi points $k = \pm k_F$ in momentum space, and with gapless, low energy excitations. Under these assumptions the Hamiltonian of the system, in the low-energy approximation, can be simplified by the linearized expression [5],

$$H = \bar{v}_F \sum_{\chi,k} (\chi k - k_F) : c^\dagger_{\chi,k} c_{\chi,k} :$$

$$+ \frac{1}{4L} \sum_{\chi,q} [V_1(q)\rho_{\chi,q}\rho_{\chi,-q} + V_2(q)\rho_{\chi,q}\rho_{-\chi,-q}]. \tag{2}$$

$\chi = \pm 1$ is here a chirality parameter, associated with the two Fermi points, and $\rho_{\chi,q} = \sum_k : c^\dagger_{\chi,k+q} c_{\chi,k} :$ are the Fourier components of the particle density of chirality χ, normal ordered relative to the filled Fermi sea. The system is assumed to be confined to an interval of length L, with periodic boundary conditions for the fermion fields. (L is assumed to be much larger than any physical length, and may be taken to infinity at places where that is convenient.) The momentum then takes discrete values $k = 2\pi n/L$, with n as an integer. The interaction is separated in two parts, with $V_1(q)$ as the interaction between fermions with the same chirality and $V_2(q)$ with opposite chiralities. The effective Fermi velocity $\bar{v}_F$ has the form

$$\bar{v}_F = v_F - \frac{1}{4\pi}(V_1(0) - V_2(0)), \tag{3}$$

with $v_F = \frac{\partial \epsilon_0}{\partial k}(k_F)$ as the Fermi velocity of the non-interacting Fermi system, and the interaction dependent term is a correction, created by interactions between the low energy fermions and the Fermi sea [11].

Although the quantum number k is, in the linearized approximation, restricted to small deviations from $\pm k_F$, this restriction can be lifted, since the low energy sector of the theory is not affected by this extension. Without the restriction, the model (2) describes in effect two types of fermions, characterized by different values of χ, both types with linear dispersion.

The standard way to analyze the system described by the Hamiltonian (2) is in terms of bosonization [5]. I briefly summarize expressions to be used in the discussion to follow. The Fourier components of the charge density operators, $q \neq 0$, define the boson annihilation and creation operators,

$$a_q = \sqrt{\frac{2\pi}{|q|L}} \sum_\chi \theta(\chi q)\, \rho_{\chi,q}, \quad a^\dagger_q = \sqrt{\frac{2\pi}{|q|L}} \sum_\chi \theta(\chi q)\, \rho_{\chi,-q}, \tag{4}$$

where $\theta(q)$ is the Heaviside step function, and the $q = 0$ components of the charge densities define the conserved fermion numbers

$$N = \sum_\chi N_\chi = \sum_{k\chi} : c_{\chi,k}^\dagger c_{\chi,k} :, \qquad J = \sum_\chi \chi N_\chi = \sum_{k\chi} \chi\, c_{\chi,k}^\dagger c_{\chi,k}, \qquad (5)$$

with N measuring the deviation of the particle number from its ground state value N_0. The bosonized form of the Hamiltonian is [5]

$$H = \frac{\pi}{2L}(v_N N^2 + v_J J^2)$$
$$+ \frac{1}{2} \sum_{q\neq 0} |q| \left[\left(\bar{v}_F + \frac{V_1(q)}{4\pi} \right) (a_q^\dagger a_q + a_q a_q^\dagger) + \frac{V_2(q)}{4\pi} (a_q^\dagger a_{-q}^\dagger + a_q a_{-q}) \right].$$

$$(6)$$

Compared to the Hamiltonian (2) it is modified by removing (non-relevant) terms that are constant or linear in N. The two velocity parameters v_N and v_J are

$$v_N = \bar{v}_F + \frac{1}{4\pi}(V_1(0) + V_2(0)) = v_F + \frac{1}{2\pi} V_2(0),$$

$$v_J = \bar{v}_F + \frac{1}{4\pi}(V_1(0) - V_2(0)) = v_F. \qquad (7)$$

One should note that v_J is identical to the original Fermi velocity v_F of the non-interacting fermions, rather than to the effective Fermi velocity $\bar{v}_F$, which appears in the Luttinger Hamiltonian (2). This can be viewed as a consequence of Galilei invariance of the Hamiltonian (see Sec. 4). The low energy sector, where (6) is valid, corresponds to situations where $|q|$, as well as N/L and $|J|/L$, are effectively restricted to values much smaller than k_F.

The bosonized Hamiltonian is diagonalized by a Bogoliubov transformation of the form

$$a_q = \cosh \xi_q\, b_q + \sinh \xi_q\, b_{-q}^\dagger,$$
$$a_q^\dagger = \cosh \xi_q\, b_q^\dagger + \sinh \xi_q\, b_{-q}, \qquad (8)$$

where ξ_q is fixed by the relation

$$\tanh 2\xi_q = -\frac{V_2(q)}{V_1(q) + 4\pi\, \bar{v}_F}. \qquad (9)$$

In terms of the new bosonic operators the Hamiltonian gets the diagonal form

$$H = \sum_{q\neq 0} \omega_q\, b_q^\dagger b_q + \frac{\pi}{2L}(v_N N^2 + v_J J^2), \qquad (10)$$

with the frequency ω_q given by

$$\omega_q = \sqrt{\left(\bar{v}_F + \frac{V_1(q)}{4\pi}\right)^2 - \left(\frac{V_2(q)}{4\pi}\right)^2} \, |q|. \tag{11}$$

The bosonized form of the low-energy Hamiltonian (10) has, for given values of N and J, a free field form, which makes it straightforward to solve the many-particle problem and in particular to determine the relevant correlation functions [5]. However, for the purpose here it will be useful to reintroduce fermion variables in the expression for the Hamiltonian.

3. Adiabatically Dressed Fermions

The two sets of bosonic operators are unitarily equivalent,

$$b_q = U a_q U^\dagger, b_q^\dagger = U a_q^\dagger U^\dagger, \tag{12}$$

with the unitary transformation given by

$$U = \exp\left[-\sum_{q\neq 0} \frac{\xi_q}{2}(a_q^2 - a_q^{\dagger 2})\right]. \tag{13}$$

The operator U preserves the particle number of the two chiralities separately and it maps energy eigenstates of the linearized, free theory continuously into the eigenstates of the interacting theory, when the parameters ξ_q are changed. With ω_q also changing smoothly, the transformation of the Hamiltonian can thus be interpreted as defining an adiabatic change from the free to the interacting theory.

For the fermion operators the corresponding transformation is

$$\phi(x) = U\psi(x)U^\dagger, \tag{14}$$

where $\psi(x) = \frac{1}{\sqrt{L}}\sum_k e^{ikx}c_k$ as the original fermion operator, and $\phi(x)$ is regarded as the *dressed* fermion operator [12]. The transformed field operator $\phi(x)$ clearly satisfies the same anticommutation relations as the original field operator $\psi(x)$, and in this sense it is a fermion field. However, the statistics of the dressed particles is not necessarily apparent in the commutation relations of the field alone, since the form of the Hamiltonian may reveal presence of a 'statistical interactions' between the particles. For this reason I will examine more closely the form of the Hamiltonian, expressed in terms of dressed fermionic variables.

To proceed the following low-energy approximation is assumed,

$$V_1(q) \approx V_1(0), \quad V_2(q) \approx V_2(0), \tag{15}$$

which for the boson frequency implies

$$\omega_q \approx v_s|q|, \quad v_s = \sqrt{v_J v_N}. \tag{16}$$

The transformation U then is approximated by

$$U \approx \exp\left[-\sum_{q \neq 0} \frac{\xi_0}{2}(a_q^2 - a_q^{\dagger 2})\right], \quad \tanh \xi_0 = \frac{g-1}{g+1}, \tag{17}$$

which implies that U, in this approximation, is uniquely determined by the interaction parameter $g = \sqrt{v_J/v_N}$.

The Hamiltonian is next separated in two parts in the following way,

$$H = U v_s \left(\sum_{q \neq 0} |q| a_q^\dagger a_q + \frac{\pi}{2L}(N^2 + J^2)\right) U^\dagger + v_s \frac{\pi}{2L}\left(\left(\frac{1}{g}-1\right)N^2 \right.$$

$$\left. + (g-1)J^2\right), \tag{18}$$

where the first term can be identified (see (6)) as a linearized free-field Hamiltonian, with v_s as Fermi velocity, and with the field variables transformed by the operator U. This implies that the Hamiltonian can be expressed in terms of the dressed fermion field as

$$H = v_s \left\{\int_0^L dx : \sum_\chi \phi_\chi^\dagger(x)(-i\chi\partial_x - k_F)\phi_\chi(x) :\right.$$

$$\left. + \frac{\pi}{2L}\sum_\chi\left[\left(\frac{1}{g}+g-2\right)N_\chi^2 + \left(\frac{1}{g}-g\right)N_\chi N_{-\chi}\right]\right\}, \tag{19}$$

where the chiral fields are defined by

$$\psi_\chi(x) = \frac{1}{\sqrt{L}}\sum_k c_{\chi,k}e^{ikx}, \quad \phi_\chi(x) = U\psi_\chi(x)U^\dagger. \tag{20}$$

This means that, under the simplification introduced above, the Hamiltonian (19) is unitarily equivalent to a free field Hamiltonian plus a term which is invariant under the unitary transformation.

4. Fermi Liquid Description

The assumption of adiabatic connection between the non-interacting and interacting system forms the basis for Landau's Fermi liquid theory. In this theory the total energy is given as a functional of the distribution of occupation numbers $n(k)$, associated with the non-interacting theory,

$$E = E[n(k)], \tag{21}$$

and the quasiparticle energies and interactions can be defined in terms of functional derivatives to first and second order in the particle density [6],

$$\delta E = \sum_k \epsilon(k)\delta n(k) + \frac{1}{2}\sum_{kk'} f(k,k')\delta n(k)\delta n(k'). \tag{22}$$

The quasiparticles, introduced by Landau in this way, will be identified here with the dressed fermions previously discussed. For variations about the filled Fermi sea, the expressions for energy and interactions will be referred to as $\epsilon_0(k)$ and $f_0(k,k')$.

In the present case the unitary transformation (17) defines an adiabatic transition from the free field Hamiltonian to the interacting one, when the parameter g is slowly changing from the initial value 1. The expression for the variation of the energy can then be extracted directly from (19), and with χ in the following being restricted by the relation $\chi = \operatorname{sgn} k$, this gives

$$\delta E = \sum_k v_s(|k| - k_F)\delta n(k) + v_s\frac{\pi}{L}\sum_{k,k'}(\lambda_1\theta(kk') + \lambda_2\theta(-kk'))\delta n(k)\delta n(k'), \tag{23}$$

where $\theta(k)$ is the Heaviside step function, and λ_1 and λ_2 are defined by

$$\lambda_1 = \frac{1}{2}\left(\frac{1}{g} + g - 2\right), \quad \lambda_2 = \frac{1}{2}\left(\frac{1}{g} - g\right). \tag{24}$$

From this follows that the single particle energy and the interaction terms are

$$\epsilon_0(k) = v_s(|k| - k_F),$$
$$f_0(k,k') = v_s\frac{2\pi}{L}(\lambda_1\Theta(kk') + \lambda_2\Theta(-kk')). \tag{25}$$

When corrections to the Hamiltonian (19) are included, the above expression for the interaction can be interpreted as being valid at the Fermi points, written as

$$f_0(k_F, k_F) = f_0(-k_F, -k_F) = v_s\frac{2\pi}{L}\lambda_1,$$
$$f_0(k_F, -k_F) = f_0(-k_F, k_F) = v_s\frac{2\pi}{L}\lambda_2. \tag{26}$$

The symmetric and antisymmetric combinations of the interaction terms define the two Landau parameters, which after normalization with respect to the density of states are,

$$F_0 = \frac{L}{2\pi v_s}(f_0(k_F, k_F) + f_0(k_F, -k_F)) = \frac{1}{g} - 1,$$

$$F_1 = \frac{L}{2\pi v_s}(f_0(k_F, k_F) - f_0(k_F, -k_F)) = g - 1. \tag{27}$$

This gives the following relation,

$$1 + F_1 = \frac{1}{1 + F_0} = g. \tag{28}$$

It is of interest to relate this result to the condition of Galilean invariance, as expressed in the Fermi liquid formulation. This condition is written as [6],

$$\int dk \, k \, n(k) = \int dk \, m \frac{\partial \epsilon(k)}{\partial k} n(k), \tag{29}$$

where m is the (bare) mass of the fermions and the occupation numbers are treated as a continuous function of k. In the following $n(k)$ is assumed to be the particle density normalized relative to the fully occupied system, which means that it takes values in the interval $0 \leq n(k) \leq 1$. The equation above states that the total momentum is conserved when the interaction is adiabatically turned on. Variation in the particle density gives

$$\int dk \frac{k}{m} \delta n(k) = \int dk \frac{\partial \epsilon(k)}{\partial k} \delta n(k) + \frac{L}{2\pi} \iint dk dk' \frac{\partial f(k, k')}{\partial k} n(k) \delta n(k'), \tag{30}$$

where the last term is the result of treating $\epsilon(k)$ as a functional of $n(k)$. With this being valid for arbitrary variations $\delta n(k)$, the following relation is implied,

$$\frac{k}{m} = \frac{\partial \epsilon(k)}{\partial k} - \frac{L}{2\pi} \int dk' \, f(k, k') \frac{\partial n(k')}{\partial k'}. \tag{31}$$

For a filled Fermi sea the derivative of the particle density is

$$\frac{\partial n_0(k')}{\partial k'} = \delta(k' + k_F) - \delta(k' - k_F), \tag{32}$$

and with $k = k_F$, (31) gets the form

$$\frac{k_F}{m} = \frac{\partial \epsilon_0(k)}{\partial k}\bigg|_{k_F} + \frac{L}{2\pi}(f_0(k_F, k_F) - f_0(k_F, -k_F)). \tag{33}$$

The following relations are now introduced,

$$\frac{k_F}{m} = v_F, \quad \frac{k_F}{m^*} \equiv \frac{\partial \epsilon_0(k)}{\partial k}\bigg|_{k_F} = v_s, \tag{34}$$

with m^* as the effective mass of the quasiparticles. This gives

$$\frac{m^*}{m} = \frac{v_F}{v_s} = 1 + F_1 = g. \tag{35}$$

By further use of the relations

$$v_s = \sqrt{v_J v_N}, \quad g = \sqrt{v_J/v_N}, \tag{36}$$

the earlier result (7) is reproduced,

$$v_J = v_F. \tag{37}$$

Here this follows as a consequence of Galilei invariance in Landau's Fermi liquid formulation, whereas the result in (7) is a consequence of the corresponding symmetry of the two-particle interaction $V(k_1-k_2, q)$. The equality between $1 + F_1$ and $(1 + F_0)^{-1}$ in Eq. (28) can be seen as a consequence of the equality between the quasiparticle velocity k_F/m^* and the velocity of sound v_s, as shown above.

5. Fractional Statistics

A central element in the Fermi liquid theory is the assumption that the elementary excitations (quasiparticles) of the theory obey Fermi-Dirac statistics. This means that the entropy function has the same form as for the non-interacting (bare) particles,

$$S = -\sum_k [n(k) \ln n(k) + (1 - n(k)) \ln(1 - n(k))]. \tag{38}$$

In the case discussed in the previous sections, this follows since the dressed particle field $\phi(x)$ is related to the original fermion field $\psi(x)$ by a unitary transformation. However, a further change of variable will now be introduced, which changes this relation. This is not done in the form of a transformation of the field operators, but rather by introducing a new momentum variable, with a stronger repulsion between neighboring values than demanded by the Pauli exclusion.

Assume a set of particles occupy places in k-space with coordinates $k_i = 2\pi n_i/L$, where n_i are integers that increase monotonically with i. The corresponding new momentum coordinate κ is then introduced in the form of a Bethe ansatz equation,

$$\kappa_i = k_i + \lambda \frac{\pi}{L} \sum_{j \neq i} \text{sgn}(k_i - k_j), \quad i = 1, 2, ..., \tag{39}$$

where λ is a new, real parameter. This equation leads to the following effective repulsion between the κ values,

$$\kappa_{i+1} = \kappa_i + \frac{2\pi}{L}(\Delta n_i + \lambda)\,, \tag{40}$$

where $\Delta n_i = n_{i+1} - n_i$ is a positive integer. The equation can be interpreted as expressing that each new particle introduced in the system will occupy a one-dimensional volume $2\pi(1+\lambda)/L$, as compared to $2\pi/L$ for fermions. This can be expressed more directly by the formula

$$\Delta d = -(1+\lambda)\Delta N\,, \tag{41}$$

where Δd is the change in the number of available single-particle states within a fixed, finite interval, when ΔN particles are introduced in the interval. This formulation corresponds to Haldane's defining relation of generalized exclusion statistics [4], where d is interpreted as the dimension of the Hilbert space that is available for a new particle that is added to the system, and $1+\lambda$ is the exclusion statistics parameter.

In the thermodynamic limit, $L \to \infty$, the relation (39) between k_i and κ_i defines a mapping between the corresponding continuous variables k and κ, which depend on the particle density $n(k)$ in the following way,

$$\kappa = k + \frac{1}{2}\lambda \int dk'\, n(k')\,\mathrm{sgn}(k - k')\,. \tag{42}$$

The density $\nu(\kappa)$ corresponding to the new variable κ is defined by

$$\nu(\kappa)\,d\kappa = n(k)\,dk\,, \tag{43}$$

which simply states that the number of occupied states is conserved (locally) under the mapping $k \to \kappa$. It follows directly that the two densities are related by

$$\nu(\kappa) = \frac{n(k)}{1 + \lambda n(k)}\,, \quad n(k) = \frac{\nu(\kappa)}{1 - \lambda\nu(\kappa)}\,, \tag{44}$$

with k and κ related as shown in (42). With $n(k)$ limited by $0 \le n(k) \le 1$, the corresponding restriction on $\nu(\kappa)$ is $0 \le \nu(\kappa) \le 1/(1+\lambda)$.

The fermion entropy (38), in the continuum form is

$$S = -\frac{L}{2\pi} \int_{-\infty}^{\infty} dk[n(k)\ln n(k) + (1 - n(k))\ln(1 - n(k))], \tag{45}$$

and as follows from (43) and (44), it takes the following form when expressed in terms of the new variables,

$$S = -\frac{L}{2\pi} \int_{-\infty}^{\infty} d\kappa [\nu(\kappa) \ln \nu(\kappa) - (1 - \lambda\nu(\kappa)) \ln(1 - \lambda\nu(\kappa))$$

$$+ (1 - (1+\lambda)\nu(\kappa)) \ln(1 - (1+\lambda)\nu(\kappa))]. \tag{46}$$

This expression agrees with expressions found earlier in Refs. [13] and [14] for the entropy of exclusion statistics particles.

However, one should note that, in the present case, the transformation introduced above is so far only a change of variables. One cannot make any conclusion about the true quantum statistics of the particles without considering what the transformation makes to the energy functional of the system. The point to be shown is that by choosing a particular value for the parameter λ, the leading part of the quasiparticle interaction, defined in the previous section by the Landau parameters F_0 and F_1, is transformed to zero. This implies that the statistics defined by the new form of the entropy is not modified by a statistical interaction term.

The next step then is to consider how the transformation (42) changes the energy functions, $E[n(k)] \to E[\nu(\kappa)]$, and thereby redefines the quasiparticle energy and interaction,

$$\tilde{\epsilon}(\kappa) = \frac{2\pi}{L} \frac{\delta E}{\delta \nu(\kappa)}, \quad \tilde{f}(\kappa, \kappa') = \frac{4\pi^2}{L^2} \frac{\delta^2 E}{\delta \nu(\kappa) \delta \nu(\kappa')}. \tag{47}$$

The idea is to express these in terms of the previous functionals $\epsilon(k)$ and $f(k, k')$. For the single particle energy the transformation gives

$$\tilde{\epsilon}(\kappa') = \frac{2\pi}{L} \int dk \frac{\delta n(k)}{\delta \nu(\kappa')} \frac{\delta E}{\delta n(k)} = \int dk \frac{\delta n(k)}{\delta \nu(\kappa')} \epsilon(k), \tag{48}$$

and for the interaction

$$\tilde{f}(\kappa'', \kappa') = \frac{4\pi^2}{L^2} \frac{\delta}{\delta \nu(\kappa'')} \int dk \frac{\delta n(k)}{\delta \nu(\kappa')} \frac{\delta E}{\delta n(k)}$$

$$= \frac{2\pi}{L} \int dk \frac{\delta^2 n(k)}{\delta \nu(\kappa'') \delta \nu(\kappa')} \epsilon(k) + \iint d\bar{k} \, dk \frac{\delta n(\bar{k})}{\delta \nu(\kappa'')} \frac{\delta n(k)}{\delta \nu(\kappa')} f(\bar{k}, k). \tag{49}$$

After some manipulations (see Ref. [7]), the following rather simple expressions are found for the transformation matrices,

$$\frac{\delta n(k)}{\delta \nu(\kappa')} = \frac{1}{2} \frac{d}{dk} [(1 + \lambda n(k)) \text{sgn}(k - k')],$$

$$\frac{\delta^2 n(k)}{\delta \nu(\kappa'') \delta \nu(\kappa')} = \frac{1}{4} \lambda \frac{d^2}{dk^2} [(1 + \lambda n(k)) \text{sgn}(k - k') \text{sgn}(k - k'')], \tag{50}$$

where the pairs of variables k', κ' and k'', κ'' are related by the transformation (42).

The expression obtained for the energy is then the following,

$$\tilde{\epsilon}(\kappa') = \frac{1}{2} \int dk\, \epsilon(k) \frac{d}{dk} [(1 + \lambda n(k))\mathrm{sgn}(k - k')]$$

$$= (1 + \lambda n(k'))\epsilon(k') + \frac{1}{2}\lambda \int dk\, \epsilon(k) n'(k)\mathrm{sgn}(k - k'), \qquad (51)$$

with $n'(k) = dn/dk$.

In the case of a filled Fermi sea, the particle density and its derivative are

$$n_0(k) = \frac{1}{2}(\mathrm{sgn}(k + k_F) - \mathrm{sgn}(k - k_F)),$$

$$n_0'(k) = \delta(k + k_F) - \delta(k - k_F). \qquad (52)$$

This gives for the pseudomomentum,

$$\kappa = k + \frac{1}{2}\lambda \int_{-k_F}^{k_F} d\bar{k}\, \mathrm{sgn}(k - \bar{k}) = \begin{cases} k + \lambda k_F & k > k_F \\ k(1 + \lambda) & -k_F < k < k_F, \\ k - \lambda k_F & k < -k_F \end{cases} \qquad (53)$$

in particular $\kappa_F = (1 + \lambda)k_F$. The transformed particle density is then

$$\nu_0(\kappa) = \frac{1}{2(1 + \lambda)}(\mathrm{sgn}(\kappa + \kappa_F) - \mathrm{sgn}(\kappa - \kappa_F)). \qquad (54)$$

Introducing this in the expression for the quasiparticle energy gives

$$\tilde{\epsilon}_0(\kappa) = \begin{cases} \epsilon_0\left(\kappa - \dfrac{\lambda}{1 + \lambda}\kappa_F\right) & \kappa > \kappa_F \\[2mm] (1 + \lambda)\epsilon_0\left(\dfrac{\kappa}{1 + \lambda}\right) - \lambda\epsilon_0\left(\dfrac{\kappa_F}{1 + \lambda}\right) & |\kappa| < \kappa_F \\[2mm] \epsilon_0\left(\kappa + \dfrac{\lambda}{1 + \lambda}\kappa_F\right) & \kappa < -\kappa_F \end{cases} \qquad (55)$$

For the interaction, results for the variables k at the Fermi points are only cited here (see Ref. [7]),

$$\tilde{f}_0(\kappa_F, \kappa_F) = f_0(k_F, k_F) + \left(\lambda + \frac{1}{2}\lambda^2\right)(f_0(k_F, k_F) - f_0(k_F, -k_F)) + \frac{\pi}{L}\lambda^2 v_s,$$

$$\tilde{f}_0(\kappa_F, -\kappa_F) = f_0(k_F, -k_F) - \left(\lambda + \frac{1}{2}\lambda^2\right)\left(f_0(k_F, k_F) - f_0(k_F, -k_F) + \frac{2\pi}{L}v_s\right).$$

$$\qquad (56)$$

If the new Landau parameters $\tilde{F}_0$ and $\tilde{F}_1$ are normalized as in (27), this gives the following relation between these and the original Landau parameters,

$$\widetilde{F}_0 = F_0 - \lambda \,,$$

$$\widetilde{F}_1 = (1 + \lambda)^2 \left(F_1 + \frac{\lambda}{1 + \lambda} \right) . \tag{57}$$

Furthermore, the relation (28) between F_0 and F_1 gives the following relation between $\tilde{F}_0$ and $\tilde{F}_1$,

$$\left(1 + \frac{\tilde{F}_0}{1 + \lambda} \right) = \left(1 + \frac{\tilde{F}_1}{1 + \lambda} \right)^{-1} . \tag{58}$$

Assuming now that the value of the parameter λ is specified as

$$\lambda = \lambda_1 + \lambda_2 = \frac{1}{g} - 1 \,, \tag{59}$$

and by using the values found earlier for F_0 and F_1 in (28), one finds that both the new Landau parameters vanish,

$$\widetilde{F}_0 = \widetilde{F}_1 = 0. \tag{60}$$

This means that both $\tilde{f}_0(\kappa_F, \kappa_F)$ and $\tilde{f}_0(\kappa_F, -\kappa_F)$ vanish, and since these functions can be shown to be continuous at the Fermi points [7], the interactions in the low energy regime are weak, in the sense

$$\lim_{|\kappa''| \to k_F} \lim_{|\kappa'| \to k_F} \tilde{f}_0(\kappa'', \kappa') = 0 \,. \tag{61}$$

The conclusion is thus that the interactions of the one-dimensional fermion system effectively change the particle statistics, and make the system appear as a weakly interacting system of particles with generalized statistics. The modified exclusion parameter is given by $1 + \lambda = 1/g$.

6. Low Energy Excitations

In the low energy approximation the interaction terms $\tilde{f}(\kappa'', \kappa')$ are negligible, and the energy function $\tilde{\epsilon}(\kappa)$ can be approximated by $\tilde{\epsilon}_0(\kappa)$, given in (55). It is of interest to check that the sum of this energy function, over occupied particle states, reproduces the energy determined by the Hamiltonian (10).

Let us first assume the particle distribution to be without holes, with all momentum states k_i being filled between a minimum value $k_{\min}$, close to the

Fermi point $-k_F$, and a maximum value k_{max}, close to k_F. k_{min} and k_{max} are then related to the particle numbers N and J in the following way,

$$k_{max} = k_F + \frac{\pi}{L}(N+J), \quad k_{min} = -k_F - \frac{\pi}{L}(N-J), \qquad (62)$$

and the relation (42) between κ and k now simplifies to

$$\kappa = (1+\lambda)k - \frac{\pi}{L}\lambda J. \qquad (63)$$

The energy contribution from the particles added to the Fermi sea, expressed in terms of the energy function $\tilde{\epsilon}_0(\kappa)$, is then

$$\begin{aligned}
\delta E &= \frac{L}{2\pi} \int \tilde{\epsilon}_0(\kappa)\delta\nu(\kappa)d\kappa \\
&= \frac{L}{2\pi}\frac{1}{1+\lambda}\left(\int_{\kappa_{min}}^{-\kappa_F} \tilde{\epsilon}_0(\kappa)d\kappa + \int_{\kappa_F}^{\kappa_{max}} \tilde{\epsilon}_0(\kappa)d\kappa\right) \\
&= \frac{L}{2\pi}\frac{1}{1+\lambda}\left(-\int_{\kappa_{min}}^{-\kappa_F} v_s(\kappa+\kappa_F)d\kappa + \int_{\kappa_F}^{\kappa_{max}} v_s(\kappa-\kappa_F)d\kappa\right) \\
&= \frac{\pi}{2L}v_s\left((1+\lambda)N^2 + \frac{1}{1+\lambda}J^2\right),
\end{aligned} \qquad (64)$$

This expression is consistent with that of the Hamiltonian (10), with the quadratic terms in N and J agreeing with those in (10). The bosonic excitation terms in (10), however, correspond to particle-hole excitations of the fermionic system, which are not included in (64).

Particle-hole excitations can be introduced by changing the (discrete) momenta k_i of the occupied states in the following way,

$$k_i = k_i^0 + \Delta k_i = \frac{2\pi}{L}(i+n_i), \quad i = i_{min}, i_{min}+1, \ldots, i_{max}. \qquad (65)$$

k_i^0 are the momentum values of the occupied states without holes, and n_i is a new set of integers, which introduce holes in the distribution. The condition $n_{i+1} \geq n_i$ is assumed. This makes the ordering of the set $\{k_i\}$, with respect to i, unchanged when the holes are introduced. For the pseudomomenta κ_i there is a similar change in the values, as consequence of the transformation formula (39),

$$\begin{aligned}
\kappa_i &= k_i + \lambda\frac{\pi}{L}\sum_{j=i_{min}}^{i_{max}} \operatorname{sgn}(k_i - k_j) \\
&= (2\pi/L)\left(i + n_i + \frac{1}{2}\lambda\sum_{j=i_{min}}^{i_{max}} \operatorname{sgn}(i-j)\right) \\
&\equiv \kappa_i^0 + \Delta k_i,
\end{aligned} \qquad (66)$$

with $\Delta k_i = (2\pi/L)n_i$. The shifts are thus the same as for the momenta k_i, which means that they are independent of the statistics parameter λ.

With the excitations restricted to the neighborhoods of the Fermi points, linearization of the energy as function of momentum can be made, which gives

$$\sum_i \tilde{\epsilon}_0(\kappa_i) = \sum_i \tilde{\epsilon}_0(\kappa_i^0) + v_s \sum_i |\Delta k_i|. \tag{67}$$

One should note that the excitation term is the same as for free fermions, although here with v_s as the effective Fermi velocity. The same effect is seen in the Hamiltonian (10), when the boson frequency is linearized in q, $\omega_q \approx v_s|q|$. Thus, the bosonic operators $b_q^\dagger b_q$ of the interacting system are unitarily equivalent with the corresponding operators $a_q^\dagger a_q$ of the free system. This implies that the expression (67) for the full energy, given as a sum over single particle energies $\tilde{\epsilon}_0(\kappa_i)$, reproduces the energy eigenvalues of the Hamiltonian (10) within the above approximation.

7. An Application

A quantum Hall system with the electrons restricted to the lowest Landau level is effectively a one-dimensional system. Thus, with x and y as orthogonal coordinates of electrons in the two-dimensional plane, the projection of these operators to the lowest Landau level will introduce a non-trivial commutation relation,

$$[x, y] = -il_B^2, \tag{68}$$

with $l_B = \sqrt{1/eB}$ as the magnetic length in a strong magnetic field B. This is like the commutator between coordinate and momentum in one dimension, and that is why the two-dimensional (x, y)-space can be regarded as the phase space of a one-dimensional system. Details about how the two-dimensional description can be re-formulated as a one-dimensional description can be found in Ref. [11]. A short version is given here.

In the Landau gauge,

$$A_x = -yB, \quad A_y = 0, \tag{69}$$

the Hamiltonian is translationally invariant in the x-direction and has the form of a harmonic oscillator in the y-direction. A complete set of (single-particle) orthonormalized wave functions is

$$\psi_k(x, y) = \mathcal{N}e^{ikx}\psi_0(y - y_k), \tag{70}$$

where $\mathcal{N}$ is a normalization constant, and $\psi_0(y - y_k)$ is the ground state of the harmonic oscillator in the y-direction. The oscillator is k-dependent, with $y_k = -l_B^2 k$ as the centre of the oscillator. The wavefunctions are assumed to be periodic in the x-direction, with period L. This implies that k takes the discrete values $k = 2\pi n/L$, with n as an integer. In the one-dimensional (1D) description, the corresponding set of orthonormalized wave functions is given by

$$\psi_k(\xi) = \frac{1}{\sqrt{L}} e^{ik\xi} . \tag{71}$$

The coordinate ξ in 1D then corresponds to the x-coordinate in two dimensions (2D) while k has taken the place of the y-coordinate.

With the electrons restricted to the lowest Landau level, the Hamiltonian is completely degenerate. However, when a confining potential is introduced the degeneracy is lifted. If the potential is invariant under translation in the x-direction, and has the form of a harmonic oscillator in the y-direction, the 2D description of the single-particle Hamiltonian is

$$H = \frac{1}{2m}(p_x + eBy)^2 + \frac{1}{2m}p_y^2 + \frac{1}{2}m\omega^2 y^2$$
$$= \frac{1}{2m}p_y^2 + \frac{1}{2}m\left[\left(\omega_c y + \frac{p_x}{m}\right)^2 + \omega^2 y^2\right] . \tag{72}$$

Here $\omega_c = \sqrt{eB/m}$ is the cyclotron frequency of the magnetic field, e is the electron charge, m the mass, and ω is the angular frequency of the harmonic confining potential. The harmonic oscillator potential can be absorbed in a stronger magnetic field $\bar{B}$ in the following way,

$$H = \frac{1}{2m}p_y^2 + \frac{1}{2}m\bar{\omega}_c^2\left(y + \frac{\omega_c}{m\bar{\omega}_c^2}p_x\right)^2 + \frac{1}{2m}\frac{\omega^2}{\bar{\omega}_c^2}p_x^2 , \tag{73}$$

with $\bar{\omega}_c = \sqrt{\omega_c^2 + \omega^2}$ as the stronger cyclotron frequency.

The first two terms in (73), which commute with the third one, is identical to the Hamiltonian of an electron in the enhanced magnetic field $\bar{B}$, without a confining potential. With the electron confined to the lowest Landau level of the enhanced magnetic field, the sum of the first two terms therefore defines a constant, which may be disregarded. This implies that only the last term remains, and the full many-particle Hamiltonian, with a two-body interaction term V_{ij} added, then has the form

$$H = \sum_i \frac{1}{2M}p_i^2 + \sum_{i<j} V_{ij} , \tag{74}$$

where

$$M = m \frac{\bar{\omega}_c^2}{\omega^2}, \tag{75}$$

is the effective particle mass. With V_{ij} as a standard two-body interaction in 2D, the interaction in 1D is not completely local, as follows from the (small) minimum width of the electron wave functions in the lowest Landau level. In second quantized form the Hamiltonian then is

$$H = \sum_k \frac{\hbar^2}{2M} k^2 c_k^\dagger c_k + \frac{1}{4L} \sum_{q,k_1,k_2} V(k_1 - k_2, q) c_{k_1}^\dagger c_{k_2}^\dagger c_{k_2-q} c_{k_1+q}, \tag{76}$$

where the non-locality is implicit in the dependence of V on the two variables $k_1 - k_2$ and q.

This expression (76) for H has precisely the same form as the Hamiltonian given in (1), here with $\epsilon_0(k) = \frac{\hbar^2}{2M} k^2$. With the ground state having the form of a filled Fermi sea, and with the low-energy states corresponding to gapless excitations, the low-energy Hamiltonian will therefore take the same form as in (2). As a consequence the discussion and results derived in the previous sections, will be applicable to the special case discussed here.

Charge fractionalization on edges of a quantum Hall system is an interesting effect, which has been discussed in several papers in the past [12, 15–22]. The effect depends on having a system where two edges, with opposite chiralities, interact. A charge inserted on of the edges will then be separated into right-moving and left-moving components, as illustrated in Fig. 1. As shown in [12], the right-moving components will carry a fraction $\frac{1}{2}(1 + g)$ of

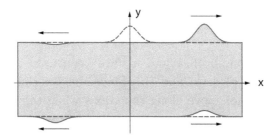

Fig. 1.   Two-dimensional illustration of charge separation in an interacting system. A charge which is injected at the upper edge (dashed curve) is separated into a right-moving and a left-moving component due to interactions between the edges. Each of these carries a density component both on the upper and on the lower edge. The ratio between the upper and lower part of the right-going charge is determined by the interaction parameter g, and is the same as the ratio between the lower and upper part of the left-going charge. The initial condition restricts the total charge on the lower edge to be zero. The illustration is taken from Ref. [12].

the inserted charge, and the left-moving components will carry the fraction $\frac{1}{2}(1-g)$ of the charge. This separation into right-moving and left-moving components can be explained in the Fermi liquid formulation, as will be shown in the following.

Consider a situation similar to that above, with the Hamiltonian of the form (76). Expressed in terms of the pseudo-momentum κ, the ground state corresponds to a filled Fermi sea, with all available states in the interval $-\kappa_F < \kappa < \kappa_F$ filled. The single-particle energy is assumed to have a quadratic form $\tilde{\epsilon}_0(\kappa) = \frac{1}{2}a\kappa^2$, with $a = v_s/k_F$, corresponding to the harmonic oscillator form of the confining potential in (72). (In reality the precise form of the confining potential is not important for what is discussed here.)

The confining potential introduces motion of the particles to the right in the upper part of the Fermi sea and to the left in the lower part. Due to the symmetry of the occupied states in the filled Fermi sea the integrated current vanishes. To make a comparison with the situation shown in Fig. 1, a charge is next added at the upper edge and the corresponding change in the current is found and compared with the result in [12]. However, instead of adding the charge locally, as shown in the illustration, an asymmetry is here introduced by occupying additional momentum states close to the upper edge.

The situation is illustrated in Fig. 2. Two cases are shown, the first one with a filled Fermi sea, with $N_0 = 21$ particles and $N = J = 0$. In the second case two particles have been added in the lowest available states close to the Fermi point k_F, so that $N = J = 2$. The statistics parameter in the plot is chosen as $\lambda = 0.5$. Since there is no hole among the occupied states, there is a simple relation between the variables k and κ, as shown in (63),

$$\kappa = (1 + \lambda)k - \frac{\pi}{L}\lambda J.$$

By use of this relation, both k and κ have been used as variables in the plots, respectively in plot (a) and (b). Since the positions of the occupied states in plot (a) do not move along the k-axis when the additional charges are included, there is no obvious appearance in this plot of a separation of the additional charge into right/left-moving components. However, even if the positions of the occupied states along the k-axis are not changed, there is a change of positions along the energy axis, which is relevant for this separation. As shown in the figure, the *curve* formed by the occupied points in the two-dimensional plane is shifted along the k-axis when the two charges are introduced.

In plot (b), the same two cases are illustrated, here with κ rather than k as variable. The charge separation is here more explicit. Thus, the two

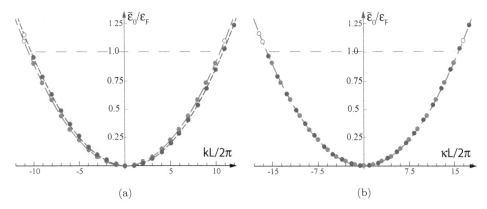

(a)   (b)

Fig. 2.   Charge separation on edges of a quantum Hall system in a 1D representation. In (a) the single particle energy $\tilde{\epsilon}_0$ is shown as a function of the momentum variable k, and in (b) as a function of κ. Filled circles correspond to occupied states and open circles to unoccupied states. Two cases are shown in both plots. The first case (red circles) corresponds to a filled Fermi sea, the second case (dark blue circles) contains two additional particles, located in the lowest available momentum states close to the Fermi point k_F. Figure (b) shows most clearly the charge separation, with the added charge introducing a shift in the κ coordinates of the particles. This shift is interpreted as causing separation of the added charge into a right-moving component (for $\kappa > 0$) and a left-moving component (for $\kappa < 0$).

curves corresponding to $J = 0$ and $J = 2$ fall on top of each other, and as a consequence the shift in energy between the two cases is linked to a shift in the variable κ. This effect is a consequence of the relation between k and κ, shown in (63), which implies that there is a difference between the two variables which is proportional to J. The interpretation now is that κ rather than k determines the right/left-motion of the particles, so that positive κ corresponds to right-moving particles and negative κ corresponds to left-moving particles. With this interpretation it is straightforward to determine how the inserted charge is divided into these components, and to compare the results with what has earlier been cited from [12].

Assume a number J of particles is added at the positive Fermi point. The shift in positions κ of the particles in Fermi sea then is

$$\Delta\kappa = -\frac{\pi}{L}\lambda J = -\frac{2\pi}{L}\left(\frac{1}{g} - 1\right)J. \tag{77}$$

The separation between occupied places in the Fermi sea is $\Delta\kappa_0 = \frac{2\pi}{L}\frac{1}{g}$, and with the combination of these expressions the result is,

$$\frac{\Delta\kappa}{\Delta\kappa_0} = -\frac{1}{2}(1 - g)J. \tag{78}$$

This can be interpreted as representing the part of the inserted charge that is transferred from the positive to the negative side of the κ-axis. The result is thus that the right-moving fraction of the inserted charge is $\frac{1}{2}(1+g)$ and the left-moving fraction is $\frac{1}{2}(1-g)$, a result which agrees with what was previously found in Ref. [12].

8. Summary

The standard approach to study interacting one-dimensional Fermi systems is to use the bosonization technique. However, here I have focussed on how Landau's Fermi liquid theory can be applied to such systems.

In the low-energy approximation, a unitary transformation between the excitations of the non-interacting and the interacting system is applied to rewrite the Hamiltonian in terms of 'dressed' fermion fields. The Hamiltonian, in this form, is then used to determine the quasiparticle energy and two-body interaction, defined as functional derivatives of the full energy of the system. With a further change of variables the interaction terms are absorbed, so that the description gets the form of a free theory. However, as shown by the transformed form of the entropy function, the quasiparticles are not fermions, but obey fractional exclusion statistics. (This means that to refer to the system as a *Fermi* liquid may be somewhat misleading.)

In the last section this is applied to a quantum Hall system, which is restricted to a narrow band, with interaction between the edges of the band. Although the physical number of dimensions of the system is two, when the particles are restricted to the lowest Landau level, the dimensions are effectively reduced to one. This system is here used as an example, to demonstrate the effect of fractional exclusion statistics in the case of a one-dimensional interacting Fermi system.

As a final comment, I would like to congratulate Frank Wilczek on the occasion of his 70th birthday.

References

[1] J.M. Leinaas and J. Myrheim, *Nuovo Cimento* **37B**, 1 (1977).
[2] F. Wilczek, *Phys. Rev. Lett.* **49**, 957 (1982).
[3] J.M. Leinaas and J. Myrheim, *Phys. Rev. B* **37**, 9286 (1988).
[4] F.D.M. Haldane, *Phys. Rev. Lett.* **67**, 937 (1991).
[5] F.D.M. Haldane, *J. Phys. C* **14**, 2585 (1981).
[6] L.D. Landau, *Sov. Phys. JETP* **3**, 920 (1956).
[7] Jon Magne Leinaas, *Phys. Rev. B* **95**, 155429 (2017).
[8] Y.S. Wu and Y. Yu, *Phys. Rev. Lett.* **75**, 890 (1995).

[9] Y.S. Wu, Y. Yu, and H.X. Yang, *Nucl. Phys. B* **604**, [FS], 551 (2001).

[10] Sergei B. Isakov, *Phys. Lett. A* **242**, 130 (1998).

[11] Mats Horsdal and Jon Magne Leinaas, *Phys. Rev. B* **76**, 195321 (2007).

[12] Jon Magne Leinaas, Mats Horsdal, and T. H. Hansson, *Phys. Rev. B* **80**, 115327 (2009).

[13] Sergei B. Isakov, *Mod. Phys. Lett. B* **8**, 319 (1994).

[14] Y.S. Wu, *Phys. Rev. Lett.* **73**, 922 (1994).

[15] M. P. A. Fisher and L. I. Glazman, in *Mesoscopic Electron Transport*, NATO Advanced Study Institute, Series E: Applied Sciences, edited by L. Kouwenhoven, G. Schoen, and L. Sohn (Kluwer Academic Publishers, 1997), Vol. 345.

[16] I. Safi, *Ann. Phys. (Paris)* **22**, 463 (1997).

[17] K.-V. Pham, M. Gabay, and P. Lederer, *Phys. Rev. B* **61**, 16 397 (2000).

[18] Björn Trauzettel, Inès Safi, Fabrizio Dolcini, and Hermann Grabert, *Phys. Rev. Lett.* **92**, 226405 (2004).

[19] Karyn Le Hur, Bertrand, I. Halperin, and Amir Yacoby, *Ann. Phys. (N.Y.)* **323**, 3037 (2008).

[20] E. Berg, Y. Oreg, E.-A. Kim, and F. von Oppen, *Phys. Rev. Lett.* **102**, 236402 (2009).

[21] Mats Horsdal, Marianne Rypestøl, Hans Hansson, and Jon Magne Leinaas, *Phys. Rev. B* **84**, 115313 (2011).

[22] H. Inoue, A. Grivnin, N. Ofek, I. Neder, M. Heiblum, V. Umanski, and D. Mahalu, *Phys. Rev. Lett.* **112**, 166801 (2014).

Breached Pair Superfluidity: A Brief Review

W. Vincent Liu*

*Department of Physics and Shenzhen Institute
for Quantum Science and Engineering
Southern University of Science and Technology
Shenzhen 518055, China and
Wilczek Quantum Center, School of Physics
and Astronomy and T. D. Lee Institute
Shanghai Jiao Tong University, Shanghai 200240, China
wvliu@pitt.edu*

Interior gap superfluidity was introduced together with Frank Wilczek. Later on together with our collaborators, we generalized this new possibility of superfluidity to a broader concept, breached pair superfluidity. On the occasion to celebrate Professor Frank Wilczek's seventieth birthday and his productive career in several major areas in physics, I dedicate this note to recall the exciting times of developing this idea, the main aspects of the proposed phase, and discussion on its stability condition.

1. Introduction

Modern history of physics has proudly recorded a group of great luminaries having broadly impacted on the areas of high energy, statistical, and condensed matter physics. Among those who are still live and active in today's physics, many would immediately point out Frank Wilczek in this class. I was lucky to have had the privilege of working with him — during my postdoctoral times at MIT — on one of the topics of great interest in such an interdisciplinary area. It was about exotic superfluidity arising from the effect of mismatched Fermi surfaces.

The phenomenon of mismatched Fermi surfaces occurs in a number of physical systems. It happens in electronic superconductors when an in-plane magnetic field is applied or when superconductivity and ferromagnetism coexist. It should happen in dense quantum chromodynamics (QCD) matter — arguably the inside of neutron stars or a quark-gluon plasma realized in the heavy ion collision experiments at CERN [1]. It can be artificially

---

*On sabbatical leave from Department of Physics and Astronomy, University of Pittsburgh, Pittsburgh, PA 15260, USA.

tuned to occur, not as a problem but as a new parameter regime for possible new effects, in cold atomic gases through the mixtures of different atomic species whose populations are separately controlled and conserved.

Understanding the Zeeman effect in the electronic superconductors was a key motivation in the early proposal by Fulde-Ferrell-Larkin-Ovchinnikov (FFLO) [2] to consider the instability of Bardeen-Cooper-Schrieffer (BCS) [3] phase towards alternative energetically favored states to accommodate the Fermi level difference due to spin polarization. This class of states are now known as FFLO phases, in which each Cooper pair carries a finite center-of-mass momentum whose scale is set by the Fermi surface difference, i.e. $\mathbf{Q} \sim 1.2\delta p_F$ by mean field theory.

Frank Wilczek and his collaborators are among the early pioneers to initiate the field of color superconductivity [4–9]. The condensed matter concept of FFLO phase was extended to the understanding of the phase diagram of dense QCD matter, for which crystalline color superconductivity was proposed [9–11]. The study of quark matter at finite density turns into a new condensed matter physics problem. A fundamental change in comparison is the role of the usual Coulomb interaction between electrons mediated by U(1) electromagnetic gauge bosons (photons) being replaced by the strong interaction mediated by SU(3) color gauge bosons known as gluons. And there are more degrees of freedom and higher symmetry involved, such as a variety of Cooper pairs with several flavors and colors present at the appropriate density level (for that matter, also the energy scale).

In high density QCD, the phenomenon of mismatched Fermi surfaces is guaranteed to exist by two facts combined: six quark flavors carry two different fractions of electrical charge and each flavor has its own unique mass, hence different from each other. Let us illustrate this by considering an intermediate high density quark matter with average chemical potential $\mu \sim 400\,\text{MeV}$, which probably corresponds to the nucleon density in the core of neutron stars. At such an energy scale, the charm, top and bottom flavors are not present due to their individual masses being significantly high above. The QCD matter then is made of (approximately) massless up and down quarks and massive strange quarks. The strange quark has a mass $M_s \sim 300\,\text{MeV}$, comparable to the chemical potential scale under consideration. It plays a crucial role, as we see below, to cause a mismatch in flavor chemical potentials. Electric neutrality requires a nonzero density of electrons present, estimated to be $\mu_e \sim 50\,\text{MeV}$. In many body physics, μ and μ_e are treated as Lagrangian multiplier to enforce the conserved quantum numbers of quark flavor and electric charge, respectively. A simple algebra shows that they are related to the individual flavor chemical potentials and

Fermi momenta as follows:

$$\mu_u = \mu - \frac{2}{3}\mu_e = 367\,\text{MeV}, \quad p_F^u = \mu_u = 367\,\text{MeV},$$

$$\mu_d = \mu + \frac{1}{3}\mu_e = 417\,\text{MeV}, \quad p_F^d = \mu_d = 417\,\text{MeV}, \tag{1}$$

$$\mu_s = \mu + \frac{1}{3}\mu_e = 417\,\text{MeV}, \quad p_F^s = \sqrt{\mu_s^2 - M_s^2} = 289\,\text{MeV}.$$

The above crude estimate shows that the three flavors would have three different Fermi surfaces. An immediate consequence is that the color-flavor-locking superconductivity would be unstable towards crystalline color superconductivity, the manifestation of FFLO in high density QCD. This was analyzed in the context of color superconductivity by Alford, Bowers, and Rajagopal [10, 11] (for reviews, see [7–9]). The BCS equivalent in this context is the color-flavor-locking (CFL) superconductivity with equal population pairing, proposed for the extreme high density limit where all flavors would enjoy approximately the same Fermi surfaces with chemical potential difference negligible at such a high-density scale. It was discussed in the 1970s and 1980s (see Bailin and Love [12, 13]) that dense quark matter might become superfluid.

Frank, together with his collaborators, pioneered in revitalizing the idea of color superconductivity [4–9]. He also knew well of the FFLO idea from his close collaborators and former students who extended the FFLO concept to the intermediate density regime of quark matter to introduce crystalline color superconductivity. I was fortunate to be exposed to this interesting interface between condensed matter and high energy physics, immediately after I went to MIT as a postdoctoral fellow with Frank in 2001. I quickly learned a great deal of color superconductivity and QCD matter phase diagram from him, and we realized that some of the ideas could be quantum simulated by ultra-cold atomic gases.

Progressive developments in ultra-cold gases have revitalized interest in some basic qualitative questions of quantum many-body theory, because they promise to make a wide variety of conceptually interesting parameter regimes, which might previously have seemed academic or excessively special, experimentally accessible. Advances in the spatiotemporal control and read-out of ultra-cold quantum gases are rapidly expanding the scientific range of current and near-future experiments in this growing field [14]. Emergent tools of quantum control in AMO physics represent an important bridge to the exploration of complex many-body problems based on fully understood few-particle subsystems. One of the most remarkable is the unprecedented flexibility to directly control the interaction between the selected atomic internal states — which play the role of "spins" or " flavors" — through the technique known as Feshbach resonance [15–19]. It has been demonstrated that interaction between fermionic atoms can be precisely tuned, by dialing an external magnetic field, from attractive to repulsive, from weak to infinitely strong. Trapping cold atoms and molecules in optical lattices brings a whole new set of quantum manipulations [20–22]. Among them, the band masses and interaction between atoms on the same or neighboring sites are all becoming experimentally controlled with unprecedented flexibilities. Novel forms in geometry or (dynamic) Floquet engineering have been demonstrated and used to explore a wide range of interesting quantum states of matter, from simulating topological insulators and fractional quantum Hall effects to exploring antiferromagnetism and orbital superfluidity [23–27].

2. Aspects of Breached Pair Superfluidity

The FFLO actually represents a class of superconducting states, because the FFLO order parameter in principle can be a superposition of Cooper pairs condensed at a set of different finite momenta,

$$\Delta(\mathbf{r}) \equiv \langle \psi_\sigma(\mathbf{r})\psi_{\sigma'}(\mathbf{r})\epsilon_{\sigma\sigma'}\rangle \sim \sum_{\{\mathbf{Q}_\alpha\}} \alpha e^{i\mathbf{Q}_\alpha\cdot\mathbf{r}}\Delta_\alpha \qquad (2)$$

where I assume a fermion model of two spins $\sigma =\uparrow,\downarrow$, $\epsilon_{\sigma\sigma'}$ is the antisymmetric tensor, and the summation over α represents a set of Cooper pair momenta chosen to minimize the postulated ground state energy. Hence, it yields a rich phase diagram of different ordering crystalline structures. In other words, generic FFLO phases break both spatial translational and rotational symmetries in addition to the phase U(1) rotation symmetry. A FFLO pairing order parameter with a single momentum component is an exception as it would still be translationally invariant. The rich phase diagram, however, poses an experimental challenge to realize, observe and identify the nature and symmetry of the actual FFLO phase being realized, in part due to an abundance of competing FFLO phases which differ in crystalline symmetry. The energy difference between similar but symmetrically different FFLO phases is often very small, from variational calculations. The overall condensation energy saved in FFLO scenario is also exponentially smaller than that of the corresponding BCS phase if the condition of Fermi surface match restores while everything else is being kept the same. The reason is quite easy to understand. Unlike the BCS case, FFLO pairing only takes place in certain spots of the Fermi surfaces, so the density of states of fermionic particle states participating in pairing and condensation is fractional, not a whole shell along the Fermi surface in a 3D setting. The energy gap and critical temperature both depend on the density of states of paired fermions exponentially, if the BCS mean field theory is taken as guidance.

The new experimental regime in cold atomic gases motivated Frank and me to think whether it was possible to have some homogeneous phase — in this regard like the BCS but not like the FFLO — that can be energetically better than the non-homogeneous FFLO. Our initial proposal, as a phenomenological trial wavefunction for the superfluid ground state was interior gap superfluidity [28]. Later on, we realize this represents just one special limit of a more general possibility [29–31]. In the following, I will first review the general state and then point the interior gap as a special situation of the general scenario.

Let us use an example of model Hamiltonian to introduce the breached pair superfluid (BP) state [29, 31],

$$
H = \sum_{\mathbf{p}\sigma} \left[\frac{\mathbf{p}^2}{2m_\sigma} - \mu_\sigma \right] \psi_{\sigma\mathbf{p}}{}^\dagger \psi_{\sigma\mathbf{p}} + \sum_{\mathbf{p}\mathbf{p}'} V_{\mathbf{p}\mathbf{p}'}(\mathbf{q}) \psi^\dagger_{\uparrow\mathbf{q}+\mathbf{p}} \psi^\dagger_{\downarrow\mathbf{q}-\mathbf{p}} \psi_{\downarrow\mathbf{q}-\mathbf{p}'} \psi_{\uparrow\mathbf{q}+\mathbf{p}'},
$$

(3)

where $\sigma = \{\uparrow, \downarrow\}$ (or $\{A, B\}$) is the spin indices, m_σ are the masses of fermions, and μ_σ are the chemical potentials to enforce the condition of spin population imbalance, say $N_\uparrow < N_\downarrow$. Unlike previous studies, a key additional feature that I believe was first explored by Frank and me [28] is the introduction of mass imbalance $m_\uparrow \neq m_\downarrow$. It was found that the larger the mass ratio, the better the BP state is favored. As a concrete example, assume that the spin down species is much heavier than the spin up species ($m_\downarrow \gg m_\uparrow$) without loss of generality. In order for the BP state to be energetically favorable, the interaction $V_{\mathbf{p}\mathbf{p}'}(\mathbf{q})$ has to be strongly momentum dependent. (A contact δ-like interaction in the real space corresponds to a $\mathbf{q}$-independent constant in momentum space by Fourier transformation, which does not work.) Two types of interaction, each of special interest, were found to work [31]. One is of the (modified) BCS type of interaction

$$
V^I_{\mathbf{p}\mathbf{p}'}(\mathbf{q}) = \begin{cases} g \ (\text{constant}) & \text{if } p, p' \in [p^F_\sigma - \lambda/2, \ p^F_\sigma + \lambda/2], \\ 0. \end{cases}
$$

(4)

where p^F_σ are the Fermi momentum for the two spins ($\sigma = \uparrow, \downarrow$) and the non-vanishing condition in the above is for momenta sitting within the stripes of width λ around each of two Fermi surfaces. Here is a subtle point — λ behaves like the ultraviolet cutoff, in the sense $\lambda \gg \Delta/v_F$ (where Δ is the energy gap due to Cooper pairing), but should be kept smaller than the Fermi surface mismatch, $\lambda < \delta p^F = p_\downarrow^F - p_\uparrow^F$. This type of model was used in the calculation of our 2003 PRL [28] when first introducing the concept of interior gap superfluidity. Such a condition was briefly indicated in a sentence put in parentheses under Eq. (1) in Ref. [28]. The work by Wu and Yip [32] was on a qualitatively different model — their interaction is point-like in the position space, which transforms into a uniform constant in momentum space with a momentum cut-off scale taken to be the largest scale, $\gg \delta p^F$. In other words, the type of interaction considered in Wu-Yip paper is not that used in our model calculation. This was the source of early debate and confusion. It was clarified in our later 2005 PRL work with Forbes *et al.* [31].

Another type is of momentum structure falling off as a Gaussian [31]

$$V_{\mathbf{pp}'}^{II}(\mathbf{q}) = ge^{-q^2/\lambda^2}, \quad \forall \mathbf{p}, \mathbf{p}'. \tag{5}$$

Similar to type I interaction in a qualitative sense, for the BP phase to prevail, the falling off momentum scale λ needs to be within the Fermi momentum difference between the two spins.

The BP state is similar to the BCS in terms of symmetry of the superfluid order parameter — Cooper pairs condensed at zero momentum and the state is uniform in position space. Then, how does the state accommodate the spin population difference $N_\uparrow < N_\downarrow$? This question can be answered precisely by contrasting the many-body wavefunctions of the well-known BCS state

$$|\Psi_{BCS}\rangle = \prod_{\mathbf{p}}(u_{\mathbf{p}} + v_{\mathbf{p}}\psi_{\mathbf{p}\uparrow}^\dagger\psi_{-\mathbf{p}\downarrow}^\dagger)|0\rangle, \tag{6}$$

and the new BP state,

$$|\Psi_{BP}\rangle = \prod_{\mathbf{p}:p<p_\Delta^-}(u_{\mathbf{p}} + v_{\mathbf{p}}\psi_{\mathbf{p}\uparrow}^\dagger\psi_{-\mathbf{p}\downarrow}^\dagger) \prod_{\mathbf{p}:p\in[p_\Delta^-,p_\Delta^+]}\psi_{\mathbf{p}\downarrow}^\dagger$$
$$\times \prod_{\mathbf{p}:p>p_\Delta^+}(u_{\mathbf{p}} + v_{\mathbf{p}}\psi_{\mathbf{p}\uparrow}^\dagger\psi_{-\mathbf{p}\downarrow}^\dagger)|0\rangle. \tag{7}$$

Momentum-space phase separation. The BP state accomplishes the population imbalance by a mechanism that I would refer to as momentum-space phase separation of superfluid and normal components. The momentum region of $\mathbf{p} : p \in [p_\Delta^-, p_\Delta^+]$ is a normal component breach: it is filled by only one fermion species, namely, the majority species (spin $\downarrow$ in our example here), hence there is no pairing. Superfluid components exist, in a way similar to what happens in BCS state, in the momentum regions outside this "normal" breach.

The BP variational wavefunction consists of the usual coherence variables $(u_{\mathbf{p}}, v_{\mathbf{p}})$ as well as additional variational parameters $p_\Delta^\pm$, to be determined by variationally minimizing the ground state energy with fixed chemical potentials and solving the energy gap equation self-consistently. The following summarizes the results obtained in this manner,

$$\left\{ \begin{array}{c} |u_{\mathbf{p}}|^2 \\ |v_{\mathbf{p}}|^2 \end{array} \right\} = \frac{1}{2} \left(1 \pm \frac{\epsilon_{\mathbf{p}}^+}{\sqrt{\epsilon_{\mathbf{p}}^{+2} + |\Delta|^2}} \right), \quad \epsilon_{\mathbf{p}}^\pm \equiv \frac{\epsilon_\uparrow(\mathbf{p}) \pm \epsilon_\downarrow(\mathbf{p})}{2} \tag{8}$$

with $\epsilon_\sigma(\mathbf{p}) = \mathbf{p}^2/2m_\sigma - \mu_\sigma$. The Bogoliubov quasi-particle spectrum in the BP superconducting state takes a different form than in the BCS state, shown as follows:

$$E_{\mathbf{p}}^\pm = \epsilon_{\mathbf{p}}^- \pm \sqrt{\epsilon_{\mathbf{p}}^{+2} + |\Delta|^2}. \tag{9}$$

Taking the usual notation, Δ denotes the excitation energy gap appearing in the superconducting state. What is special in the BP excitation spectrum is the presence of gapless Fermi surface while being superconducting (or superfluid for charge neutral fermions). The gapless surfaces are the zero mode solution of the quasi-particle excitation in momentum space,

$$E_{\mathbf{p}}^+ E_{\mathbf{p}}^- = 0 \ \Rightarrow \ p = p_\Delta^\pm. \tag{10}$$

The peculiar features of the BP state are illustrated in Fig. 1. The momentum dependence of the fermion occupation numbers, $n_\sigma(\mathbf{p})$, tells two important points. First, it shows where the pairing spectral weight is taking place most. That is the region where $n_\sigma(\mathbf{p})$ deviates from 1 most due to fermion pairing. Note this is the ground state property ($T = 0$) under discussion. In the example we adopt here ($m_\uparrow \ll m_\downarrow$ and $p_F^\uparrow < p_F^\downarrow$), Cooper pairing occurs mostly around the smaller Fermi surface, hence initially called "interior gap" superfluidity [28]. If one had considered the opposite case (still $m_\uparrow \ll m_\downarrow$ but $p_F^\uparrow > p_F^\downarrow$), one would find fermion pairing should occur most along the larger Fermi surface, and then one would see something like "exterior gap" [29]. Second, the occupation numbers tell where the breach (a region of no Cooper pairing) is precisely located. It is the place in momentum where the minority species is 0 and the majority is 1. In both "interior" and "exterior" gap case, the breach is the hallmark of the new superfluid [29, 31].

Let us summarize the characteristic features of the BP phase:

(a) It realizes a momentum-space phase separation to accommodate the population imbalance between two spins.

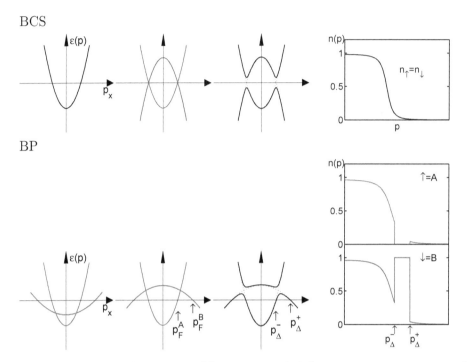

Fig. 1.   Comparison of BP and BCS states revealed from excitation spectra and fermion occupation numbers. In this illustration of example, we assume the condition $m_\uparrow \ll m_\downarrow$ and $N_\uparrow < N_\downarrow$ with two species fermions denoted as A, B (or $\uparrow, \downarrow$ exchangeably). The region bounded between $p_\Delta^\pm$ is a breach in the momentum space, where only the majority species is present and no pairing takes place. Within the breach, the occupation numbers are 1 and 0 for the majority and minority fermion, respectively (right panel).

(b) It exhibits coexisting superfluid and normal Fermi liquid components in the quantum ground state through such a momentum-space phase separation.

(c) It is a superfluid with a full surface of gapless quasiparticle excitations. In the case illustrated in Fig. 1, the BP phase has 2 gapless surfaces (BP2). At certain critical point, one gapless surface is found possible (BP1) [30, 33–35].

(d) Unlike the fully gapped BCS phase, the superfluid density is not equal to the total fermion density, but to the density of only those fermions filled outside the breach.

(e) Unlike the FFLO phase, it does not spontaneously break the translational and rotational symmetries.

3. Remarks

Since the initial proposal, the concept of interior gap and BP phase has received much attention and debates regarding its stability and competition with other viable phases [32, 36–38]. The confusion has something to do with that the BP phase we proposed is related to one of the solutions to the superconducting gap equation studied by Sarma [39] in early years, which was correctly realized as an unstable solution in his analysis. (It is sometime jointly called Sarma or BP phase in the literature.) The key point is that we introduced the BP phase, despite some similarity to Sarma's state in the structure of wavefunction, with a large mass ratio. This is one of the key ingredients to have a physically stable state, to be highlighted next.

Based on studies and discussions so far, our general conclusion is that the BP phase requires two crucial conditions: [31] (a) a relatively large mass ratio between the two fermion species and (b) strong momentum dependence of a two-body attractive s-wave interaction. The latter is equivalent to requiring strong spatial dependence of the interaction in position space, by Fourier transformation. The examples we have found include the Gaussian type of long range interaction in position space or the type of interaction restricted to a narrow momentum strip as in the BCS model. The BP phase has been found as a competing phase in the phase diagram by other studies. An effective field theory approach by Son and Stephanov [33] showed a universal phase diagram of a homogenous gapless superfluid phase which corresponds to the BP phase. The quantum critical theory based on the renormalization group analysis by Yang and Sachdev [34, 35] showed the gapless BP phase is stable in a 2D superfluid. Dynamical mean field theory by Dao *et al.* [40] found that the attractive Hubbard model yields a polarized phase closely connected to the physics of the Sarma or BP phase (with two fermi surfaces) down to very low temperatures. Furthermore, Dukelsky *et al.* [41] obtained the phase diagram of an exact solvable model by using the algebraic Richardson-Gaudin techniques, which shows not only a breached pair (BP) phase but also another exotic phase that they dubbed "breached" LOFF phase [41]. This model generalizes what was introduced by me with Frank [28].

The presence of gapless Fermi surfaces was found to manifest itself by some remarkable, unconventional aspects such as inducing a spatially oscillating potential between superfluid vortices, akin to the RKKY indirect-exchange interaction in non-magnetic metals [42]. It was remarked that the "interior gap"/BP superfluidity might be relevant to explain the experimental observation of unpaired electrons present in the heavy-fermion superconductor CeCoIn$_5$ [43]. In the context of high density QCD, gapless color superconductivity — a phase related to the Sarma/BP — was proposed as a natural candidate for quark matter in cores of compact stars at zero and finite temperature by Huang and Shovkovy through a detailed analysis [44] and their earlier paper [45].

For trapped cold ensembles of atoms, the effect of mass and population imbalance in gapless superfluidity was analyzed by Bedaque, Caldas, and Rupak [46, 47] (where the authors did not consider momentum-dependent interaction) suggesting real-space phase separation of normal and superfluid components and by Yi and Duan and later by Lin with them [48, 49] putting forward experimental signatures detecting breached pair phases with 1 or 2 Fermi surfaces (BP1 and BP2).

Acknowledgments

I am grateful to M. Forbes, E. Gubankova, M. Huang, Y. B. Kim, G. Ortiz, K. Rajagopal, L. Taillefer, F. Wilczek, and K. Yang for valuable discussions. This work is supported by AFOSR Grant No. FA9550-16-1-0006, the MURI-ARO Grant No. W911NF17-1-0323 through UC Santa Barbara, and the Shanghai Municipal Science and Technology Major Project (Grant No. 2019SHZDZX01).

References

[1] R. Pasechnik and M. Šumbera, Phenomenological review on quarkgluon plasma: Concepts vs. observations, *Universe.* **3**(1), (2017). doi: 10.3390/universe3010007. URL https://www.mdpi.com/2218-1997/3/1/7.

[2] P. Fulde and R. A. Ferrell, *Phys. Rev.* **135**, A550 (1964); A. I. Larkin and Yu. N. Ovchinnikov, *Sov. Phys. JETP* **20**, 762 (1965).

[3] J. Bardeen, L. N. Cooper, and J. R. Schrieffer, Theory of superconductivity, *Phys. Rev.* **108**, 1175–1204 (1957).

[4] M. Alford, K. Rajagopal, and F. Wilczek, QCD at finite baryon density: Nucleon droplets and color superconductivity, *Phys. Lett. B.* **422**(1), 247–256 (1998). doi: https://doi.org/10.1016/S0370-2693(98)00051-3. URL https://www.sciencedirect.com/science/article/pii/S0370269398000513.

[5] R. Rapp, T. Schäfer, E. Shuryak, and M. Velkovsky, Diquark bose condensates in high density matter and instantons, *Phys. Rev. Lett.* **81**, 53–56 (1998). doi: 10.1103/PhysRevLett.81.53. URL https://link.aps.org/doi/10.1103/PhysRevLett.81.53.

[6] M. Alford, K. Rajagopal, and F. Wilczek, Color-flavor locking and chiral symmetry breaking in high density QCD, *Nucl. Phys. B* **537**(1), 443–458 (1999). doi: https://doi.org/10.1016/S0550-3213(98)00668-3. URL https://www.sciencedirect.com/science/article/pii/S0550321398006683.

[7] K. Rajagopal and F. Wilczek. The condensed matter physics of QCD. In *Frontier of Particle Physics/Handbook of QCD*, ed. M. Shifman, chapter 35. World Scientific, Singapore (2002).

[8] R. Casalbuoni and G. Nardulli, Inhomogeneous superconductivity in condensed matter and QCD, *Rev. Mod. Phys.* **76**(1), 263–320 (2004). doi: 10.1103/RevModPhys.76.263.

[9] M. G. Alford, A. Schmitt, K. Rajagopal, and T. Schäfer, Color superconductivity in dense quark matter, *Rev. Mod. Phys.* **80**, 1455–1515 (2008). doi: 10.1103/RevModPhys.80.1455. URL https://link.aps.org/doi/10.1103/RevModPhys.80.1455.

[10] M. Alford, J. A. Bowers, and K. Rajagopal, Crystalline color superconductivity, *Phys. Rev. D* **63**, 074016 (2001).

[11] J. A. Bowers and K. Rajagopal, Crystallography of color superconductivity, *Phys. Rev. D.* **66**, 065002 (2002). doi: 10.1103/PhysRevD.66.065002. URL https://link.aps.org/doi/10.1103/PhysRevD.66.065002.

[12] D. Bailin and A. Love, Superfluid quark matter, *J. Phys. A: Mathematical and General.* **12**(10), L283–L289 (1979). doi: 10.1088/0305-4470/12/10/009. URL https://doi.org/10.1088/0305-4470/12/10/009.

[13] D. Bailin and A. Love, Superfluidity and superconductivity in relativistic fermion systems, *Physics Reports.* **107**(6), 325–385 (1984). doi: https://doi.org/10.1016/0370-1573(84)90145-5. URL https://www.sciencedirect.com/science/article/pii/0370157384901455.

[14] For a review, see *Nature* **416**, 205–246 (2002).

[15] W. Ketterle and M. W. Zwierlein. Making, probing and understanding ultracold fermi gases. In *Proceedings of the International School of Physics "Enrico Fermi", Ultra-cold Fermi Gases*, eds. M. Inguscio, W. Ketterle, and C. Salomon, Vol. 164, pp. 95–287. IOS Press, Amsterdam (2008).

[16] S. Giorgini, L. P. Pitaevskii, and S. Stringari, Theory of ultracold atomic fermi gases, *Rev. Mod. Phys.* **80**(4), 1215–1274 (2008). doi: 10.1103/RevModPhys.80.1215.

[17] L. D. Carr, D. DeMille, R. V. Krems, and J. Ye, Cold and ultracold molecules: Science, technology and applications, *New J. Phys.* **11**(5), 055049 (2009). URL http://stacks.iop.org/1367-2630/11/i=5/a=055049.

[18] C. Chin, R. Grimm, P. Julienne, and E. Tiesinga, Feshbach resonances in ultracold gases, *Rev. Mod. Phys.* **82**, 1225–1286 (2010). doi: 10.1103/RevModPhys.82.1225. URL https://link.aps.org/doi/10.1103/RevModPhys.82.1225.

[19] K. Levin and R. G. Hulet, The Fermi Gases and Superfluids: Short Review of Experiment and Theory for Condensed Matter Physicists, ArXiv e-prints (2012). Chapter in *Contemporary Concepts of Condensed Matter Science*, Elsevier.

[20] D. Jaksch and P. Zoller, The cold atom Hubbard toolbox, *Ann. Phys.* **315**(1), 52–79 (2005). doi: https://doi.org/10.1016/j.aop.2004.09.010. URL https://www.sciencedirect.com/science/article/pii/S0003491604001782. Special Issue.

[21] M. Lewenstein, A. Sanpera, V. Ahufinger, B. Damski, A. Sen(De), and U. Sen, Ultracold atomic gases in optical lattices: Mimicking condensed matter physics and beyond, *Adv. Phys.* **56**(2), 243–379 (2007). doi: 10.1080/00018730701223200.

[22] I. Bloch, J. Dalibard, and W. Zwerger, Many-body physics with ultracold gases, *Rev. Mod. Phys.* **80**, 885–964 (2008). doi: 10.1103/RevModPhys.80.885. URL https://link.aps.org/doi/10.1103/RevModPhys.80.885.

[23] T. Esslinger, Fermi-hubbard physics with atoms in an optical lattice, *Annu. Rev. Condens. Matter Phys.* **1**, 129–152 (2010).

[24] D. M. Stamper-Kurn and M. Ueda, Spinor bose gases: Symmetries, magnetism, and quantum dynamics, *Rev. Mod. Phys.* **85**, 1191–1244 (2013). doi: 10.1103/RevModPhys.85.1191. URL http://link.aps.org/doi/10.1103/RevModPhys.85.1191.

[25] O. Dutta, M. Gajda, P. Hauke, M. Lewenstein, D.-S. Lühmann, B. A. Malomed, T. Sowiński, and J. Zakrzewski, Non-standard Hubbard models in optical lattices: A review, *Rep. Prog. Phys.* **78**(6), 066001 (2015). URL http://stacks.iop.org/0034-4885/78/i=6/a=066001.

[26] T. Kock, C. Hippler, A. Ewerbeck, and A. Hemmerich, Orbital optical lattices with bosons, *J. Phys. B* **49**(4), 042001 (2016). URL http://stacks.iop.org/0953-4075/49/i=4/a=042001.

[27] X. Li and W. V. Liu, Physics of higher orbital bands in optical lattices: A review, *Rep. Prog. Phys.* **79**(11), 116401 (2016). URL http://stacks.iop.org/0034-4885/79/i=11/a=116401.

[28] W. V. Liu and F. Wilczek, Interior gap superfluidity, *Phys. Rev. Lett.* **90**, 047002 (2003).

[29] E. Gubankova, W. V. Liu, and F. Wilczek, Breached pairing superfluidity: Possible realization in QCD, *Phys. Rev. Lett.* **91**, 032001 (2003).

[30] W. V. Liu, F. Wilczek, and P. Zoller, Spin-dependent Hubbard model and a quantum phase transition in cold atoms, *Phys. Rev. A* **70**, 033603 (2004).

[31] M. M. Forbes, E. Gubankova, W. V. Liu, and F. Wilczek, Stability criteria for breached pair superfluidity, *Phys. Rev. Lett.* **94**, 017001 (2005).

[32] S.-T. Wu and S. Yip, Superfluidity in the interior-gap states, *Phys. Rev. A* **67**, 053603 (2003).

[33] D. T. Son and M. A. Stephanov, Phase diagram of a cold polarized Fermi gas, *Phys. Rev. A* **74**, 013614 (2006). doi: 10.1103/PhysRevA.74.013614.

[34] K. Yang and S. Sachdev, Quantum criticality of a Fermi gas with a spherical dispersion minimum, *Phys. Rev. Lett.* **96**, 187001 (2006).

[35] S. Sachdev and K. Yang, Fermi surfaces and Luttinger's theorem in paired fermion systems, *Phys. Rev. B* **73**, 174504 (2006). URL doi: 10.1103/PhysRevB.73.174504.

[36] C. H. Pao, S.-T. Wu, and S. K. Yip, Superfluid stability in BEC-BCS crossover, *Phys. Rev. B* **73**, 132506 (2006).

[37] D. E. Sheehy and L. Radzihovsky, BEC-BCS crossover in "magnetized" Feshbach-resonantly paired superfluids, *Phys. Rev. Lett.* **96**, 060401 (2006).

[38] A. Bulgac, M. M. Forbes, and A. Schwenk, Induced p-wave superfluidity in asymmetric Fermi gases, *Phys. Rev. Lett.* **97**, 020402 (2006).

[39] G. Sarma, On the influence of a uniform exchange field acting on the spins of the conduction electrons in a superconductor, *Phys. Chem. Solid.* **24**, 1029 (1963).

[40] T.-L. Dao, M. Ferrero, A. Georges, M. Capone, and O. Parcollet, Polarized superfluidity in the attractive Hubbard model with population imbalance, *Phys. Rev. Lett.* **101**, 236405 (2008). doi: 10.1103/PhysRevLett.101.236405. URL https://link.aps.org/doi/10.1103/PhysRevLett.101.236405.

[41] J. Dukelsky, G. Ortiz, S. M. A. Rombouts, and K. Van Houcke, Integrable models for asymmetric Fermi superfluids: Emergence of a new exotic pairing phase, *Phys. Rev. Lett.* **96**, 180404 (2006). doi: 10.1103/PhysRevLett.96.180404. URL https://link.aps.org/doi/10.1103/PhysRevLett.96.180404.

[42] V. M. Stojanovic, W. V. Liu, and Y. B. Kim, Unconventional interaction between vortices in a polarized Fermi gas, *Ann. Phys.* **323**, 989 (2008).

[43] M. A. Tanatar, J. Paglione, S. Nakatsuji, D. G. Hawthorn, E. Boaknin, R. W. Hill, F. Ronning, M. Sutherland, L. Taillefer, C. Petrovic, P. C. Canfield, and Z. Fisk, Unpaired electrons in the heavy-fermion superconductor cecoin$_5$, *Phys. Rev. Lett.* **95**, 067002 (2005) doi: 10.1103/PhysRevLett.95.067002.

[44] M. Huang and I. Shovkovy, Gapless color superconductivity at zero and at finite temperature, *Nucl. Phys. A* **729**(2), 835–863 (2003). doi: https://doi.org/10.1016/j.nuclphysa.2003.10.005.

[45] I. Shovkovy and M. Huang, Gapless two-flavor color superconductor, *Phys. Lett. B* **564**(3), 205–211 (2003). doi: https://doi.org/10.1016/80370:2693(03)00748-2.

[46] P. F. Bedaque, H. Caldas, and G. Rupak, Phase separation in asymmetrical fermion superfluids, *Phys. Rev. Lett.* **91**, 247002 (2003).

[47] H. Caldas, Cold asymmetrical fermion superfluids, *Phys. Rev. A* **69**, 063602 (2004).

[48] W. Yi and L.-M. Duan, Detecting the breached pair phase in a polarized ultracold fermi gas, *Phys. Rev. Lett.* **97**, 120401 (2006).

[49] G.-D. Lin, W. Yi, and L.-M. Duan, Superfluiel shells for trapped fermions with mass and population imbalance, *Phys. Rev. A* **74**, 031604 (Sep, 2006).

© 2022 World Scientific Publishing Company
https://doi.org/10.1142/9789811251948_0014

A Musical Tribute to Anyons

Siddhardh C. Morampudi

*Center for Theoretical Physics, Massachusetts
Institute of Technology, Cambridge, MA 02139, USA*
msid@mit.edu

The theoretical concept of an anyon [1–3] is a simple, yet profound one. The diverse places where anyons pop up such as the fractional quantum Hall effect [3, 4] and quantum spin liquids [5, 6], alongside unforeseen practical uses such as topological quantum computing [3, 7, 8] is a source of much intrigue. There's a nice quote by Heinrich Hertz which comes to mind[a] — "One cannot escape the feeling that these mathematical formulae have an independent existence and an intelligence of their own, that they are wiser than we are, wiser even than their discoverers, that we get more out of them than was originally put into them." In a spirit of attempting to get even more out of these wise ideas, here is a musical tribute inspired by a Pauli X gate realized through anyons in a $\nu = 5/2$ fractional quantum Hall system made of interacting electrons (Fig. 1).

The various aspects of the physics suggest a natural structure to the piece. The gates in a topological quantum computer can be represented by knots of anyon worldlines and the Pauli X gate maps to four instruments. The time signature of 10/4 is suggested by the $\nu = 5/2$ quantum Hall setting. The Compton frequency of the electron transposed down to sensible frequencies lands exactly between an A and a $\sharp G$. This inspires a bitonal piece where the two notes act as the major and minor third in the key of F, with a piano and cello taking on the different roles. The two knots of the gate show up as places where the piano and cello exchange their keys (points A and F in the score). There is also a secret key change to Dflat (point B) since the $\sharp G$ and A can also be viewed as the 5th and augmented 5th of Dflat.

---

[a]One of Frank's favourite quotes.

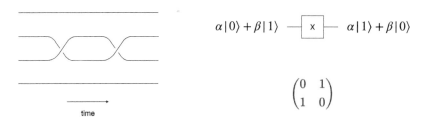

$$\alpha|0\rangle + \beta|1\rangle \longrightarrow \boxed{\text{x}} \longrightarrow \alpha|1\rangle + \beta|0\rangle$$

$$\begin{pmatrix} 0 & 1 \\ 1 & 0 \end{pmatrix}$$

Fig. 1.   (*Left*) Pauli X gate formed by a braid of 4 anyons [9,10]. (*Top right*) Action of the Pauli X gate on a state. (*Bottom right*) Matrix representation of the Pauli X gate.

In any case, for a reader uninterested in music theory and/or physics, the ears are the final judge.[b]

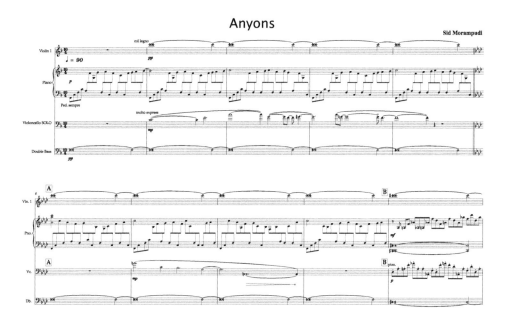

---

[b]An electronic rendering can be heard at https://www.youtube.com/channel/ UCIyLHTTEX6BR0Qdq9RVyBSQ.

Acknowledgments

The author has benefitted greatly from discussions with Anne Hager and Tim Maryon.

References

[1] J. M. Leinaas and J. Myrheim, On the theory of identical particles, *Il Nuovo Cimento B* (1971–1996) **37**, 1 (1977).

[2] F. Wilczek, Quantum mechanics of fractional-spin particles, *Phys. Rev. Lett.* **49**, 957 (1982).

[3] C. Nayak, S. H. Simon, A. Stern, M. Freedman, and S. D. Sarma, Non-abelian anyons and topological quantum computation, *Rev. Mod. Phys.* **80**, 1083 (2008).

[4] B. I. Halperin, Statistics of quasiparticles and the hierarchy of fractional quantized hall states, *Phys. Rev. Lett.* **52**, 1583 (1984).

[5] L. Savary and L. Balents, Quantum spin liquids: a review, *Rep. Prog. Phys.* **80**, 016502 (2016).

[6] J. Knolle and R. Moessner, A field guide to spin liquids, *Annual Review of Condensed Matter Physics* **10**, 451 (2019).

[7] A. Y. Kitaev, Fault-tolerant quantum computation by anyons, *Ann. Phys.* **303**, 2 (2003).

[8] G. P. Collins, Computing with quantum knots, *Sci. Amer.* **294**, 56 (2006).

[9] S. D. Sarma, M. Freedman, and C. Nayak, Topologically protected qubits from a possible non-abelian fractional quantum hall state, *Phys. Rev. Lett.* **94**, 166802 (2005).

[10] L. S. Georgiev. Topological quantum computation with non-abelian anyons in fractional quantum hall states. In *Quantum Systems in Physics, Chemistry, and Biology* (Springer 2017), pp. 75–94.

https://doi.org/10.1142/9789811251948_0015

Working with Frank Wilczek to Make the Invisible, Visible

Nathan Newman

Materials Science and Engineering Program, Arizona State University
Tempe, Arizona, USA
Nathan.Newman@asu.edu

I have had the pleasure of working with Frank Wilczek in a new venture called the Science Hub, or SciHub for short. Frank sees our mission as giving everyone superpowers. Frank says "there is more out there" and indicates "it would enrich all of our lives if we could visualize microwaves, IR and UV light and even magnetic and electric fields." So, we are doing this by making advanced portable, inexpensive instruments that can do this. Frank is motivated to commercialize our inventions for household, industrial, and educational applications. Although he values his great contributions in basic science, he explains that he is motivated to make devices that solve real-world problems, as his father did while working in an engineering laboratory.

As you might expect, Frank works in a very different way and at a different level than other scientists. Although I have had the great privilege to work with and "rub shoulders" with some of the great technical leaders of the 20th century, including those who established the foundations of what is now Silicon Valley and the foundations of superconductivity, I find Frank to be in a class by himself. Although he, like the others, is brilliant and has many interests far outside his own field, it seems that he spends much of time observing the beauty and elegance of the world around us. He almost seems to be mesmerized by it. I notice the same trait in many of the artists that I have known.

Unlike all technical presentation that I have been to, Frank's public lectures are delivered in a slow and thoughtful way, poetically. He gives his audience enough time to ponder between passages. I also notice that he asks uninhibited questions, much like we all did when we were very young.

I believe that the combination of these traits, combined with an unprecedented knowledge of advanced mathematics and physics, gives Frank the machinery to do the amazing things that he does every day.

Since the SciHub work is done with different goals and in a different environment than theoretical physics, I share some insight about this brilliant and kind gentleman scholar. To accomplish the SciHub goals of producing innovative end-products, Frank and I created an integrated research, teaching, outreach, and product development lab. We brought in world-renown designers Prof. Walter Herbst (*Business Week's* designer of decade award, Northwestern University) and Prof. Deana McDonagh (famous empathic designer, University of Illinois at Urbana-Champagne) to help round out our leadership team. The overall SciHub effort has involved over 75+ individuals from scientific, engineering, design and art disciplines working together in an integrated entrepreneurial environment. These include university faculty, staff and students, as well as local engineers, medical professionals, artists, and high school students.

Having such a diverse group working together has been productive, educational and a lot of fun for all of us.

And because the SciHub effort is within a university, one of our most important missions is to inspire and mentor the future generation of scientists, engineers and innovators. In our PHY 498 class for undergraduate students and PHY 598 for graduate students, Frank, Walter, Deanna and I teach a class on perception theory and product design. The students develop concepts and ideas there that they use to make prototypes of devices that address real-world problems. And this has worked surprisingly well. A good fraction of the SciHub products that we are currently developing have come from their projects.

In the class, Frank first teaches the fundamentals of perception theory, i.e. the physics and chemistry of sensing light, sound, and taste. In the lectures, Frank has mostly focused on the science behind color vision. He started with Maxwell's discovery that one can produce all visible colors by illuminating with various intensities of red, green, and blue light. And that this result from our eye's retina having 3 types of cone cell color detectors. Then, he takes the class through an elegant set of linear algebra steps using the properties of our light receptors to describe how to add in light of various wavelengths and intensities that do not change the color. A simple example is that you can add nearly equal intensities of red and green to yellow, without observing a color change. Such combinations of light illuminations are called metamers. Then, using the light absorption curves of the 3 different cones, Frank showed that subjects with normal-vision and those with each type of color blindness have very different sets of metamers. Using this approach, a team of SciHub students is building a new portable, inexpensive instrument that can detect the type, and even subtype, of color acuity of a subject faster and with greater resolution than the currently used methods. I can imagine that we will one day all go to our optometrist to get our eyeglasses with our prescription that corrects both our vision and optimizes our ability to see colors.

Following Frank's lectures, I teach the engineering principles behind seeing, hearing and taste sensing, with again the focus on light detection, from single photon detection to night-vision goggles. I also team with Professor Herbst to teach the industrial design process. Walter covers the critical marketing techniques needed to make a successful commercial product. Professor McDonagh teaches empathic design, focusing on how important it is for the designer to involve those that have a mental or physical limitation. Of course, the classes are aimed at the students, but I can say all of the faculty involved are learning in areas that they have not thought much about before. So, the faculty instructors all get involved in the student activities. Frank participated in a student exercise designed by Prof. McDonagh to emulate the challenges which a subject with restricted sight, hearing and motion experiences. Frank is pictured below in front of the screen, along with a couple of students behind him. I wasn't sure how he felt about the exercise, but after the class ended, I asked and he proclaimed, "The exercise was what I live for. It was beyond mind expanding."

Another exercise was done to appreciate the limitations of those paralyzed or with limited control of the upper body. The class was asked to draw their partner using a pencil and their feet. Again, Frank was very animated about the challenges and the outcome. I have kept it and in fact treasure it, not only because it is on interesting drawing but it reminds me how much Frank enjoys being out of his element. I have learned a lot from Frank, far beyond physics and science.

https://doi.org/10.1142/9789811251948_0016

From Schrödinger to Sisyphus

Antti J. Niemi

Nordita, Stockholm University and Uppsala University
Hannes Alfvéns väg 12, SE-106 91 Stockholm, Sweden
Pacific Quantum Center, Far Eastern Federal University
690950 Sukhanova 8, Vladivostok, Russia
School of Physics, Beijing Institute of Technology
Haidian District, Beijing 100081, China
antti.niemi@su.se

A Hamiltonian time crystal can emerge when a Noether symmetry is subject to a condition that prevents the energy minimum from being a critical point of the Hamiltonian. A somewhat trivial example is the Schrödinger equation of a harmonic oscillator. The Noether charge for its particle number coincides with the square norm of the wave function, and the energy eigenvalue is a Lagrange multiplier for the condition that the wave function is properly normalized. A more elaborate example is the Gross-Pitaevskii equation that models vortices in a cold atom Bose-Einstein condensate. In an oblate, essentially two-dimensional harmonic trap the energy minimum is a topologically protected timecrystalline vortex that rotates around the trap center. Additional examples are constructed using coarse grained Hamiltonian models of closed molecular chains. When knotted, the topology of a chain can support a time crystal. As a physical example, high precision all-atom molecular dynamics is used to analyze an isolated cyclopropane molecule. The simulation reveals that the molecular D_{3h} symmetry becomes spontaneously broken. When the molecule is observed with sufficiently long stroboscopic time steps it appears to rotate like a simple Hamiltonian time crystal. When the length of the stroboscopic time step is decreased the rotational motion becomes increasingly ratcheting and eventually it resembles the back-and-forth oscillations of Sisyphus dynamics. The stroboscopic rotation is entirely due to atomic level oscillatory shape changes, so that cyclopropane is an example of a molecule that can rotate without angular momentum. Finally, the article is concluded with a personal recollection how Frank's and Betsy's Stockholm journey started.

1. Introduction

Wilczek [1] together with Shapere [2] envisioned a *time crystal* to be a state that extends the notion of spontaneous breakdown of space translation symmetry to include time translation symmetry. They argued that if time translation symmetry becomes spontaneously broken, the lowest energy state of a physical system can no longer be time independent but has to change with time. If the symmetry breaking leaves behind a discrete group the ensuing time evolution will be periodic, and in analogy with space crystals we have a time crystal.

The proposal drew immediate criticism: In a canonical Hamiltonian setting the generator of time translations is the Hamiltonian itself. Thus energy is a conserved charge. But if time translation symmetry becomes spontaneously broken, the ground state energy can no longer be a conserved quantity. Accordingly, a time crystal must be impossible in any kind of isolated and energy conserving physical system, governed by autonomous Hamiltonian equation of motion [3, 4, 5].

As a consequence the search of spontaneously broken time translation symmetry focused on driven, non-equilibrium quantum systems [6, 7, 8, 9, 10, 11, 12]. The starting point is a many-body system with intrinsic dynamics governed by a time independent Hamiltonian H. The system is then subjected to an external explicitly time periodic driving force, with period T, that derives from an extrinsic time dependent potential $U(t + T) = U(t)$. The total Hamiltonian is the sum of the two $H_{tot}(t) = H + U(t)$ so that the total Hamiltonian is also explicitly time dependent, with the same period T of the drive. Floquet theory asserts that there can be solutions to the corresponding time dependent Schrödinger equation, with a time period that is different from T where the difference is due to a Floquet index. As a consequence it is plausible that in such a periodically driven many-body system, a spontaneous self-organization of time periodicity takes place so that the system starts evolving with its own characteristic period, which is different from that of the external driving force. It was first shown numerically that this kind of self-organisation can take place in certain many-body localized spin systems [6, 7, 8, 9, 10, 11, 12]. Experiments were then performed in appropriate material realizations [13, 14, 15] and they confirmed the presence of sustained collective oscillations with a time period that is indeed different from the period of the external driving force. It is now widely accepted that this kind of driven non-equilibrium Floquet time crystals do exist, but the setting is quite distant from Wilczek's original idea.

Here I describe how, in spite of the *No-Go* arguments, *genuine* (semi)classical and quantum Hamiltonian time crystals do exist[16, 17, 18]. They could even be widespread. I start with an explicit *proof-of-concept* construction that shows how to go around the *No-Go* arguments: I show that whenever a Hamiltonian system supports conserved Noether charges that are subject to appropriate conditions, the lowest energy ground state can be both time dependent and have an energy value that is conserved. This can occur whenever the lowest energy ground state, as a consequence of the conditions, is not a critical point of the Hamiltonian. I explain how such a time dependent ground state can be explicitly constructed by the methods of constrained optimization [19, 20], using the Lagrange multiplier theorem [21]. Whenever the solution for *any* Lagrange multiplier is non-vanishing, the lowest energy ground state is time dependent: A time crystal is simply a time dependent symmetry transformation that converts the time evolution of a Hamiltonian system into an equivariant time evolution. In particular, since time translation symmetry is not spontaneously broken but equivariantized, unlike in the case of conventional spontaneous symmetry breaking now there is no massless Goldstone boson that can be associated with a time crystal. But the two concepts can become related in a limit where the period of a time crystal goes to infinity and its energy approaches a (degenerate) critical point of the Hamiltonian.

I present a number of examples, starting with the time dependent Schrödinger equation of a harmonic oscillator. I continue with the Gross-Pitaevskii equation that models vortices in a cold atom Bose-Einstein condensate, and with a generalized Landau-Lifschitz equation that can describe closed molecular chains in a coarse grained approximation. I then analyze cyclopropane as an actual molecular example of timecrystalline Hamiltonian dynamics. For this I employ high precision all-atom molecular dynamics to investigate the ground state properties of a single isolated cyclopropane molecule. I conclude that the maximally symmetric configuration, with the D_{3h} molecular symmetry, can become spontaneously broken. I follow the time evolution of the minimum energy configuration stroboscopically, at very low but constant internal temperature values. I find that with a proper internal temperature and for sufficiently long stroboscopic time steps the molecule becomes a Hamiltonian time crystal with time evolution that is described by the generalization of the Landau-Lifschitz equation. But when the length of the stroboscopic time step is decreased, there is a cross-over transition to an increasingly ratcheting time evolution. In the limit where the stroboscopic time step is very small the motion of the cyclopropane molecule resembles Sisyphus dynamics [22]. I propose that this kind of cross-over transition between the Sisyphus dynamics that describes the limit of very short stroboscopic time steps, and the uniform timecrystalline dynamics that describes the limit of very long stroboscopic time steps, is a universal phenomenon. It exemplifies that the coarse graining of an apparently random microscopic many-body system can lead to a separation of scales and self-organization towards an effective theory Hamiltonian time crystal.

Finally, the rotational motion that I observe in a cyclopropane in the limit of long stroboscopic time steps, can occur even with no angular momentum. Thus, cyclopropane is a molecular level example of a general phenomenon of rotation by shape deformation, and without any angular momentum: The short time scale vibrational motions of the individual atoms that are driven e.g. by thermal or maybe even by quantum mechanical zero point fluctuations can become converted into a large scale rotational motion of the entire molecule, even when there is no angular momentum. This kind of phenomenon was first predicted by Guichardet[23], and independently by Shapere and Wilczek[24], and an early review can be found in [25].

2. Hamiltonian Time Crystals

A Hamiltonian time crystal describes the minimum of a Hamiltonian that is not a critical point of the Hamiltonian. To show how this can occur, I start with the Hamiltonian action

$$S = \int dt \, p_i \dot{q}_i - H(p,q) \tag{1}$$

where (p_i, q_i) $(i, j = 1, \ldots, N)$ are the local Darboux coordinates with non-vanishing Poisson bracket

$$\{q_i, p_j\} = \delta_{ij} \tag{2}$$

and Hamilton's equation is

$$\frac{dq_i}{dt} = \{q_i, H\} = \frac{\partial H}{\partial p_i}$$
$$\frac{dp_i}{dt} = \{p_i, H\} = -\frac{\partial H}{\partial q_i} \tag{3}$$

On a compact closed manifold the minimum of $H(p,q)$ is also its critical point, and in that case the Hamiltonian can not support any time crystal [3, 4, 5]. Thus for a time crystal we need additional structure, and for this I focus on a canonical Hamiltonian system that is subject to appropriate conditions

$$G_a(p,q) - g_a = 0 \quad a = 1, \ldots, n \leq N \tag{4}$$

where the g_a are some constants and the G_a's define a Noether symmetry,

$$\{G_a, G_b\} = f_{abc} G_c \quad \text{for all } a, b, c$$
$$\{G_a, H\} = 0 \tag{5}$$

I then search for a solution to the following problem [17]:

First, find a minimum of $H(p,q)$ that is subject to appropriate conditions (4) but is not a critical point of $H(p,q)$. Then, solve (3) with this minimum as the initial condition.

The first step is a classic problem in constrained optimization [19, 20] and it can be solved using the Lagrange multiplier theorem [21]. The theorem states that the minimum of H can be found as a critical point of

$$H_\lambda(p,q;\lambda) = H(p,q) + \lambda_a(G_a(p,q) - g_a) \tag{6}$$

where the λ_a are independent, *a priori* time dependent auxiliary variables. The critical point of (6) is a solution of

$$\frac{\partial H}{\partial p_i} + \lambda_a \frac{\partial G_a}{\partial p_i} = 0$$

$$\frac{\partial H}{\partial q_i} + \lambda_a \frac{\partial G_a}{\partial q_i} = 0 \tag{7}$$

$$G_a(p,q) = g_a$$

Since the number of equations (7) equals the number of unknowns (p, q, λ) a solution $(p^\star, q^\star, \lambda^\star)$ including the Lagrange multiplier, can be found at least in principle. Under proper conditions, in particular if $H(p,q)$ is strictly convex and the $G^a(p,q)$ are affine functions, existence and uniqueness theorems can also be derived. But if there are more than one solution I choose the one with the smallest value of $H(p,q)$.

Suppose the solutions $\lambda_a^\star$ for the Lagrange multipliers do not all vanish. By combining (7) with (3) I conclude that I have a time crystal[17] with the initial condition

$$p_i(t=0) = p_i^\star \;\&\; q_i(t=0) = q_i^\star \;\&\; \lambda_a(t=0) = \lambda_a^\star \tag{8}$$

and with the time evolution

$$\frac{dq_i}{dt} = -\lambda_a^\star \frac{\partial G_a}{\partial p_i} = -\lambda_a^\star \{q_i, G_a\}$$

$$\frac{dp_i}{dt} = \lambda_a^\star \frac{\partial G_a}{\partial q_i} = -\lambda_a^\star \{p_i, G_a\} \tag{9}$$

and the Lagrange multipliers can be shown to be time independent $\lambda_a(t) \equiv \lambda_a^\star$. In particular, the timecrystalline evolution (9) determines a time dependent symmetry transformation of the minimum energy configuration (8), one that is generated by the linear combination

$$G_a^\lambda = \lambda_a^\star G_a$$

of the Noether charges.

Since the Hamiltonian H has no explicit time dependence I immediately conclude that the energy of the time crystal is a conserved quantity

$$\frac{dH}{dt} = -\lambda_a^\star \{H, G_a\} = 0$$

This contrasts some of the early arguments, to exclude a time crystal on the grounds that the minimum energy should be time dependent.

In the sequel I consider exclusively such energy conserving Hamiltonian time crystals, with a time evolution that is a symmetry transformation.

3. Schrödinger as Time Crystal

For a simple example of the general formalism, I start with the following canonical action

$$S = \int dt d\mathbf{x} \{\bar\psi(i\partial_t)\psi - \bar\psi(-\nabla^2 + |\mathbf{x}|^2)\psi\} \tag{10}$$

in D space dimensions. This action yields the non-vanishing Poisson bracket

$$\{\bar\psi(\mathbf{x}_1), \psi(\mathbf{x}_2)\} = -i\delta(\mathbf{x}_1 - \mathbf{x}_2) \tag{11}$$

The Hamiltonian energy is

$$H = \int d\mathbf{x}\, \bar\psi(-\nabla^2 + |\mathbf{x}|^2)\psi \tag{12}$$

and Hamilton's equation coincides with the time dependent Schrödinger equation

$$i\partial_t \psi = -\nabla^2 \psi + |\mathbf{x}|^2 \psi \tag{13}$$

The Hamiltonian is strictly convex and its unique critical point is the absolute minimum

$$\psi(\mathbf{x}) = 0$$

At this point I have an example of the situation governed by (3). In particular, there is no time crystal.

To obtain a time crystal, I follow the general formalism of the previous section: I introduce the square norm

$$N = \int d\mathbf{x}\, \bar{\psi}\psi \tag{14}$$

This is the Noether charge for the symmetry of (10) under a phase rotation, and I subject it to the following familiar condition (4),

$$G_1 \equiv N - 1 = \left(\int d\mathbf{x}\, \bar{\psi}\psi\right) - 1 = 0 \tag{15}$$

I then proceed with the Lagrange multiplier theorem and search for the critical point of the corresponding functional (6)

$$H_E = \int d\mathbf{x}\, \bar{\psi}(-\nabla^2 + |\mathbf{x}|^2)\psi - E\left(\int d\mathbf{x}\, \bar{\psi}\psi - 1\right)$$

where $E \equiv -\lambda$ is the Lagrange multiplier: The corresponding equations (7) coincide with the time independent Schrödinger equation for a harmonic oscillator

$$-\nabla^2\psi + |\mathbf{x}|^2\psi = E\psi$$

$$\int d\mathbf{x}\, \bar{\psi}\psi = 1$$

In general there are many solutions, all the harmonic oscillator eigenstates are solutions. But I pick up the solution $(\psi_{min}^\star(\mathbf{x}), E_{min}^\star)$ that minimizes the energy (12). This is exactly the textbook lowest energy ground state wave function $\psi_{min}^\star(\mathbf{x})$ of the D dimensional harmonic oscillator, and $E_{min}^\star$ is the corresponding lowest energy eigenvalue.

In line with (8), (9) I can write the time dependent Schrödinger equation (13) as follows,

$$i\partial_t\psi = E_{min}^\star\{N, \psi\} \equiv E_{min}^\star\left\{\int \bar{\psi}\psi, \psi\right\} \quad \text{with} \tag{16}$$

$$\psi(\mathbf{x}, t = 0) = \psi_{min}^\star(\mathbf{x})$$

That is, the time evolution of the harmonic oscillator wave function is a symmetry transformation generated by the Noether charge N i.e. a phase rotation, with the familiar solution

$$\psi(\mathbf{x}, t) = e^{-iE_{min}^\star t}\, \psi_{min}^\star(\mathbf{x}) \tag{17}$$

Normally, a time dependent phase factor is not an observable. But it can be made so, e.g. in a proper double slit experiment. Note that unlike in the case of standard spontaneous symmetry breaking, even though time translation invariance is spontaneously broken into an *equivariant* time translation, there is no Goldstone boson in a quantum harmonic oscillator.

The previous example is *verbatim* a realization of the general formalism in Sec. 2. Albeit quite elementary in its familiarity and simplicity, it nevertheless makes the point. Conditions such as (4) on Noether charges are commonplace, they often have a pivotal role in specifying the physical scenario. When that happens, a time crystal can appear. Moreover, without additional structure the appearance of a time crystal does not entail the emergence of a massless Goldstone boson: A time crystal does not break the time translation symmetry. Instead, it equivariantizes a time translation into a combination of a time translation and a symmetry transformation.

4. Nonlinear Schrödinger and Time Crystalline Vortices

I now proceed with additional examples of the general formalism. For this I observe that besides phase rotations generated by the Noether charge N, the Schrödinger action (10) has also a Noether symmetry under space rotations. Accordingly I introduce the corresponding Noether charges

$$\mathbf{L} = \int d\mathbf{x} \bar{\psi}(-i\mathbf{x} \wedge \nabla)\psi$$

Their Poisson brackets coincide with the Lie algebra $SO(D)$ in D dimensions, and have vanishing Poisson brackets with the conserved charge (14),

$$\{\mathbf{L}, N\} = 0$$

I follow the general formalism: I impose additional conditions to the harmonic oscillator using the maximal commuting subalgebra of space rotations; in three dimensions this amount to the familiar conditions $\mathbf{L}^2 = l(l+1)$ and $L_z = m$ with $l \in \mathbb{Z}^+$ and $m \in \mathbb{Z}$ and $|m| \leq l$. I can take results from any quantum mechanics textbook and confirm that all the higher angular momentum eigenstates of the harmonic oscillator yield the appropriate minimum energy solutions of the time dependent Schrödinger equation.

For a more elaborate structure, I introduce a quartic self-interaction and consider the following nonlinear Schrödinger action,

$$S = \int dt d\mathbf{x} \left\{ \bar{\psi}(i\partial_t)\psi - \bar{\psi}(-\nabla^2 + |\mathbf{x}|^2)\psi - \frac{g}{2}(\bar{\psi}\psi)^2 \right\} \tag{18}$$

This action also supports both N and $\mathbf{L}$ as conserved Noether charges. It defines the Gross-Pitaevskii model that describes e.g. the Bose-Einstein condensation of cold alkali atoms at the level of a mean field theory [26], with $g > 0$ the quartic nonlinearity models short distance two-body repulsion. For clarity I specify to two space dimensions so that there is only one conserved charge $L \equiv L_z$. The set-up is that of a spheroidal, highly oblate three dimensional trap, with atoms confined to a disk by a very strong trap potential in the z-direction, and much weaker harmonic trap potential in the (x, y) direction. Thus, besides the condition (15) I also introduce the following condition

$$G_2 \equiv L_z - l_z = \int dx dy \; \bar{\psi}(-i\mathbf{x} \times \nabla)\psi - l_z = 0 \qquad (19)$$

so that I have the scenario (4), (5) with two Noether charges.

I keep the normalization (15) but I leave the numerical value l_z of the angular momentum as a free parameter. The choice (15) is entirely for convenience: I can always rescale the square norm to set N to any non-vanishing value, and compensate for this by adjusting the length and time scales. But l_z and the parameter g in (18) remain as freely adjustable parameters [27]. Note that even though the microscopic, individual atom angular momentum is certainly quantized, the macroscopic angular momentum L_z does not need to be quantized: In applications to cold atoms the wave function $\psi(x, y)$ is a macroscopic condensate wave function that describes a very large number of atoms. Thus, it can support arbitrary values of the macroscopic angular momentum L_z.

Following [27] I search for a solution of the nonlinear time dependent Schrödinger equation of (18) a.k.a. the Gross-Pitaevskii equation

$$i\partial_t \psi = -\nabla^2 \psi + |\mathbf{x}|^2 \psi + g|\psi|^2 \psi \qquad (20)$$

that minimizes the Hamiltonian i.e. energy

$$H = \int d\mathbf{x} \left\{ \bar{\psi}(-\nabla^2 + |\mathbf{x}|^2)\psi + \frac{g}{2}(\bar{\psi}\psi)^2 \right\} \qquad (21)$$

subject to the two conditions (15) and (19). The Hamiltonian is strictly convex, its global minimum coincides with the only critical point $\psi(\mathbf{x}) \equiv 0$. But when it is subject to the conditions (15) and (19) the minimum does not longer need to be a critical point. Instead, the Lagrange multiplier theorem states that the minimum is a critical point $(\psi^\star, \lambda_1^\star, \lambda_2^\star)$ of

$$H_\lambda = H + \lambda_1 G_1 + \lambda_2 G_2 \qquad (22)$$

That is, the minimum is a solution of

$$\frac{\delta H_\lambda}{\delta \psi} = -\nabla^2 \psi + |\mathbf{x}|^2 \psi + g|\psi|^2 \psi + \lambda_1 \psi + \lambda_2(-i\mathbf{x} \times \nabla)\psi = 0$$

$$\frac{\delta H_\lambda}{\delta \lambda_1} = \int d\mathbf{x} \, \bar{\psi}\psi - 1 = 0 \tag{23}$$

$$\frac{\delta H_\lambda}{\delta \lambda_2} = \int d\mathbf{x} \, \bar{\psi}(-i\mathbf{x} \times \nabla)\psi - l_z = 0$$

If there are several solutions, I choose $(\psi^\star, \lambda_1^\star, \lambda_2^\star)$ for which $H(\psi)$ has the smallest value. The minimum energy $\psi^\star(\mathbf{x})$ then defines the initial condition

$$\psi(\mathbf{x}, t = 0) = \psi^\star(\mathbf{x}) \tag{24}$$

for the putative timecrystalline solution of (20); recall that the corrresponding Lagrange multipliers are space-time independent, $\lambda_{1,2}(\mathbf{x}, t) \equiv \lambda_{1,2}^\star$.

Remarkably, when I combine (23) and (20), the *nonlinear* time evolution equation of $\psi^\star(\mathbf{x})$ becomes converted to the following *linear* time evolution equation

$$i\partial_t \psi = -\lambda_1^\star \psi + i\lambda_2^\star \mathbf{x} \times \nabla \psi \equiv -\lambda_1^\star \{G_1, \psi\} - \lambda_2^\star \{G_2, \psi\} \tag{25}$$

This is the equation (9) in the present case. In particular, (25) states that the time evolution of $\psi^\star(\mathbf{x})$ is a symmetry transformation; the pertinent symmetry is a combination of phase rotation by N and a spatial rotation by L_z.

Since the Hamiltonian H has vanishing Poisson brackets with both G_1 and G_2, the energy is conserved during the timecrystalline evolution,

$$\frac{d}{dt}H = \lambda_1^\star \{H, G_1\} + \lambda_2^\star \{H, G_2\} = 0$$

The solutions of (23), (20) describe vortices that rotate uniformly, with angular velocity $-\lambda_2^\star$ around of the trap center. For this I define

$$\mathbf{L}_z = -i\mathbf{x} \times \nabla \quad \& \quad \mathbf{A} = \nabla \tan^{-1}\left(\frac{x}{y}\right)$$

to write (25) as follows:

$$i\partial_t \psi = -\lambda_2^\star \left(\mathbf{L}_z + \frac{\lambda_1^\star}{\lambda_2^\star}\mathbf{x} \times \mathbf{A} \right) \psi \equiv \omega \mathbf{L}_z^{\text{cov}} \psi \tag{26}$$

Here $\mathbf{L}_z^{\text{cov}}$ is the covariant angular momentum that generates the rotations around the trap center in the presence of the "analog gauge field" $\mathbf{A}$. Note that $\mathbf{A}$ supports a "magnetic" flux with "strength" $\lambda_1^\star/\lambda_2^\star$ along the z-axis, that can have non-integer values. Notably, $\mathbf{L}_z^{\text{cov}}$ has the same form as the

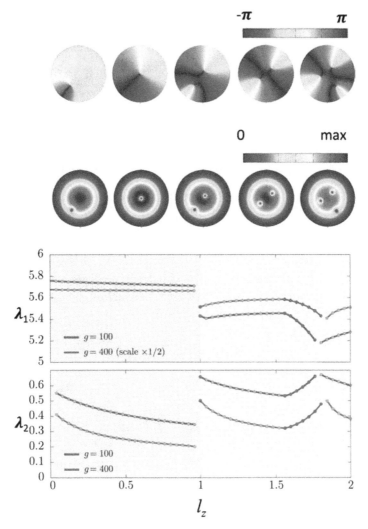

Fig. 1.   The first line shows the phase of the wave function $\psi^\star(\mathbf{x}, t)$. The second line shows the density $|\psi^\star(\mathbf{x}, t)|$ for five representative instantaneous minimum energy vortex solutions of (20), (24): From left to right $0 < l_z < 1.0$, $l_z = 1$, $0 < l_z < 1.5$, $1.5 < l_z < 1.8$, $1.8 < l_z < 2.0$; the numerical values $1.5, 1.8$ are approximative, and depend on the coupling g. The vortices rotate around the trap center with angular velocity determined by $\lambda_2^\star$. In these figures the value of coupling is $g = 400$ which is representative for cold atom Bose-Einstein condensates [27]. The bottom panels show the evolution of Lagrange multipliers $\lambda_{1,2}^\star$ for $g = 100$ and $g = 400$.

angular momentum operator introduced by Wilczek [28, 29], in the case of an anyon pair, in terms of the relative coordinate.

Figure 1 summarizes the results from the numerical investigations in [27]. The number of vortices and their relative positions including the distances from the trap center, depend on the free parameter l_z. The two top lines of Fig. 1 show how the phase and the cores of the vortex structure evolve for $0 < l_z < 2$. The bottom panels show the corresponding values of the Lagrange multipliers $\lambda_1^\star$ and $\lambda_2^\star$. Remarkably, when $l_z \to 0$ neither of these multipliers vanish,

$$\lim_{l_z \to 0} \lambda_{1,2}^\star(l_z) \neq 0 \qquad (27)$$

Since $\lambda_2^\star$ determines the angular velocity around the trap center (26), this means that for any $l_z \neq 0, 1$ the minimum energy solution describes a rotating vortex configuration.

For $l_z = 1$ the vortex core coincides with the trap center, only its phase has time dependence. For $l_z = 0$ the minimum energy solution is a real valued function, up to a constant phase factor. For $0 < |l_z| < 1$ the distance between the vortex core, located at point $\mathbf{p} \in \mathbb{R}^2$, and the trap center increases as $|l_z|$ decreases. Notably, the limit $l_z \to 0$ is discontinuous and to inspect this I introduce the superfluid velocity

$$\mathbf{v}(\mathbf{x}, t) = \nabla \arg[\psi](\mathbf{x}, t) \qquad (28)$$

and I define its integer valued circulation

$$i_\mathbf{v}(\mathbf{p}; \Gamma) = \frac{1}{2\pi} \oint_\Gamma d\boldsymbol{\ell} \cdot \mathbf{v} \qquad (29)$$

where Γ is a closed trajectory on the plane that does not go through any singular point of $\mathbf{v}(\mathbf{x}, t)$. For any given $l_z \neq 0$ I can always choose Γ to be a circle around the trap center and with a large enough radius, so that the core $\mathbf{p}$ of a given vortex is inside this circle. For a single vortex the value of (29) is $i_\mathbf{v}(\mathbf{p}; \Gamma) = \pm 1$, with positive sign for $l_z > 0$ and negative for $l_z < 0$. For $l_z = 0$ the value of the integral (29) vanishes, and for this value the phase of $\psi(\mathbf{x}, t)$ can be chosen to vanish; the entire plane is a fixed point of (28) for $l_z = 0$.

The circulation (29) is an integer valued topological invariant. In particular it can not be continuously deformed as a function of l_z, when l_z varies between $i_\mathbf{v}(\mathbf{p}; \Gamma) = +1$ for $l_z > 0$ and $i_\mathbf{v}(\mathbf{p}; \Gamma) = -1$ for $l_z < 0$. When $|l_z|$ continues to increase to values $|l_z| > 1$ the value of (29) increases but always in integer steps, as new vortex cores enter inside the (sufficiently large radius) circle Γ. Thus the vortex structures are topologically protected timecrystalline solutions of (20).

5. Timecrystalline Molecular Chains

I now proceed to a general class of Hamiltonian time crystals. The Hamiltonians describe discrete, piecewise linear chains[16, 18]. One can think of the vertices $\mathbf{r}_i$ $(i = 1, \ldots, N)$ as point-like interaction centers, they can e.g. model atoms or small molecules in a coarse grained description of a linear polymer. The links $\mathbf{n}_i = \mathbf{r}_{i+1} - \mathbf{r}_i$ between the vertices then model e.g. the covalent bonds, or peptide planes in the case of a protein chain. For clarity I only consider cyclic chains, with the convention $\mathbf{r}_{N+1} = \mathbf{r}_1$.

In an actual molecule, the covalent bonds are very rigid and oscillate rapidly, with a characteristic period as short as a few femtoseconds. I am mostly interested in timecrystalline dynamics at much longer time scales. Thus I assume that the lengths of the links are constant, and equal to their time averaged values in the underlying atomistic system. For simplicity I take all the links to have an equal length with the numerical value

$$|\mathbf{n}_i| \equiv |\mathbf{r}_{i+1} - \mathbf{r}_i| = 1 \tag{30}$$

The link variables $\mathbf{n}_i$ are the dynamical coordinates in my set-up. I subject them to the Lie-Poisson bracket [16]

$$\{n_i^a, n_j^b\} = \pm \epsilon^{abc} \delta_{ij} n_i^c \tag{31}$$

where I can choose either sign on the r.h.s. and for clarity I choose +-sign; the two signs are related by parity i.e. change in direction of $\mathbf{n}_i$. The bracket is designed to generate all possible local motions of the chain except for stretching and shrinking of its links,

$$\{\mathbf{n}_i, \mathbf{n}_k \cdot \mathbf{n}_k\} = 0$$

for all pairs (i, k), so that (30) is preserved for all times, independently of the Hamiltonian details.

Remarkably, the same bracket (31) appears in Kirchhoff's theory of a rigid body that moves in an unbounded incompressible and irrotational fluid that is at rest at infinity [30].

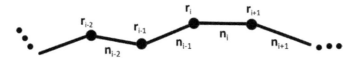

Fig. 2.   The dynamical variables $\mathbf{n}_i = \mathbf{r}_{i+1} - \mathbf{r}_i$ are links that connect the vertices $\mathbf{r}_i$ of a piecewise linear chain.

Hamilton's equation coincides with the Landau-Lifschitz equation

$$\frac{\partial \mathbf{n}_i}{\partial t} = \{\mathbf{n}_i, H\} = \mathbf{n}_i \times \frac{\partial H}{\partial \mathbf{n}_i} \tag{32}$$

and the condition that the chain is closed gives rise to the first class constraints

$$\mathbf{G} \equiv \sum_{i=1}^{N} \mathbf{n}_i = 0$$

$$\{G^a, G^b\} = \epsilon^{abc} G^c \tag{33}$$

$$\{\mathbf{G}, H\} = 0$$

The last equation restricts the form of Hamiltonian functions I consider. Such Hamiltonians $H_i(\mathbf{n})$ can be constructed e.g. as linear combinations of the Hamiltonians that appear in the integrable hierarchy of the Heisenberg chain:

$$H_1 = \sum_i a_i \mathbf{n}_i \cdot \mathbf{n}_{i+1}$$

$$H_2 = \sum_i b_i \mathbf{n}_i \cdot (\mathbf{n}_{i-1} \times \mathbf{n}_{i+1})$$

$$H_3 = \sum_i c_i \mathbf{n}_i \cdot (\mathbf{n}_{i-1} \times (\mathbf{n}_{i+1} \times \mathbf{n}_{i+2})) \tag{34}$$

$$H_4 = \sum_i d_i \mathbf{n}_{i-1} \cdot \mathbf{n}_{i+1}$$

etc.

where a_i, b_i, c_i, d_i are parameters. Furthermore,

$$\mathbf{r}_i - \mathbf{r}_j = \frac{1}{2}(\mathbf{n}_j + \cdots + \mathbf{n}_{i-1} - \mathbf{n}_i - \cdots - \mathbf{n}_{j-1}) \tag{35}$$

where I have symmetrized the distance, since there are two ways to connect $\mathbf{r}_i$ and $\mathbf{r}_j$ along the chain. As a consequence I can also introduce two-body interactions between distant vertices as contributions in a Hamiltonian, such as a combination of electromagnetic Coulomb potential and the Lennard-Jones potential:

$$U(\mathbf{x}_1, \ldots, \mathbf{x}_N) = \frac{1}{2}\sum_{\substack{i,j=1 \\ i \neq j}}^{N} \frac{e_i e_j}{|\mathbf{x}_i - \mathbf{x}_j|} + \frac{\epsilon}{2}\sum_{\substack{i,j=1 \\ i \neq j}}^{N} \left\{ \left(\frac{\sigma_P}{|\mathbf{x}_i - \mathbf{x}_j|}\right)^{12} - \left(\frac{\sigma_{vdW}}{|\mathbf{x}_i - \mathbf{x}_j|}\right)^{6} \right\}$$

$$\tag{36}$$

Here e_i is the charge at the vertex $\mathbf{x}_i$, σ_P characterizes the extent of the Pauli exclusion that prevents chain crossing, and σ_{vdW} is the range of the van der Waals interaction. All are commonplace in molecular modeling, and in particular they comply with the conditions (33).

Thus, the combination of (34) and (36) can be employed to construct realistic coarse grained Hamiltonian functions H that describe dynamics of (closed) molecular chains, in a way that only depends on the vectors $\mathbf{n}_i$.

Note in particular that (33) implies that an initially closed chain remains a closed chain during the time evolution (32).

I follow the general formalism of Sec. 2 to search for a time crystal as a minimum of $H(\mathbf{n})$ that is subject to the chain closure condition (33). The minimum is a critical point of the following version of (7), (9)

$$H_\lambda = H + \boldsymbol{\lambda} \cdot \mathbf{G}$$

$$\frac{\partial H}{\partial \mathbf{n}_i}\Big|_{\mathbf{n}^\star} = -\boldsymbol{\lambda}^\star \;\&\; \mathbf{G}(\mathbf{n}^\star) = 0 \tag{37}$$

$$\Rightarrow \frac{\partial H}{\partial t} = \boldsymbol{\lambda}^\star \times \mathbf{n}_i \;\&\; \mathbf{n}_i(t=0) = \mathbf{n}_i^\star$$

Whenever the solution $\boldsymbol{\lambda}^\star \neq 0$ I have a time crystal as a closed polygonal chain that rotates like a rigid body. The direction of its rotation and its angular velocity are both determined by the direction and the magnitude of the time independent vector $\boldsymbol{\lambda}^\star$. Thus, the present timecrystalline Hamiltonian framework provides an effective theory framework for modeling the autonomous dynamics of rotating cyclic molecules.

In practice, to construct the minimum of $H(\mathbf{n})$ I extend (32) to the Landau-Lifschitz-Gilbert equation for H_λ [17, 18]

$$\frac{\partial \mathbf{n}_i}{\partial t} = -\mathbf{n}_i \times \frac{\partial H_\lambda}{\partial \mathbf{n}_i} + \mu \mathbf{n}_i \times \left(\mathbf{n}_i \times \frac{\partial H_\lambda}{\partial \mathbf{n}_i} \right) \tag{38}$$

with $\mu > 0$ the large-t limit is a critical point of H_λ since (38) gives

$$\frac{dH_\lambda}{dt} = -\frac{\mu}{1+\mu^2} \sum_{i=1}^{N} \left| \frac{\partial \mathbf{n}_i}{\partial t} \right|^2 \tag{39}$$

so that the time evolution (38) proceeds towards decreasing values of H_λ and the flow continues until a critical point $(\mathbf{n}_i^\star, \boldsymbol{\lambda}^\star)$ is reached. Whenever more than one solution exist, I choose the one with smallest value of H.

5.1. *Simple examples*

5.1.1. *Triangular time crystal*

The first simple example is an equilateral triangle, with Hamiltonian[16]

$$H = \sum_{i=1}^{3} a_i \mathbf{n}_i \cdot \mathbf{n}_{i+1} + b\mathbf{n}_1 \cdot (\mathbf{n}_2 \times \mathbf{n}_3) \tag{40}$$

Hamilton's equation (32) gives

$$\partial_t \mathbf{n}_1 = \mathbf{n}_1 \times (a_1 \mathbf{n}_2 + a_3 \mathbf{n}_3) + b\mathbf{n}_1 \times (\mathbf{n}_2 \times \mathbf{n}_3)$$

$$\partial_t \mathbf{n}_2 = \mathbf{n}_2 \times (a_2 \mathbf{n}_3 + a_1 \mathbf{n}_1) + b\mathbf{n}_2 \times (\mathbf{n}_3 \times \mathbf{n}_1) \tag{41}$$

$$\partial_t \mathbf{n}_3 = \mathbf{n}_3 \times (a_3 \mathbf{n}_1 + a_2 \mathbf{n}_2) + b\mathbf{n}_3 \times (\mathbf{n}_1 \times \mathbf{n}_2)$$

By summing these equations I obtain

$$\frac{d}{dt}(\mathbf{n}_1 + \mathbf{n}_2 + \mathbf{n}_3) = 0$$

This confirms that an initially closed chain remains closed for all t. Moreover, for general choice of parameters (a_i, b) the r.h.s. of (41) never vanishes; the minimum of H for a closed chain is not a critical point of H; the minimum is time dependent i.e. a time crystal. The time crystal describes rotation with an angular velocity around an axis, with direction determined by the parameters. See Fig. 3.

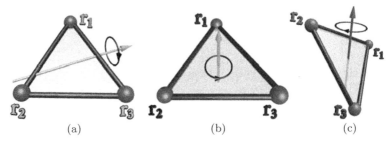

Fig. 3. (a): A timecrystalline triangle with $b = 0$ and rotation axis determined by the a_i. (b): A timecrystalline triangle with $a_i = 0$, $b \neq 0$ and the rotation axis is the symmetric normal to the triangular plane. (c): For generic (a_i, b) the rotation axis points to generic direction.

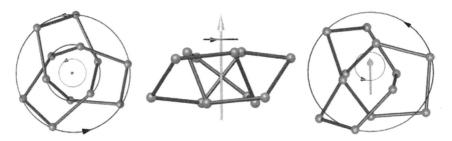

Fig. 4. A topological time crystal, with the topology of a trefoil knot, viewed from three different directions. The energy function is given by (42), the rotation axis points in the direction of $\boldsymbol{\lambda}^\star$ and the angular velocity is proportional to $|\boldsymbol{\lambda}^\star|$.

5.1.2. *Knotted time crystals*

The second concrete, simple example involves only the long range energy function (36), with Hamiltonian [18]

$$H = \frac{1}{2} \sum_{\substack{i,j=1 \\ i \neq j}}^{12} \left\{ \frac{1}{|\mathbf{r}_i - \mathbf{r}_j|} + \left(\frac{3/4}{|\mathbf{r}_i - \mathbf{r}_j|} \right)^{12} \right\} \tag{42}$$

The first term is a Coulomb repulsion between the vertices and the second term is a short range Pauli repulsion that prevents chain crossing; in an actual molecule the covalent bonds can not cross each other. The links connecting the $N = 12$ vertices are chosen to have the topology of a trefoil knot. The initial knot geometry is otherwise random. The Hamiltonian is first minimized using the Landau-Lifschitz-Gilbert equation (38). The set-up is an example of (32), (33). Figure 4 shows the resulting minimum energy time crystal, how it rotates according to (32) around the axis that coincides with the vector $\boldsymbol{\lambda}^\star$.

Various combinations of the local angles (34) and the long distance interactions (36) can be introduced. The ensuing energy functions can describe time crystalline structures, also with more elaborate knot topologies than a trefoil. At a higher level of realism, the interaction centers at the vertices can be given their internal atomic structure. Eventually, one ends up with a highly realistic all-atom molecular dynamics description of a polymer chain, which is the subject of the next section.

6. Cyclopropane and Sisyphus

6.1. *Cyclopropane as a time crystal*

All-atom molecular dynamics simulations are the most realistic descriptions that are presently available to model chain-like molecules. CHARMM [31] is an example of such a molecular dynamics energy function, and GROMACS[32] is a user-friendly package for performing simulations. A typical molecular dynamics energy function contains the following terms; here the summations cover all atoms of the molecule and can also extend e.g. over ambient water molecules.

$$V(\mathbf{x}_i) = \sum_{bonds} k_{bi}(l_i - l_{i0})^2 + \sum_{angles} k_{ai}(\theta_i - \theta_{i0})^2$$

$$+ \sum_{torsions} V_i^n [1 - \cos(n\omega_i - \gamma_i)]$$

$$+ \sum_{i \neq j} \left\{ \frac{e_i e_j}{|\mathbf{x}_i - \mathbf{x}_j|} + \frac{\epsilon_{ij}}{2} \left[\left(\frac{r_{\min}}{|\mathbf{x}_i - \mathbf{x}_j|} \right)^{12} - 2 \left(\frac{r_{\min}}{|\mathbf{x}_i - \mathbf{x}_j|} \right)^6 \right] \right\} \quad (43)$$

The first term describes the stretching and shrinking of covalent bonds; it is not present in (34), (36) where the Lie-Poisson bracket (31) preserves the bond lengths. The second and third terms account for the bending and twisting in the covalent bonds. These terms are akin quadratic/harmonic approximations to non-linear terms that are listed in (34). The last term is a combination of the electromagnetic and Lennard-Jones interactions (36). There can also be additional terms such as the Urey-Bradley interaction between atoms separated by two bonds (1,3 interaction), and improper dihedral terms for chirality and planarity; these can also be descrobed by the higher order terms in (34). The time evolution is always computed from Newton's equation, with the force field that derives from (43).

In the case of a molecular chain, a typical characteristic time scale for a covalent bond oscillation that is due to stretching and shrinking of the bond described by the first term in (43), can be as short as a few femtoseconds. In practical observations of molecular motions the time scales are usually much longer, and the observed covalent bond lengths commonly correspond to time averaged values. For the bending and twisting motions the characteristic time scales are much longer than for stretching and shrinking. Thus a separation of scales should take place so that an effective theory description becomes practical. Indeed, many phenomena that are duly consequences of the free energy (43) can often be adequately modeled by an effective theory description. The effective theory energy function can be a combination of terms such as those in (34), (36) and its dynamics can be described by the Lie-Poisson bracket (31), in a useful approximation.

To investigate how the separation of scales takes place, and how an effective theory description emerges, in [33] all-atom molecular dynamics has been

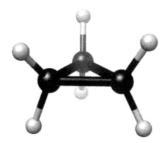

Fig. 5.   Cyclopropane C_3H_6 with full D_{3h} molecular symmetry.

used to simulate the ground state of an isolated cyclopropane molecule C_3H_6 shown in Fig. 5. The force field is CHARMM36m, in combination with GROMACS. The simulation starts with a search of the minimum energy configuration, at a given ultra low internal temperature factor value; very low temperature thermal oscillations could be interpreted as mimicking quantum oscillations in a semiclassical description. The initial atomic coordinates can be found from the PubMed site [34] where the positions of the carbon and hydrogen atoms are specified with 10^{-14} m precision. In [33] the structure is further optimized so that it describes a local minimum of the CHARMM36m energy function, with full D_{3h} molecular symmetry where the carbon-carbon bond angles are $60°$ and the hydrogen pairs are in full eclipse. Starting from this energy minimum all-atom trajectories are constructed, to simulate $10\,\mu s$ of cyclopropane dynamics, at different ultra low internal temperature factor values. The simulations use double precision floating point accuracy and the length of the simulation time step is $1.0 fs$; for the detailed set-up and for simulation details I refer to [33]. All the individual atom coordinates are followed and recorded, and analysed at different stroboscopic time steps $\Delta_s t$, during the entire $10\,\mu s$ molecular dynamics trajectory.

When the cyclopropane is simulated with the very low $\sim 0.067\,K$ internal temperature factor value, and the all the atom positions are observed at every $\Delta_s t = 100\,ns$ (or longer) stroboscopic time step, the molecule rotates uniformly at constant angular velocity. The axis of rotation coincides with the (time averaged) center of mass axis that is normal to the plane of the three carbon atoms. Remarkably, this stroboscopic rotational motion is *identical* to the motion of a triangular Hamiltonian time crystal shown in Fig. 3(b): The dynamics is described by the generalized Landau-Lifschitz equation (32), with the Hamiltonian H_2 in (34). The results confirm that the timecrystalline Hamiltonian H_2 is an effective theory for this stroboscopic motion, in the limit of long stroboscopic time steps.

6.2. *Spontaneous symmetry breaking*

Notably, the Lie-Poisson bracket (31) breaks parity; if the sign on the r.h.s. is changed, the rotation direction in Fig. 3)(b) also changes. Obviously something similar needs to take place in cyclopropane for it to rotate in a particular direction: The cyclopropane is *a priori* a highly symmetric molecule with D_{3h} molecular symmetry; the carbon-carbon bond angles are all 60° and the dihedrals of all hydrogen pairs are fully eclipsed. In this maximally symmetric state there can not be any unidirectional rotational motion around the molecular symmetry axis that is normal to the plane of carbons, as there is no way to select between clockwise and counterclockwise rotational direction. However, the bond angles are much smaller than the optimum 109.5° angles of a normal tetrahedral carbon atom, and there is considerable torsional strain between the fully eclipsed hydrogen pairs[35]. Thus one can expect that in the lowest energy ground state the D_{3h} symmetry becomes spontaneously broken. By rigidity of covalent bond lengths I expect that the symmetry breakdown should be mainly due to a twisting of the dihedral angles, between the hydrogen pairs. This spontaneous symmetry breakdown selects a rotation direction, since parity is no longer a symmetry. The simulation results that I have described show that this indeed occurs: The unidirectional rotation around the triangular symmetry axis in the limit of long stroboscopic time steps is a manifestation of broken parity.

A simple model free energy can be introduced, to demonstrate how the spontaneous symmetry breaking due to strain in hydrogen pair dihedral angles can take place. With θ_i ($i = 1, 2, 3$) the dihedrals, the free energy is

$$F(\theta_1, \theta_2, \theta_3) = \frac{1}{4} \sum_{i=1}^{3} g(\theta_i^2 - \alpha^2)^4 \tag{44}$$

The eclipsed configuration with all $\theta_i = 0$ is a local maximum, and a critical point of the free energy. The minimum of (44) occurs when $\theta_i = \pm\alpha$, the value of α corresponds to the optimal value of the dihedral angle for two staggered hydrogen pairs. But in the cyclopropane molecule the three dihedrals are subject to the condition

$$\theta_1 + \theta_2 + \theta_3 = 0 \tag{45}$$

Thus $\theta_i^{\min} = \pm\alpha$ is not achievable for non-vanishing α. Instead I need to find the minimum of (44) subject to the condition (45). This is (again) a problem in constrained optimization, so I search for critical points of

$$F_\lambda = \frac{1}{4} \sum_{i=1}^{3} g(\theta_i^2 - \alpha^2)^4 + \lambda(\theta_1 + \theta_2 + \theta_3)$$

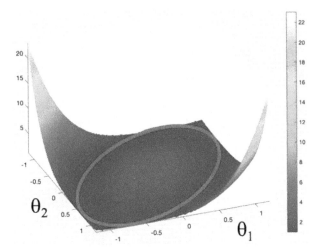

Fig. 6.   Free energy (44) with θ_3 given by (45), and its minimum.

with λ the Lagrange multiplier; I can rescale the angles, and set $a = g = 1$ in which case the critical points obey

$$\theta_i(\theta_i^2 - 1) + \lambda = 0 \qquad (46)$$

in addition of (45). I eliminate θ_3 and plot the minimum of the rescaled (44) as a function of θ_1 and θ_2. The result is shown in Fig. 6. The minimum forms a circular curve on the (θ_1, θ_2) plane around the origin. In particular, the D_{3h} symmetry becomes spontaneously broken, by the minimum. The Lagrange multiplier can be solved from (46). It is non-vanishing except when θ_1 has the value 0 or ± 1 and θ_2 is ± 1 or 0, respectively. The non-vanishing of λ is suggestive of a time crystal, in line with the general theory of Section 2.

6.3. *Sisyphus*

The Newtonian dynamics with the CHARMM36m force field is much more complex than the generalized Landau-Lifschitz evolution (32) with the Hamiltonian H_2 in (34). Thus one can not expect that the cyclopropane molecule continues to display the same uniform, timecrystalline rotational motion when one decreases the length of the stroboscopic time step $\Delta_s t$. Figure 7 shows how the rotational motion proceeds as function of the decreasing length of the stroboscopic time step; these figures display the instantaneous stroboscopic value of the rotation angle $\theta(t)$ around the normal axis of the carbon triangle.

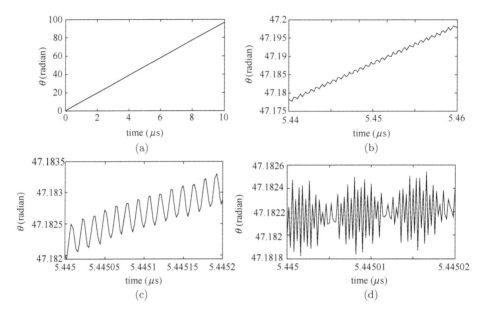

Fig. 7. The evolution of the cyclopropane rotation angle during a $10\,\mu s$ CHARMM36m simulation and with $T = 0.067K$ internal temperature factor value, recorded with decreasing stroboscopic time steps: a) The regime of uniform rotation, here with $\Delta_s t = 100\,ns$. b) and c) describe ratcheting regime, with $\Delta_s t = 20\,ps$ in b) and $\Delta_s t = 2.0\,ps$ in c). Finally d) with $\Delta_s t = 200\,fs$ is in the regime dominated by Sisyphus dynamics.

- Figure 7(a) shows the result for $\Delta_s t = 100ns$, when the effective theory description (32) with the Hamiltonian H_2 in (34) is accurate: The rotation is uniform, with a constant angular velocity.

- In Figure 7(b) the length of the stroboscopic time step is decreased to $\Delta_s t = 20\,ps$. There is a very small amplitude ratcheting, with an almost constant amplitude oscillations around the average value of the increasing rotation angle.

- In Figure 7(c) the stroboscopic time step is decreased to $\Delta_s t = 2.0\,ps$. The amplitude of ratcheting oscillations around the average value of θ has substantially increased: The molecule turns around regularly and rotates in the opposite direction, but at a slightly smaller relative value of angular velocity $\omega_s \equiv \dot{\theta}$. The period of ratcheting oscillations in $\theta(t)$ are also shorter than in Figure 7(b).

- Finally, in Fig. 7(d) the molecule is sampled with stroboscopic time steps $\Delta_s t = 200\,fs$. Now the motion is becoming more chaotic, it consists of a superposition of very rapid back-and-forth rotations with different amplitudes and frequencies, and with only a slow relative drift towards increasing values of $\theta(t)$.

The results shown in Fig. 7 demonstrate how the separation of scales takes place in the simulated cyclopropane: There is a continuous, smooth cross-over transition from a large-$\Delta_s t$ regime of a uniform timecrystalline rotation, through an intermediate $\Delta_s t$ regime with increasingly ratcheting rotational motion, to a small-$\Delta_s t$ regime that is dominated by rapid back-and-forth oscillations, with different amplitudes and frequencies. Remarkably, when the stroboscopic time step decreases, the time evolution of the cyclopropane becomes qualitatively increasingly similar to the Sisyphus dynamics reported in [22]. Thus, the Sisyphus dynamics appears to provide a microscopic level explanation how timecrystalline effective theory Hamiltonian dynamics emerges, at least in a small molecule such as cyclopropane.

6.4. *Rotation without angular momentum*

Newton's equation with the CHARMM36m all-atom molecular dynamics force field preserves the angular momentum, and angular momentum is also well preserved in a GROMACS numerical simulation. Since the initial cyclopropane has no angular momentum, the rapid back-and-forth oscillations and in particular the uniform timecrystalline rotational motion that is observed, are in apparent violation of angular momentum conservation. The resolution of the paradox is that the cyclopropane is not a rigid body. It is a deformable body, and a deformable body with at least three movable components can rotate simply by changing its shape [23, 24]. A falling cat is a good example, how it can maneuver and rotate in air to land on its feet.

In the case of a cyclopropane molecule, when the internal temperature factor has a non-vanishing value, the covalent bonds oscillate so that the shape of the molecule continuously changes; in an actual molecule there are also quantum mechanical zero-point oscillations. Such shape changes are minuscule, but over a long trajectory their effects can accumulate and self-organize into an apparent rotational motion. This is what is described in the Fig. 7.

The analysis of results in [33] confirm that the angular momentum of the simulated cyclopropane is conserved, and vanishes with numerical precision during the entire $10\,\mu s$ simulation trajectory. For this, one evaluates the accumulation of infinitesimal rotations, with each rotation corresponding to that of an instantaneous rigid body. An infinitesimal rigid body rotation can be defined using e.g. Eckart frames, in terms of the instantaneous positions and velocities of all the carbon and hydrogen atoms around the center of mass. In our simulations these are recorded at every $\Delta \tau = 10^{-15}\,fs$ time step n during the entire $10\,\mu s$ production run. The instantaneous values

$L(n)$ of the corresponding rigid body angular momentum component along the normal to the instantaneous plane of the three carbon atoms can then be evaluated, together with the corresponding instantaneous moment of inertia values $I(n)$. This gives the following instantaneous "rigid body" angular velocity values

$$\omega(n) = L(n)/I(n)$$

When these are summed up the result is the accumulated "rigid body" rotation angle, at each simulation step n:

$$\vartheta(n) = \omega(n)\Delta\tau + \vartheta(n-1) = \sum_{i=1}^{n} \frac{L(i)}{I(i)}\Delta\tau \tag{47}$$

In full compliance with the conservation of angular momentum and the vanishing of its initial value, it is found [33] that in all the $10\,\mu s$ production run simulations the accumulated values (47) always remains less than $\sim 10^{-6}$ radians, for all n, and Fig. 8 shows a typical example: There is no observable net rotation of the cyclopropane molecule due to "rigid body" angular momentum, with numerical precision. Accordingly any systematic rotational motion that exceeds $\sim 10^{-6}$ radians during a production run simulation must be emergent, and entirely due to shape deformations.

The original articles on rotation by shape deformations are [23, 24]. Reviews can be found in [25, 18]] and here I follow [18]:

Consider the (time) t-evolution of three equal mass point particles that form the corners $\mathbf{r}_i$ $(i = 1, 2, 3)$ of a triangle. I assume that there are no

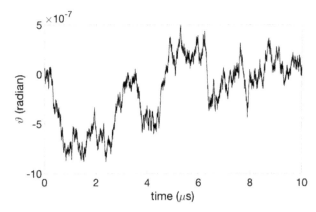

Fig. 8.   The evolution of the rigid body rotation angle $\vartheta(n)$ in (47), during a typical cyclopropane simulation.

external forces so that the center of mass does not move,

$$\mathbf{r}_1(t) + \mathbf{r}_2(t) + \mathbf{r}_3(t) = 0 \tag{48}$$

for all t. I also assume that the total angular momentum vanishes,

$$\mathbf{L} = \mathbf{r}_1 \times \dot{\mathbf{r}}_1 + \mathbf{r}_2 \times \dot{\mathbf{r}}_2 + \mathbf{r}_3 \times \dot{\mathbf{r}}_3 = 0 \tag{49}$$

I now show that nevertheless, the triangle can rotate by changing its shape. To describe this rotational motion, I place the triangle to the $z = 0$ plane and with the center of mass at the origin $(x, y) = (0, 0)$. Two triangles then have the same shape if they only differ by a rigid rotation on the plane, around the z-axis. I can describe shape changes by shape coordinates $\mathbf{s}_i(t)$ that I assign to each vertex of the triangle. They describe all possible triangular shapes, in an unambiguous fashion and in particular with no extrinsic rotational motion, when I demand that the vertex $\mathbf{s}_1(t)$ always lies on the positive x-axis with $s_{1x}(t) > 0$ and $s_{1y}(t) = 0$, and the vertex $\mathbf{s}_2(t)$ has $s_{2y}(t) > 0$ but $s_{2x}(t)$ can be arbitrary. The coordinates $\mathbf{s}_3(t)$ of the third vertex are then fully determined by the demand that the center of mass remains at the origin:

$$\mathbf{s}_3(t) = -\mathbf{s}_1(t) - \mathbf{s}_2(t)$$

Now, let the shape of the triangle change arbitrarily, but in a T-periodic fashion. As a consequence the $\mathbf{s}_i(t)$ evolve also in a T-periodic fashion,

$$\mathbf{s}_i(t + T) = \mathbf{s}_i(t)$$

as the triangular shape traces a closed loop Γ in the space of all possible triangular shapes.

At each time t the shape coordinates $\mathbf{s}_i(t)$ and the space coordinates $\mathbf{r}_i(t)$ are related by a rotation around the $z = 0$ plane,

$$\begin{pmatrix} r_{ix}(t) \\ r_{iy}(t) \end{pmatrix} = \begin{pmatrix} \cos\theta(t) & -\sin\theta(t) \\ \sin\theta(t) & \cos\theta(t) \end{pmatrix} \begin{pmatrix} s_{ix}(t) \\ s_{iy}(t) \end{pmatrix} \tag{50}$$

Initially $\theta(0) = 0$, but if there is any net rotation due to shape changes we have $\theta(T) \neq 0$ so that the triangle has rotated during the period, by an angle $\theta(T)$. I substitute (50) into (49) and I get

$$\theta(T) \equiv \int_0^T dt \, \frac{d\theta(t)}{dt} = \int_0^T dt \, \frac{\sum_{i=1}^3 \{s_{iy}\dot{s}_{ix} - s_{ix}\dot{s}_{iy}\}}{\sum_{i=1}^3 \mathbf{s}_i^2} \tag{51}$$

and in general this does not need to vanish, as I show in the next sub-section.

6.5. *Towards timecrystalline universality*

I now evaluate (51) in the case of a time dependent triangular structure, with three point-like interaction centers at the corners. The shape changes are externally driven so that the shape coordinates evolve as follows:

$$\mathbf{s}_1(t) = \frac{1}{\sqrt{3}} \begin{pmatrix} \cos[a \sin \omega_1 t] \\ 0 \end{pmatrix} \quad \& \quad \mathbf{s}_2(t) = \frac{1}{\sqrt{3}} \begin{pmatrix} \cos\left[a \sin \omega_2 t + \frac{2\pi}{3}\right] \\ \sin\left(\frac{2\pi}{3}\right) \end{pmatrix} \tag{52}$$

I choose $a = 0.1$ and $\omega_2 = 2\omega_1 = 3$, substitute in (51) and evaluate the time integral numerically. Figures 9(a)–(d) show how the angle $\theta(t)$ evolves, when observed with different stroboscopic time steps.

When I compare Figs. 7 and 9 I observe a striking qualitative similarity: Except for the scales, the corresponding panels are almost identical. In particular, even though the shape changes (52) are externally driven, at large stroboscopic time scales the time evolution again coincides with that of the autonomous Hamiltonian time crystal in Fig. 3(b).

The strong qualitative similarity between results in Figs. 7 and 9 proposes that the Sisyphus dynamics of [22] and the ensuing ratcheting at larger stroboscopic time scales, is akin a universal route, how an oscillatory short

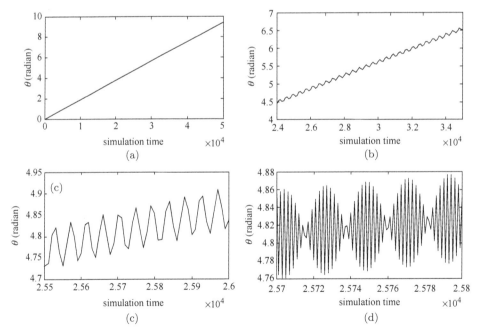

Fig. 9. The evolution of the angle $\theta(t)$ of (51) for the shape changes (52), and with stroboscopic time steps. In panel a) $\Delta_s t = 10^3$, In panel b) $\Delta_s t = 10^2$, In panel c) $\Delta_s t = 10$, and in panel d) $\Delta_s t = 1$.

time scale stroboscopic evolution becomes self-organized into a Hamiltonian time crystal, at large stroboscopic time scale.

Finally, when I expand the integrand (51), (52) in powers of the amplitude a, the result is

$$\frac{d\theta}{dt} = -\frac{1}{2}\omega_2 a \cos \omega_2 t + \frac{\sqrt{3}}{12} a^2 \{\omega_2 \sin 2\omega_2 t - \omega_1 \sin 2\omega_1 t\} - \frac{1}{8}\omega_2 a^3 \cos 3\omega_2 t$$

$$+ \frac{1}{16}\omega_2 a^3 \{\cos(\omega_2 + 2\omega_1)t + \cos(\omega_2 - 2\omega_1)t\} + \mathcal{O}(a^4) \tag{53}$$

Thus, exactly when $\omega_2 = \pm 2\omega_1$ will the large time limit of the rotation angle $\theta(t)$ increase linearly in time as follows,

$$\theta(t) \xrightarrow{\text{large}-t} \frac{1}{16}\omega_2 a^3 t \tag{54}$$

in line with Fig. 9(a). But when $\omega_2 \neq \pm 2\omega_1$ the large-T limit of the integral (51) vanishes, by Riemann's lemma. Similar high sensitivity of the rotation angle is also observed in the case of the cyclopropane, where the role of the parameter a is played by the internal temperature factor of the molecule.

7. Concluding Remarks

The concept of a time crystal has made a long journey. It started as a beautiful idea that was soon ridiculed as a fantasy. From there it has progressed to the frontline of theoretical physics research, with high expectations for remarkable future applications. But the notion is still very much under development. The conceptual principles are still under debate and remain to be finalized, there are several parallel and alternative lines of research to follow. The present article describes only my own personal way, how I try to understand what is a time crystal. My interest in the subject started from discussions with Frank, and I am only able to describe what I have learned myself, by doing things on my own, with Frank, and with my close colleagues. There is undoubtedly much that I have not covered, but I leave it to others who know things better.

Acknowledgements

I thank Anton Alekseev, Jin Dai, Julien Garaud, Xubiao Peng and Frank Wilczek for collaboration on various aspects of the original work described here. My research is supported by the Carl Trygger Foundation Grant CTS 18:276 and by the Swedish Research Council under Contract No. 2018-04411 and by Grant No. 0657-2020-0015 of the Ministry of Science and Higher Education of Russia. I also acknowledge COST Action CA17139.

Personal Recollections

I conclude with a short personal recollection of the remarkable way how Betsy and Frank have ended up, to spend part of their time in Sweden and Stockholm University.

I first met Betsy and Frank personally in Aspen, during the summer 1984 session. Incidentally, we overlapped there with Michael Green and John Schwarz, during the time when they gave birth to the modern string theory. At that time Frank and I shared a more modest interest, and we discussed certain ideas around the SU(3) Skyrme model. Unfortunately my self-confidence at the time was not at a level, to meet his challenges.

After Aspen we met several times, including Santa Barbara, Cambridge, Uppsala, Tours, Stockholm and elsewhere, not to forget their lovely summer house in New Hampshire. Our discussions were always very enjoyable. Frank even included me in his official delegation to attend the events during the Nobel Week, when he received the 2004 Physics Prize.

In 2007, around the time when Nordita was moving to Stockholm, Frank told me that he had plans for a sabbatical. I succeeded in attracting him to spend half a year in Sweden, jointly between Nordita and my Department at Uppsala University. The other half of his sabbatical he spent at Oxford University, where I also visited him. There, he told me about his dream to walk across Great Britain. Apparently he hatched the first, very early ideas of a time crystal during this walk. I now regret I did not ask to join him.

While in Uppsala, Frank and I got the idea to organize a Nobel Symposium in graphene. The Symposium took place in Summer 2010, only a few months before the discovery of graphene was awarded the Physics Nobel Prize: Ours was the first ever Nobel Symposium that took place the same year the Prize was awarded on the subject of a Symposium. I understand that the many great talks, walks and discussions during the Symposium helped to decide who got the Prize. Two years later, I hosted Frank when he became honorary doctor at Uppsala University. A little later Frank came back to Uppsala, this time to collect Nobel chocolates that he won from a bet with Janet Conrad, on the discovery of the Higgs boson.

Both Betsy and Frank seemed very happy with their sabbatical stay, and with all other experiences they had at Stockholm and Uppsala. So I started to talk with Frank about the idea, that they could spend a little longer time in Sweden, on a regular basis. In particular, I told Frank that the Swedish Research Council had occasional calls on a funding program for International Recruitments, with very generous conditions. In 2014 the opportunity raised: Soon after the Nobel Symposium on topological insulators at Högberga where Frank gave the summary talk, I learned that the call was again being opened, and that this was probably the last call in the program. I contacted Frank, now with more determination. He was at least lukewarm, so I proposed my colleagues at Uppsala University that we should make an application to try and recruit Frank. Initially, I received several very positive, in fact some enthusiastic, replies from my colleagues at the Department of Physics and Astronomy. But then came one strongly negative reply, from Maxim Zabzine who at the time was responsible for the administration of theoretical physics. Maxim stated that he did not want Uppsala University to make any effort, whatsoever, to apply for a Research Council grant for Frank.

I did not see any point to try and change Maxim's strong opinion, in particular since the deadline for the application was approaching. Instead, I immediately contacted Lars Bergström at Stockholm University. I asked him if Stockholm University would be willing to submit an application to the Research Council, on Frank's behalf. I reckon that I contacted Lars only two days before the Nobel Prize for Physics 2014 was announced. Lars was at the time the Permanent Secretary of the Nobel Physics Committee and for sure he had his hands full in preparing the announcement. However, already the next day I received a reply from Anders Karlhede, then Vice President of Stockholm University. Anders wrote that my proposal had been discussed with the President of Stockholm University Astrid Söderberg Widding, and that Stockholm University is delighted to submit an application to the Research Council.

Soon after the Nobel Prize in Physics 2014 was announced and Lars became more free, he and Anders started to work on the formal application; I understand they were also joined by Katherine Freese who was then Director of Nordita. At that time I was in China with Frank. Frank was on his first-ever trip to China, and I coordinated the visits in Beijing together with Vincent Liu. From Beijing we all continued to Hangzhou for the memorable inaugural events of Wilczek Quantum Center at Zhejiang Institute of Technology.

During our travel in China I had several long discussions with Frank about the Research Council grant application. He had his doubts, and I made my best to persuade him. I remember vividly the decisive discussion: After a breakfast at our hotel, a historic place that used to be Mao Zedong's favorite retreat at the West Lake in Hangzhou, Frank and I was sitting together in the lobby. In Stockholm, the Research Council application was ready to be submitted, the deadline was only a couple of days away. But Stockholm University still needed Frank to sign a formal letter of interest for the application, and Frank was hesitant. However, after some lengthy discussion I got his signature, and I sent the signed letter right away to Anders. In two months time we received a decision from the Research Council that Stockholm University's application for the International Recruitement Grant for Frank had been approved.

However, it was too early to call it a home run. For that, I still needed some advice from Anders Bárány, who is the creator of Nobel Museum. Anders came up with the brilliant idea, of a curator position for Betsy at Nobel Museum. To launch this, I teamed up with Gérard Mourou who invited Frank and Betsy, and a delegation from Nobel Museum, to the Symposium on Fresnel, Art and Light at Louvre in Paris. Frank gave a beautiful talk, and Betsy made contacts with Louvre art curators. With strong support from Astrid and Anders things worked out great for Betsy to start at the Nobel Museum, where her achievements inlcuded the most impressive Feynman Exhibition at ArtScience Museum at Marina Bay in Singapore 2018–2019 that she largely organized with Frank's support and great help from K K Phua. With some additional aid and support from here and there, including grand hospitality by Katherine Freese at a right time in summer 2015, and in particular with the consistent and very strong support from Astrid and Anders, Betsy and Frank were finally convinced to try and start their present journey in Stockholm. I am really grateful that I can follow and share so much of it with them.

References

[1] F. Wilczek, *Phys. Rev. Lett.* **109**, 160401 (2012).
[2] A. Shapere and F. Wilczek, *Phys. Rev. Lett.* **109**, 160402 (2012).
[3] P. Bruno, *Phys. Rev. Lett.* **111**, 070402 (2013).
[4] H. Watanabe and M. Oshikawa, *Phys. Rev. Lett.* **114**, 251603 (2015).
[5] N. Yamamoto, *Phys. Rev. D* **92**, 085011 (2015).
[6] K. Sacha, *Phys. Rev. A* **91**, 033617 (2015).
[7] K. Sacha and D. Delande, *Phys. Rev. A* **94**, 023633 (2016).
[8] V. Khemani, A. Lazarides, R. Moessner, and S.L. Sondhi, *Phys. Rev. Lett.* **116**, 250401 (2016).
[9] D.V. Else and C. Nayak, *Phys. Rev. B* **93**, 201103 (2016).
[10] D.V. Else, B. Bauer, and C. Nayak, *Phys. Rev. Lett.* **117**, 090402 (2016).
[11] D.V. Else, B. Bauer, and C. Nayak, *Phys. Rev. X* **7**, 011026 (2017).
[12] N.Y. Yao, A.C. Potter, I.-D. Potirniche, and A. Vishwanath, *Phys. Rev. Lett.* **118**, 030401 (2017).
[13] J. Zhang *et al.*, *Nature* **543**, 217 (2017).
[14] S. Choi *et al.*, *Nature* **543**, 221 (2017).
[15] J. Rovny, R.L. Blum, and S.E. Barrett, *Phys. Rev. Lett.* **120**, 180603 (2018).
[16] J. Dai, A.J. Niemi, X. Peng, and F. Wilczek, *Phys. Rev. A* **99**, 023425-9 (2019).

[17] A. Alekseev, J. Dai, and A.J. Niemi, *JHEP* **08**, 035 (2020).

[18] X. Peng, J. Dai, and A.J. Niemi, *New J. Phys.* **22**, 085006 (2020).

[19] R. Fletcher, *Practical Methods of Optimization* (Wiley, 1987).

[20] J. Nocedal and S.J. Wright, *Numerical Optimization*, Springer Series in Operations Research (Springer, Heidelberg, 1999).

[21] J.E. Marsden and T.S. Ratiu, *Introduction to Mechanics and Symmetry: A Basic Exposition of Classical Mechanical Systems*, Second Edition (Springer Verlag, New York, 1999).

[22] A.D. Shapere and F. Wilczek, *Proc. Natl. Acad. Sci. U.S.A.* **116**, 18772 (2019).

[23] A. Guichardet, *Ann. l'Inst. Henri Poincaré* **40**, 329 (1984).

[24] A. Shapere and F. Wilczek, *Am. J. Phys.* **57**, 514 (1989).

[25] R.G. Littlejohn and R.G. Reinsch, *Rev. Mod. Phys.* **69**, 213 (1997).

[26] E.B. Sonin, *Dynamics of Quantised Vortices in Superfluids* (Cambridge University Press, 2016).

[27] J. Garaud, J. Dai, and A.J. Niemi, *JHEP* **2021**, 7 (2021).

[28] F. Wilczek, *Phys. Rev. Lett.* **48**, 1144 (1982).

[29] F. Wilczek, *Phys. Rev. Lett.* **49**, 957 (1982).

[30] L.M. Milne-Thomson, *Theoretical Hydrodynamics*, 5th edition (Dover, New York, 1996).

[31] J. Huang *et al.*, *Nature Meth.* **14**, 71 (2017).

[32] http://manual.gromacs.org/.

[33] X. Peng, J. Dai, and A.J. Niemi, *New J. Phys.* **23** 073024 (2021).

[34] https://pubchem.ncbi.nlm.nih.gov/compound/6351.

[35] V. Dragojlovic, *Chem. Texts* **1**, 14 (2015).

Vision Crystallized in Time

Krzysztof Sacha

Instytut Fizyki Teoretycznej, Uniwersytet Jagielloński
ulica Profesora Stanisława Łojasiewicza 11, PL-30-348 Kraków, Poland
krzysztof.sacha@uj.edu.pl

In 2019 Alfred Shapere and Frank Wilczek published a paper in PNAS on "Regularizations of time-crystal dynamics" [1] and together with Peter Hannaford we were invited to write a commentary article [2]. The work by Alfred and Frank concerned a classical time crystal where a particle performed Sisyphus motion in order to minimize its energy. We wanted to start our commentary paper with a humorous paragraph:

> *The history of scientific discoveries is full of surprising plot twists because it often happens that it is not the person we had in mind who was first to come up with the scientific idea but somebody else who did it earlier. It seems that this is the case with time crystals. We heard that the ideas of time crystals were proposed by Alfred Shapere and Frank Wilczek in 2012 [3, 4]. However, when we dig sufficiently deeply into the literature we find that a long time ago — we do not even know when precisely — there was a guy who invented a time crystal earlier and even demonstrated it experimentally. He was the king of Ephyra, Sisyphus, who was forced to roll a boulder up a hill, and then allow it to roll back down again, which was repeated for eternity. Certainly Shapere and Wilczek were not aware of his discovery otherwise they would have cited Sisyphus in their papers. Probably, in order to give appropriate credit to the king of Ephyra, they decided to write the article about the Sisyphus time crystal which is published in this issue of PNAS [1].*

We also wanted to illustrate the paragraph by a picture of the Sisyphus laboratory, see Fig. 1. Unfortunately, PNAS did not find our idea appropriate for a serious scientific journal and the paragraph and the picture had to wait till now.

Ordinary space crystals are so common that we do not often appreciate their uniqueness. Despite the fact that interactions between electrons and between electrons and nuclei do not favor any particular positions of particles we observe a solid state system at a certain location with particles

Fig. 1.   Demonstration of a time crystal in the Sisyphus laboratory. Illustration by Andrzej Mleczko.

distributed regularly in space. It is an example of spontaneous breaking of the continuous space translation symmetry and the emergence of a discrete space translation symmetry and it can occur at the lowest energy state of a solid state system. It is unbelievable how many years had to pass until someone asked the question if similar crystallization phenomenon could take place also in the time dimension?

I did not know anything about time crystals when in 2012 my colleague, Kuba Zakrzewski, came to my office with the seminar papers [3,4] by Alfred and Frank. My initial skepticism was gone when I realized that the vision for a completely new area had just been crystallized. Extensive description of the time crystal field can be found in review papers and even in a book [5–8]. Here, I will sketch the basic idea of time crystals only and describe the current research directions.

Ordinary space crystals can form in lowest energy states of condensed matter systems. Temporal counterparts of space crystals would be systems which in the lowest energy state perform periodic motion in time. If we consider a classical particle which can move periodically on a ring and which is described by the Hamiltonian $H(x, p)$, the minimal energy should correspond to $\partial H/\partial x = 0$ and $\partial H/\partial p = 0$. However, it implies $\dot{x} = \partial H/\partial p = 0$

and no motion seems to be possible if we want to minimize energy. On the other hand, when the energy E of a particle is expressed in terms of the velocity, then for $E = \dot{x}^4/4 - \dot{x}^2/2$ the minimal value of E corresponds to $\dot{x} = \pm 1$. Alfred Shapere and Frank Wilczek analyzed such a system and they showed that when one tries to calculate the velocity by means of the Hamilton equation, $\dot{x} = \partial H/\partial p$, there is a problem because H has a cusp at p corresponding to the minimal value of the energy and $\partial H/\partial p$ is not well defined [4]. It resolves the puzzle why in the Hamilton formalism it seems impossible to observe motion of a particle when the energy is minimal while in the Lagrangian formulation, classical time crystal behavior is allowed. In the PNAS paper [1], Alfred and Frank considered a similar classical system but in the presence of a harmonic potential. Then, the kinetic energy is the smallest for $\dot{x} = \pm 1$ but the potential energy is minimized if a particle stays at $x = 0$. To reconcile these two contradicting requirements, a particle decides to perform Sisyphus motion. It slowly moves with the velocity $\dot{x} = 1$ (or $\dot{x} = -1$), crosses the position $x = 0$ and next quickly comes back and starts the slow motion again.

Quantum time crystals were proposed by Frank Wilczek in the second seminar paper published in 2012 [3]. In quantum mechanics symmetries are very important things and if the Hamiltonian of a system is time-independent, its eigenstates do not evolve in time apart from trivial oscillations of a phase. Frank proposed a many-body system which, due to interactions between particles, was expected to self-organize its motion and spontaneously start moving periodically in time even if it was prepared in the ground state. Initially he wanted to call the phenomenon: "Spontaneous breaking of time translation symmetry" but his wife, Betsy Devine, criticized him and suggested: "Call it time crystals" [9]. It turned out that to observe spontaneous breaking of the continuous time translation into a discrete time translation symmetry and consequently emergence of a time crystal is not easy if a quantum many-body system with two-body interactions is in the ground state [10]. However, Frank's idea opened people's eyes and a novel research field began.

Science often walks its own way and leads to astounding territories. While quantum time crystals in their original version could not be realized, isolated but periodically driven quantum many-body systems could demonstrate spontaneous breaking of time translation symmetry. In driven systems the time translation symmetry is not continuous but discrete because the Hamiltonian returns to the same form after a driving period T only. Despite the fact that an external force drives a system with a period T, in steady states a system prefers to evolve with its own period. Thus, we observe spontaneous breaking of a discrete time translation symmetry into another discrete time translation symmetry and such phenomea are dubbed "discrete time crystals". First they were proposed in an atomic system [11] and later in condensed matter systems [12, 13] and soon after they were demonstrated in the laboratories [14, 15].

How can a discrete time crystal form? Imagine that a T-periodic state of interacting particles (i.e. a state which obeys the discrete time translation symmetry of the Hamiltonian) is a superposition of two macroscopic states each evolving in time with the period $2T$ but after each period T they exchange their roles so that the entire state is T-periodic. The macroscopic superposition means we deal with a Schrödinger cat-like state which decoheres very quickly in any contact with the environment or after any tiny measurement and collapses to one of the states that formed the initial superposition. Then, the system starts moving with the period $2T$ and a discrete time crystal forms [11]. Lifetime of such a symmetry broken state increases quickly to infinity with increasing number of particles in a system. It is worth mentioning that not only discrete time crystals but also time quasi-crystals can spontaneously form in periodically driven systems [16].

Discrete time crystals break ergodicity because a generic quantum many-body system is expected to heat to infinite temperature if it is periodically driven. Mechanisms of the ergodicity breaking are under intensive investigation but simply speaking they are related to integrability inherited either from the underlining non-interacting driven system [8] or many-body localization phenomenon of the corresponding static many-body system [6]. There is hope for practical applications of discrete time crystals. DARPA announced a funding program [17] which states that a new paradigm for overcoming the limitations of coherence in quantum systems involves systems driven out of equilibrium, with discrete time crystals singled out as the prime example.

Spontaneous breaking of the continuous time translation symmetry in the lowest energy state of time-independent systems with two-body interactions is not possible [10] but hunting for such a genuine time crystal continues. It turns out that spontaneous breaking of the continuous time translation symmetry into a discrete time translation symmetry can be observed in the ground state of many-body systems but with multi-body interactions [18]. While it is not easy to realize such systems in the laboratory, they open new horizons for novel research directions in the time crystal field.

Crystals can spontaneously form in real time but Frank Wilczek in his paper in 2012 provided also an idea for crystalline structures in imaginary time [3]. Equilibrium thermodynamics can be formulated in terms of a path integral if inverse temperature is associated with an imaginary time parameter. If the partition function is dominated by paths evolving periodically in the imaginary time with the same period, we can say that an imaginary time crystal is formed [3, 19]. In order to achieve it, interaction between a system and a thermal bath has to be sufficiently strong. If it is so, eliminating a thermal bath from the description of a system we end up with effective interactions between particles which can be retarded in the imaginary time and minimal at some imaginary time delay [19]. These are suitable conditions for the formation of imaginary time crystals whose signatures can be measured in the laboratory because system observables change in an oscillatory way with a change of the inverse temperature [19].

The development of science needs a seed and the seed sown by Frank Wilczek is growing brilliantly. If crystalline structures can form in the time dimension why not condensed matter physics in time crystals? [20] When we look at a space crystal at a certain moment of time (which corresponds to a detection moment) we can see regular distribution of atoms in space. If one wants to switch from space to time crystals, the roles of space and time have to be exchanged. We fix a space point, where we locate a detector, and ask if the probability of clicking of a detector reveals periodic behavior in time. Is a detector able to show various condensed matter-like behavior in the time dimension? The answer is affirmative and periodically driven systems again turn out to be a perfect playground to investigate such phenomena. If a particle is resonantly driven by periodic force, quasi-energies of a system (i.e. eigenvalues of the so-called Floquet Hamiltonian $H_F = H(x, p_x, t) - i\hbar\partial_t$) form bands and the corresponding Floquet eigenstates have the form of Bloch waves but in the time domain [21, 22]. In other words we can create time crystalline structures which fulfil periodic boundary conditions in time. If it is so, one can engineer different solid state phases in the time dimension by means of appropriate time periodic driving of a single particle or many-body systems [5, 7, 8]. For example when driving possesses a weak randomly fluctuating component, Bloch waves in time turn into states exponentially localized around a certain moment of time and Anderson localization in the time domain can be observed. The presence of randomly fluctuating force in periodically driven many-body systems can result in temporal version of the many-body-localization phenomenon. Time crystals with topological properties can reveal edge states in time because it is possible to create an *edge* in time. Despite the fact that time is a single *degree of freedom*, time lattices which possess properties of two- or three-dimensional space lattices can be realized. All these crystalline structures in time are created intentionally by proper time periodic driving [5, 7, 8]. That is, one deals with similar situation like in the case of photonic crystals which do not form spontaneously because periodic modulation of the refractive index in space is engineered by fabrication of a dielectric material. The field of time crystals, despite being in its infancy, is developing rapidly and it is hard to predict what will emerge in the future. Maybe combining space and time crystalline structures will allow us to build time-space electronics?

I had a wonderful teacher, professor Andrzej Strauszkiewicz. I remember that during one lecture he showed us the formula for π discovered by Srinivasa Ramanujan and commented: "Scientists investigate responses of human neurons to perceptual input but I would like to see how such beautiful formulas are born in a man's brain." I am also curious how can the vision, I have described in the present chapter, crystallize in mind?

Acknowledgments

Support of the National Science Centre, Poland via Project No. std./31/ B/ST2/00349 is acknowledged.

References

[1] A. D. Shapere and F. Wilczek, Regularizations of time-crystal dynamics, *Proceedings of the National Academy of Sciences* **116**(38), 18772–18776 (2019). doi: 10.1073/pnas.1908758116. URL https://www.pnas.org/content/116/38/18772.

[2] K. Sacha and P. Hannaford, Time crystal minimizes its energy by performing sisyphus motion, *Proceedings of the National Academy of Sciences* **116**(38), 18755–18756 (2019). doi: 10.1073/pnas.1913075116. URL https://www.pnas.org/content/116/38/18755.

[3] F. Wilczek, Quantum time crystals, *Phys. Rev. Lett.* **109**, 160401 (2012). doi: 10.1103/PhysRevLett.109.160401. URL http://link.aps.org/doi/10.1103/PhysRevLett.109.160401.

[4] A. Shapere and F. Wilczek, Classical time crystals, *Phys. Rev. Lett.* **109**, 160402 (2012). doi: 10.1103/PhysRevLett.109.160402. URL http://link.aps.org/doi/10.1103/PhysRevLett.109.160402.

[5] K. Sacha and J. Zakrzewski, Time crystals: A review, *Rep. Prog. Phys.* **81**, 016401 (2018). URL https://doi.org/10.1088/1361-6633/aa8b38.

[6] V. Khemani, R. Moessner, and S. L. Sondhi, A Brief History of Time Crystals, arXiv e-prints. art. arXiv:1910.10745 (2019).

[7] L. Guo and P. Liang, Condensed matter physics in time crystals, *New Journal of Physics.* **22**(7), 075003 (2020). doi: 10.1088/1367-2630/ab9d54. URL https://doi.org/10.1088/1367-2630/ab9d54.

[8] K. Sacha, *Time Crystals*, Springer International Publishing, Cham (2020). doi: 10.1007/978-3-030-52523-1. URL https://doi.org/10.1007/978-3-030-52523-1.

[9] F. Wilczek, The exquisite precision of time crystals, *Sci. Am.* **321**, 28–35 (2019).

[10] H. Watanabe and M. Oshikawa, Absence of quantum time crystals, *Phys. Rev. Lett.* **114**, 251603 (2015). doi: 10.1103/PhysRevLett.114.251603. URL http://link.aps.org/doi/10.1103/PhysRevLett.114.251603.

[11] K. Sacha, Modeling spontaneous breaking of time-translation symmetry, *Phys. Rev. A.* **91**, 033617 (2015). doi: 10.1103/PhysRevA.9.033617. URL http://link.aps.org/doi/10.1103/PhysRevA.91.033617.

[12] V. Khemani, A. Lazarides, R. Moessner, and S. L. Sondhi, Phase structure of driven quantum systems, *Phys. Rev. Lett.* **116**, 250401 (2016). doi: 10.1103/PhysRevLett.116.250401. URL http://link.aps.org/doi/10.1103/PhysRevLett.116.250401.

[13] D. V. Else, B. Bauer, and C. Nayak, Floquet time crystals, *Phys. Rev. Lett.* **117**, 090402 (2016). doi: 10.1103/PhysRevLett.117.090402. URL http://link.aps.org/doi/10.1103/PhysRevLett.117.090402.

[14] J. Zhang, P. W. Hess, A. Kyprianidis, P. Becker, A. Lee, J. Smith, G. Pagano, I.-D. Potirniche, A. C. Potter, A. Vishwanath, N. Y. Yao, and C. Monroe, Observation of a discrete time crystal, *Nature* **543**(7644), 217–220 (2017). URL http://dx.doi.org/10.1038/nature21413. Letter.

[15] S. Choi, J. Choi, R. Landig, G. Kucsko, H. Zhou, J. Isoya, F. Jelezko, S. Onoda, H. Sumiya, V. Khemani, C. von Keyserlingk, N. Y. Yao, E. Demler, and M. D. Lukin, Observation of discrete time-crystalline order in a disordered dipolar many-body system, *Nature* **543**(7644), 221–225 (2017). URL http://dx.doi.org/10.1038/nature21426. Letter.

[16] K. Giergiel, A. Kuroś, and K. Sacha, Discrete time quasicrystals, *Phys. Rev. B* **99**, 220303 (2019). doi: 10.1103/PhysRevB.99.220303. URL https://link.aps.org/doi/10.1103/PhysRevB.99.220303.

[17] See www.gizmodo.com.au/2018/03/darpa-is-funding-time-crystal-research/.

[18] V. K. Kozin and O. Kyriienko, Quantum time crystals from hamiltonians with long-range interactions, *Phys. Rev. Lett.* **123**, 210602 (2019). doi: 10.1103/PhysRevLett.123.210602. URL https://link.aps.org/doi/10.1103/PhysRevLett.123.210602.

[19] Z. Cai, Y. Huang, and W. V. Liu, Imaginary time crystal of thermal quantum matter, *Chinese Physics Letters* **37**(5), 050503 (2020). doi: 10.1088/0256-307x/37/5/050503. URL https://doi.org/10.1088/0256-307x/37/5/050503.

[20] P. Hannaford and K. Sacha, Time crystals enter the real world of condensed matter, *Physics World* **33**, 42 (2020).

[21] L. Guo, M. Marthaler, and G. Schön, Phase space crystals: A new way to create a quasienergy band structure, *Phys. Rev. Lett.* **111**, 205303 (2013).

doi: 10.1103/PhysRevLett.111.205303. URL https://link.aps.org/doi/10.1103/PhysRevLett.111.205303.

[22] K. Sacha, Anderson localization and Mott insulator phase in the time domain, *Sci. Rep.* **5**, 10787 (2015). http://dx.doi.org/10.1038/srep1078710. 1038/srep10787. URL https://www.nature.com/articles/srep10787.

https://doi.org/10.1142/9789811251948_0018

Clean Energy from Dark Matter?

P. Sikivie

Department of Physics, University of Florida
Gainesville, FL 32611, USA
sikivie@phys.ufl.edu

A contribution to Frank Wilczek's 70th birthday's festschrift, this brief note considers how much power can be extracted from dark matter.

Frank Wilczek achieved great things as a theoretical physicist: asymptotic freedom of quantum chromodynamics, the axion as a consequence of the Peccei-Quinn solution to the Strong CP Problem, the proposal that the axion is the constituent particle of dark matter, anyonic quasi-particles in 2-dimensional condensed matter systems, and more yet. Underlying these successes, I believe, is a view of physics as one large topic without the common place, but largely artificial, divisions into particle physics, cosmology and astrophysics, condensed matter physics, theory and experiment. This view encourages one to explore outside one's own box. Frank emboldened us when he said: "If you are not making mistakes, you are working on things that are too easy." So, his 70th birthday festschrift may be a good place to consider whether a significant amount of power can be extracted from dark matter.

To start off on a hopeful note, consider that the amount of energy stored in dark matter is truly enormous. Our cosmic neighborhood, defined as a $(kpc)^3$ volume surrounding the Sun, contains on the order of 10^{35} terawatt·year in rest mass energy. Whether it can be tapped as an energy source on Earth may be a laudable question. It is certainly quixotic for two unrelated reasons:

- The density of dark matter on Earth is very small.
- The dark matter is very weakly coupled to ordinary matter.

I'll argue below that if the dark matter is axions, or axion-like particles, the first difficulty largely disappears. Unfortunately, the second difficulty remains for the time being.

The density of dark matter on Earth is commonly stated to be 0.5×10^{-24} gr/cc. It should be kept in mind, however, that this number, derived from observation, signifies the average dark matter density on a length scale of order kpc ($\simeq 3 \times 10^{21}$ cm). Any dark matter detector on Earth is much smaller than that, by approximately 19 orders of magnitude. The dark matter density on Earth may be very different from its kpc scale average, for example if the dark matter is clumpy. In fact there is a straightforward reason why the dark matter density on Earth may be much larger than the above average value: dark matter particles form sharp caustics because they are collisionless and have very small primordial velocity dispersion. At the caustics the dark matter density is much larger than average.

For the purpose of making estimates below, we will assume 1) that dark matter has been detected on Earth and 2) that its density has been found to be the standard average value. Let us keep in mind, however, that the density could be much larger. The dark matter particles move with speeds of order 300 km/s since they form an extended halo around the Milky Way. The rest mass energy flux density implied by the average density and typical velocity is 13 W/m^2. For comparison the solar energy flux density averaged over the sunlit half of the Earth is 680 W/m^2.

The most popular candidate for dark matter has been the WIMP, an acronym for Weakly Interacting Massive Particle. WIMP detectors on Earth are instrumented to detect collisions of WIMPs with nuclei in the bulk of the detector. In each collision, the amount of energy deposited is at most of order the kinetic energy of the WIMP, which is 10^{-6} times its rest mass energy. The largest average amount of kinetic energy is obtained when the nuclear target mass is of order the WIMP mass. If all WIMPs going through a detector were to collide with nuclei in it, the amount of energy obtained would be of order 1.3×10^{-5} W/m^2 times the surface area of the detector. But of course only a tiny fraction of WIMPs collide with nuclei. Present upper limits on their scattering cross-section, of order 10^{-45} cm^2, imply that the scattering length of WIMPs through material bodies is of order kpc. The notion of extracting significant power from WIMPs after they have been discovered to be the dark matter is truly a non-starter.

The situation is different and more tantalizing with the axion, the other leading dark matter candidate, whose popularity has been rising lately [1]. First, axions can be made to convert to photons or other forms of energy so that they yield all their energy, their rest mass energy as well as their kinetic energy. Second, dark matter axions are a highly degenerate Bose gas and therefore behave in first approximation as a classical field, whereas WIMPs are highly non-degenerate. WIMPs have de Broglie wavelength of order 10^{-10} cm $\left(\frac{\text{GeV}}{m_W}\right)$ where m_W is the WIMP mass ($\hbar = c = 1$). A WIMP that misses a detector cannot deposit any energy into it. Furthermore, when a WIMP is detected no precise information is obtained regarding the location and velocity of any other WIMP. Axions are bosons and much lighter than WIMPs. A typical expectation for the mass of dark matter axions is $m_a \sim 10^{-5}$ eV. In some models they are lighter than this by several orders of magnitude. Their de Broglie wavelength is of order $\lambda \sim 100$ m $\left(\frac{10^{-5} \text{ eV}}{m_a} \right)$. The number of axions in a volume of size λ^3 is of order $3 \times 10^{25} \left(\frac{10^{-5} \text{ eV}}{m_a} \right)^4$. The axion fluid surrounding us is therefore, in first approximation, a classical field oscillating at the frequency

$$\nu_a = 2.42 \text{ GHz } \left(\frac{m_a}{10^{-5} \text{ eV}} \right) \tag{1}$$

with frequency dispersion $\delta\nu_a \sim 10^{-6}\nu_a$ due to the spread in kinetic energy. The axion field has a coherence time of order

$$t_{\text{coh}} \sim \frac{1}{\delta\nu_a} \sim 0.4 \text{ ms } \left(\frac{10^{-5} \text{ eV}}{m_a} \right). \tag{2}$$

The coherence time of individual caustic forming cold flows is much longer.

Once axion dark matter has been detected, the frequency of the axion field oscillations is known. We also know the phase of the axion field at all times provided we keep measuring it on time scales short compared to t_{coh}. This should be achievable since the existing ADMX detector [2], on resonance, converts on the order of thousand axions to photons per second. If the cavity is driven with power and the oscillation frequency of the cavity is adjusted in time so that the phase of the axion field stays 90° ahead of the phase of the oscillation stored in the cavity, a maximum amount of power is extracted from the axion field.

When tuned to the axion mass, the cavity detector of dark matter axions behaves as a driven harmonic oscillator:

$$\frac{d^2 X}{dt^2} + \gamma \frac{dX}{dt} + \omega^2 X = f \cos(\omega t). \tag{3}$$

The quality factor of the oscillator is $Q = \frac{\omega}{\gamma}$. The steady state solution in case the cavity is driven only by the axion field is $X(t) = \frac{f}{\gamma\omega} \sin(\omega t)$. The power deposited into the cavity is then

$$P = \frac{Q}{2\omega} f^2 = g^2 \rho_a B^2 V C Q \frac{1}{m_a} \tag{4}$$

where g is the coupling of the axion to two photons, ρ_a is the axion dark matter density at the detector, V is the volume of the cavity, B the strength of the magnetic field permeating the cavity, and C a number of order one describing how strongly the relevant cavity mode couples to the axion field.

The power is of order 10^{-22} watt for the ADMX cavity detector which has a volume of order 125 liters, a magnetic field of order 7.5 Tesla, and a quality factor of order 10^5. Higher quality factors, of order 10^{10}, have been achieved with superconducting cavities. Unfortunately, the need for a magnetic field inside the cavity makes the use of superconducting cavities problematic. If the cavity is driven with power P_0, with phase 90° behind that of the driving force due to the axion field, the power transfered to the cavity from axion dark matter is $\sqrt{P_0 P}$. Thus, if one drives the cavity with 10 MW of power on resonance, the axion field contributes an additional 0.3×10^{-7} W. Of course, no one would want to go through so much trouble to generate such a small amount of power!

The difficulty with extracting power from axion dark matter is that the coupling g and the other factors on the right-hand side of Eq. (4), B, V and Q, are too small. However let us imagine that the problem of weak coupling to the axion field has been solved by some clever trick, and derive the maximum amount of power that can be extracted from the axion fluid when the coupling is arbitrarily large. We model the axion detector/power plant as a harmonic oscillator coupled to the axion field $\phi(\vec{x}, t)$

$$\left(\frac{d^2}{dt^2} + \gamma \frac{d}{dt} + \omega^2\right) X(t) = h\phi(\vec{0}, t)$$

$$(\partial_t^2 - \nabla^2 + m_a^2)\phi(\vec{x}, t) = hX(t)\delta^3(\vec{x}). \tag{5}$$

The detector is located at $\vec{x} = \vec{0}$. h is a coupling with dimension $(\text{time})^{-\frac{1}{2}}$, which we are imagining to be large for the sake of argument. In zeroth order in an expansion in powers of h, the axion field is taken to be a monochromatic wave coming by the detector:

$$\phi^{(0)}(\vec{x}, t) = A\cos(\vec{k} \cdot \vec{x} - \omega t) \tag{6}$$

where $\omega = \sqrt{\vec{k} \cdot \vec{k} + m_a^2}$. There is no prejudice in assuming the wave to be monochromatic if the phase of the actual wave is known at all times. Let us assume that the oscillator, tuned to the same frequency ω, is oscillating with amplitude X_0 and phase δ relative to the local axion field:

$$X(t) = X_0 \cos(\omega t + \delta). \tag{7}$$

The power transferred from the axion field to the oscillator is then

$$P_X = <h\frac{dX}{dt}\phi(\vec{0}, t)> = -\frac{1}{2}\omega h X_0 A \sin(\delta). \tag{8}$$

P_X is largest when the oscillator lags 90° behind the local axion field. The oscillator is a source of axion waves:

$$\phi^{(1)}(\vec{x}, t) = \frac{hX_0}{4\pi r} \cos(kr - \omega t - \delta) \tag{9}$$

where $r = |\vec{x}|$. For $r \gg \lambda$, the axion field Poynting vector is

$$\vec{\mathcal{P}}(\vec{x}) = \langle -\partial_t \phi \vec{\nabla} \phi \rangle = \langle -\partial_t(\phi^{(0)} + \phi^{(1)}) \vec{\nabla}(\phi^{(0)} + \phi^{(1)}) \rangle$$

$$= \frac{1}{2}\omega \vec{k} A^2 + \frac{hX_0 A}{8\pi r}\omega k(\hat{k} + \hat{r})\cos(\vec{k} \cdot \vec{x} - kr + \delta) + \frac{h^2 X_0^2 \omega k}{32\pi^2 r^2}\hat{r} \tag{10}$$

where $\hat{k}$ and $\hat{r}$ are unit vectors in the directions of $\vec{k}$ and $\vec{x}$, respectively. The first term in Eq. (10) is the energy flux density in the original axion wave, Eq. (6). The last term is the energy flux density in the field radiated by the oscillator, Eq. (9). The total power radiated is

$$P^{(2)} = \frac{h^2 X_0^2 \omega k}{8\pi}. \tag{11}$$

The second term in Eq. (10) is the interference term between the original axion wave and the radiated wave. The corresponding outgoing power within a solid angle $\Delta\Omega$ is

$$P^{(1)} = \lim_{r \to \infty} \int_{\Delta\Omega} d\Omega \; r^2 \; \hat{r} \cdot \vec{\mathcal{P}}^{(1)}(\vec{x})$$

$$= 0 \qquad\qquad\qquad \text{if } \hat{k} \text{ points outside } \Delta\Omega$$

$$= +\frac{1}{2}\omega h X_0 A \sin(\delta) \qquad \text{if } \hat{k} \text{ points inside } \Delta\Omega. \tag{12}$$

The interference term $P^{(1)}$ accounts for the power P_X extracted by the oscillator from the axion field. Equation (11) implies a limit on how much power can be obtained. Even if we find a way to increase h, we will want to keep $P^{(2)} < P_X$. Otherwise we lose more power in radiation than we extract from the axion field. This requires $hX_0 < \frac{4\pi}{k}A$ and hence

$$P_X < \frac{4\pi}{k^2}\mathcal{P}^{(0)} = 1.3 \cdot 10^4 \text{ W} \left(\frac{10^{-5} \text{ eV}}{m_a}\right)^2. \tag{13}$$

In the axion case, if we were able to increase the coupling h, we would be able to collect up to the energy flowing within a radius $\frac{2}{k} = \frac{\lambda}{\pi}$ of the detector/power plant, but no more than that. There is no physics principle that limits the size of h. Unfortunately we do not know at present how to increase h much in practice.

Let us also consider dark matter constituted of axion-like particles (ALPs). These are light spin zero bosons like axions [3] but they do not solve the Strong CP Problem of the Standard Model of particle physics. ALPs are much less constrained than axions. In particular their coupling strengths are not necessarily proportional to their mass (as is the case for axions) and they may be very light. Consider, for example, dark matter constituted of ALPs of mass 10^{-15} eV. Equations (1), (2) and (13) apply, so their oscillation frequency is 0.24 Hz, their coherence time is of order 4 months and the maximum amount of power that can be extracted from them is $1.3 \cdot 10^{12}$ TW, which is quite a lot more than needed. The remaining issue is the coupling strength. We may consider the ALP coupling to two photons which gives rise to Eq. (4). Let us assume that a high quality resonator can be found that exploits that coupling in the ALP case and that $B^2 V C Q$ has the same value as achieved in ADMX. The power is boosted by the factor $1/m_a$. Although g is unrelated to m_a, it is bounded by the CAST solar axion search [4]. Assuming g saturates the CAST bound, we would get $P \sim 10^{-2}$ W.

Happy Birthday Frank, and many happy returns!

Acknowledgments

This work was supported in part by the U.S. Department of Energy under grant DE-SC0010296 at the University of Florida.

References

[1] F. Chadha-Day, J. Ellis and D.J.E. Marsh, arXiv:2105.01406.
[2] R. Khatiwada *et al.* (the ADMX Collaboration), arXiv:2010.00169.
[3] P. Arias *et al.*, *JCAP* **06**, 013 (2012).
[4] K. Zioutas *et al.*, *Phys. Rev. Lett.* **94**, 121301 (2005).

© 2022 World Scientific Publishing Company
https://doi.org/10.1142/9789811251948_0019

The Third Cosmological Paradigm

Michael S. Turner*

The Kavli Foundation and the University of Chicago
mturner@uchicago.edu

I begin by briefly discussing the first two cosmological paradigms, the hot big-bang model and ΛCDM. In discussing the third paradigm, I focus on the issues it must address, what its aspirations should be, and how it might be initiated. I end with a brief history of my collaborations with Frank Wilczek.

1. The First Epoch (circa 1920 to 1980): The Emergence of the Hot Big Bang Paradigm

The Universe is big in both space and time and for much of human history most of it has been beyond the reach of our boldest ideas and most powerful instruments. I mark the birth of modern cosmology at roughly 100 years ago. Einstein had introduced general relativity, the first theory of gravity and spacetime capable of describing the Universe, and the first cosmological solutions had been found (e.g., the deSitter, Friedmann and Lemaître solutions as well as Einstein's static model). At about the same time, George Ellery Hale and George Ritchey invented the (modern) reflecting telescope, and Hale moved astronomy to the mountain tops of California, first Mt. Wilson and later Mt. Palomar. With bold ideas and new instruments, we were ready to explore the Universe beyond our own Milky Way galaxy and begin to discover and understand the larger picture.

Hale's second big reflector, the 100-inch Hooker telescope, enabled Hubble to discover that galaxies are the building blocks of the Universe today and that the Universe is expanding, the signature of its big bang beginning. While it took a few years to connect the solutions of general relativity to the observational data, by the early 1930s the basic big bang model was in place (and Hubble was on the cover of *Time* magazine).

---

*The author is Senior Strategic Advisor at The Kavli Foundation and Rauner Distinguished Service Professor emeritus at UChicago.

The final element of the hot big bang model came with Arno Penzias and Robert Wilson's discovery of the cosmic microwave background (CMB) in 1964.[a] While the idea of a hot beginning was introduced by George Gamow and his collaborators in 1948, to explain the non-equilibrium origin of the chemical elements,[b] the 1964 discovery was accidental, an interesting and oft-told story.

In 1972, years before Standard Model referred to the remarkable theory that describes quarks and leptons, Steven Weinberg coined the term "Standard Model" for the hot big bang model and described it in his classic textbook [1]. In brief, the model traces the Universe from a hot soup of hadrons at around 10^{-5} sec through the synthesis of the light elements (largely ^{4}He with traces amounts of D, ^{3}He and ^{7}Li) at a few seconds to the formation of neutral atoms and the last-scattering of CMB photons at around 400,000 years after the big bang to the formation of stars and galaxies.

The first paradigm laid out the basic architecture of the Universe — expansion from a hot big bang beginning to a Universe filled with galaxies moving away from one another today. General relativity, nuclear physics (for big bang nucleosynthesis, or BBN), and atomic physics (for the CMB) physics provided a strong theoretical foundation. The triad of the expansion, the light-element abundances, and the blackbody spectrum of the CMB provided an equally strong observational foundation.

Allan Sandage summed up cosmology in 1970 as the search for two numbers, H_0 and q_0, the expansion rate of the Universe and the deceleration rate of the Universe respectively [2]. It would take until 2000 and the completion of the Hubble Space Telescope Key Project to pin down H_0 to 10% with a reliable error estimate: $H_0 = 72 \pm 2 \pm 6$ km/s/Mpc [3], and as I will discuss later, H_0 is still a lively topic today. As for the deceleration parameter, the Universe is actually accelerating; further, q_0 is not even measurable with both precision and accuracy, another story [4]. Bottom line, H_0 continues to live up to its reputation as the most important number in cosmology, and q_0, whose inferred value is about -0.55 give or take 10%, has fallen by the wayside.

---

[a]Radio astronomy, a field pioneered by physicists Karl Jansky and Grote Reber in the 1930s, was the first of many new windows on the heavens–beyond visible light–to be opened.

[b]In an odd twist, Gamow's version of big-bang nucleosynthesis was largely wrong; in fact, it was a description of what is known today as the r-process. Hoyle, worried that his steady state model lacked the ability to explain the chemical elements, produced the modern version of the r-process in his landmark paper with the Burbidges and Willy Fowler.

There were important open issues in the first epoch. Chief among them, precisely how structure formed and what happened during the first microsecond when the soup of hot hadrons would have been strongly-interacting and overlapping.

One last thought on this first period: the sociology. The field was largely the province of astronomers and only a handful at that (certainly less than 30). There were the occasional physicists, e.g., Einstein, Gamow, and Tolman, who dabbled. The discovery of the CMB began to bring in physicists: Penzias and Wilson (radio astronomy physicists), Wagoner and Fowler (who with Hoyle carried out the first modern calculation of BBN [5]) and the Princeton gang who interpreted the Penzias and Wilson discovery (Dicke, Peebles, Roll, and Wilkinson [6]). This foreshadowed the large number of physicist-cosmologists we see today, who began coming in big numbers during the second epoch.

2. The Second Epoch (Circa 1980 to 20??): The Emergence of the ΛCDM Paradigm

Exactly when and how the paradigm shift occurred is hard to precisely pin down and likely involved two steps. According to Thomas Kuhn, the push behind a paradigm shift are anomalies that the current paradigm cannot explain or account for. There is also the pull of a better theory. Both elements were at play here.

Dark matter most clearly conforms to a Kuhnian shift. Around 1980, through the work of Vera Rubin and others [7], it became clear that bulk of matter that holds together galaxies is not in the form of stars, but rather in extended haloes of non-luminous (dark) matter. This, together with Zwicky's earlier work about dark matter in clusters of galaxies and Ostriker and Peebles's work on the theoretical need for massive halos to stabilize the disk structure of spiral galaxies, brought astronomers to the realization that there is much more to the Universe than meets the eye. But what is it?

New ideas in particle physics that trace to the discovery of asymptotic freedom by Gross & Wilczek and Politzer provided a powerful pull: During the first microsecond after the big bang the Universe was comprised of a soup of weakly-interacting, point-like quarks, leptons, gauge and Higgs bosons of the Standard Model and probably other fundamental particles. Weinberg's "hadron wall" fell and early-Universe cosmology was open for business! Further, the convergence of the three coupling constants led to grand unified theories and a flood of cosmological consequences including baryogenesis, inflation, magnetic monopoles, and particle dark matter. By 1990, particle dark matter had caught on, even among astronomers.[c]

Equally important, the "heavenly lab" can extend the reach of ground-based accelerators with its great variety of densities, temperatures, energies and magnetic fields that are not available in terrestrial labs. Zel'dovich called the early Universe "the poor man's accelerator."

The successes of these powerful ideas from particle physics at addressing big puzzles in cosmology has established a lasting and deep connection between the very small — elementary particle physics — and the very large — cosmology. The connection between quarks and the cosmos not only changed how we think about cosmology and the very vocabulary we use, but it also brought in a host of new players, theorists and experimentalists from both particle physics and nuclear physics, dramatically increasing the numbers of scientists engaged in cosmology one way or another.

The quarks/cosmos connection goes far beyond the simple fact of an early, quark-soup phase of the Universe. The events that occurred during (and before) the quark-soup phase have shaped the Universe we see today: from the baryon asymmetry and dark matter to the origin of the large-scale regularity of the Universe and the seeds for all the structure seen today.

Beyond the influx of new players and new ideas from physics, important technological advances were occurring in astronomy — the widespread use of CCD cameras that today exceed a gigapixel in size, the opening of additional windows on the Universe from infrared and UV to x-rays and gamma-rays, more powerful CMB instruments and experiments (e.g., HEMT and bolometer detectors and the use of interferometry). And the exponentially-increasing power of computing has made possible numerical simulations of the Universe and the analysis of the ever-larger datasets being created.

By the beginning of 21st century, a new kind of astronomy had been born — digital surveys of large portions of the sky, both imaging and spectra. By 1980, the total number of redshifts measured was around a thousand with the highest redshift galaxy having a redshift of less than 1! The pioneering Sloan Digital Sky Survey (a collaboration of astronomers and particle physicists) imaged more than 100 million galaixies and measured redshifts for one million of them. Today, galaxy redshifts extend to 10 and the number redshifts measured is approaching one billion (or about 0.5% of the galaxies in our visible Universe).

---

[c]Interestingly, Vera Rubin was amongst the astronomers who was never a fan of particle dark matter.

Building upon the strong foundation of the hot big bang model, a new set of questions were asked during the second epoch — and by 2000 were mostly answered:

- How did structure form and what is the origin for the seeds of that structure?
- Why is the Universe — at least the observable Universe — so regular, i.e., isotropic and homogeneous, on the largest scales?
- Why does the Universe contain only matter and not equal amounts of matter and antimatter?
- What is dark matter comprised of?
- What explains the early flatness of the Universe and is it is still flat today?
- Where did all the magnetic monopoles (and other nasty relics of the early phases of the Universe) go?
- What explains the smallness or absence of a cosmological constant (in the form of quantum vacuum energy)?

Beginning with baryogenesis — the theory of how B, C and CP violating processes in the early Universe allowed the evolution of a small excess of baryons over antibaryons — ideas motivated by grand unification, supersymmetry and eventually superstrings gave rise to the basic elements of ΛCDM: inflation, particle dark matter and dark energy. By 1985, the inflation and cold dark matter (slowly-moving dark-matter particles) paradigm was guiding cosmology.

Dark Energy did not arrive until 1995, when it became increasingly clear that the simplest version of inflation + CDM, a flat Universe comprised of 95% CDM and 5% baryons didn't work. There was increasing evidence that the total amount of matter was only about 30% of critical density [8], large-scale structure observations fit, but only if $(\Omega_M H_0/100 \, \text{km/sec/Mpc}) \simeq$ 0.2–0.3, requiring a really small Hubble constant or $\Omega_M \neq 1$, as well as other discrepancies. The fix which resolved all the problems, as ugly as it seemed, was $\Omega_\Lambda \sim 0.7$ [9]. Voila! The first evidence for the acceleration of the Universe was found in 1998 [10], and almost overnight,[d] ΛCDM became the new paradigm. Thomas Kuhn would smile. (Dark energy is the generalization of a

---

[d]My mentor, David Schramm, was supposed to debate Jim Peebles in April 1998 on whether or not $\Omega_0 = 1$. In December 1997, shortly before he died in a plane crash, he was worried about having to take the $\Omega_0 = 1$ side of the question. I filled in for David, Peebles was no longer willing to debate $\Omega_0 < 1$ and the title of the debate was changed to, *Cosmology Solved?*. Months after the discovery of cosmic acceleration, ΛCDM was firmly in place.

smooth, negative pressure component whose equation-of-state $w \equiv p_{DE}/\rho_{DE}$ is close to -1 [11].)

Today, a wealth of cosmological data supports the ΛCDM model. It began with the BBN abundance of deuterium that pinned down the baryons density at around 5% of the critical density, too small to account for the total amount of matter, pointing to the existence of particle dark matter. In 1992, COBE made the first detection of the anisotropy of the CMB. Twenty-five years later, the anisotropy has been precisely characterized by the all-sky measurements of the WMAP and Planck satellites and the ground-based measurements down to tiny angular scales of DASI, SPT, and ACT and other experiments. The CMB frontier has moved to polarization and the search for the B-mode signature of inflation produced gravitational waves.

Precision CMB measurements have been and will continue to be crucial to testing the inflationary predictions of almost scale-invariant, nearly-Gaussian curvature perturbations, a spatially flat Universe and an almost scale-invariant spectrum of gravitational waves. In addition, measurements of the acoustic oscillations imprinted upon the CMB by baryons falling into the dark matter gravitational potential wells have led to unprecedentedly accurate measurements of many important cosmological parameters including the matter and baryon densities, Hubble constant, and the amount of ionized material between us and the surface of last scattering.

Large redshift-surveys beginning with the SDSS and 2dF surveys have quantitatively characterized the large-scale structure in the Universe. The large and sophisticated numerical simulations of how structure formed in a ΛCDM Universe, together with the CMB and LSS results provide strong evidence for both CDM and the gravitational instability theory of structure formation (namely, that structure arose from the gravitational amplification of small density inhomogeneities).

Summing up the second paradigm, ΛCDM provides a tested account of the Universe from a very early time ($\ll 10^{-6}$ sec) to the present, some 13.8 Gyr later: A very-early period of accelerated expansion driven by the potential energy of a scalar field gave rise to a very-large, smooth, spatially-flat patch that became all that we can see today (and more). Quantum fluctuations during this accelerated phase grew in size and became the density perturbations that seeded galaxies and other structures. The conversion of scalar field potential energy into particles produced the quark soup that evolved a baryon asymmetry and long-lived dark-matter particles. The excess of quarks over antiquarks gave rise to neutrons and protons, and later the nuclei of the lightest chemical elements and finally atoms. The gravity of the cold (slowly moving) dark matter particles drove the formation of structure from galaxies to superclusters and a mere 5 billion years ago the repulsive gravity of dark energy (at present, indistinguishable from quantum vacuum energy) initiated another period of accelerated expansion.

ΛCDM has little to say about the beginning or the ending,[e] but it does provide sufficient detail about the "in between" to make the paradigm very testable. Further, ΛCDM has revealed new physics not contained in the Standard Model: the additional C, CP violation needed to produce the baryon asymmetry, dark matter particles, dark energy whose repulsive gravity drives today's accelerated expansion and an early, inflationary phase that lasted for at least 60 or so e-foldings of the scale factor of the Universe.

ΛCDM has exceeded the expectations of most 1980 cosmologists (certainly this one). Moreover, its account of the Universe from a very early time when galaxies and all the structures we see today were mere quantum fluctuations to the birth and formation of stars and galaxies is a remarkable achievement. All of this, with little or no need to discuss or rely upon initial conditions.

However, I suspect that few cosmologists today would simply want to *settle* for ΛCDM (Success in science is its own worst enemy! — it breeds ever higher expectations). Here is a list of some of its shortcomings:

- ΛCDM is not a fundamental theory in the sense of the Standard Model; it is a highly successful phenomenological model, with some fundamental aspects, e.g., BBN and structure formation
- What is the dark matter particle? or is there a dark matter particle?
- While baryogenesis likely involves neutrino mass and $B + L$ violation arising in the SM, it still remains just an attractive framework with few details.
- Inflation is still a paradigm, with a Landau-Ginzburg like description of this epoch that so fundamentally shaped the Universe we observe today.
- Cosmic acceleration and "the lightness of the quantum vacuum" remain profound mysteries which are likely related.
- What happened before inflation (big bang?) and what is the destiny of the Universe?
- And the crazy uncle in the attic of cosmology: the multiverse. Born of inflation and the bane of science because of its inability to be tested, it can't stay in the attic forever!

---

[e]Of course, if the cause of cosmic acceleration is just Λ, then a gloomy future is easy to predict.

3. Aspirations for the Third Paradigm

What it should address. The third paradigm must aspire to address the big puzzles left unanswered by the second paradigm: baryogenesis, dark matter, dark energy and inflation. Or, explain why they are the wrong questions to be asking (not an uncommon occurrence in science). The issue of the energy of the quantum vacuum and why it is small — likely related to dark energy and cosmic acceleration is absolutely central as well. And of course, it would be nice if the third paradigm either illuminated or told us to ignore the multiverse. Lastly, I am certain that the foundation of the third paradigm will be built upon the deep connections between the very big and very small: we have yet to plumb the full depths of this profound connection.

What it need not address. Modern cosmology started with stars and galaxies. ΛCDM provides the framework necessary to describe the birth, evolution and future of stars, galaxies and large-scale structure. It does so with such breadth and in such detail that some of the oldest questions of cosmology — e.g., the origin of the Hubble sequence of galaxies — can be addressed. And further, the CDM part of ΛCDM could be falsified.[f]

I believe cosmology has now bifurcated into two branches: astrophysical cosmology (the story from quarks to us) and fundamental cosmology (the cosmological framework) to the benefit of each. Martin Rees colorfully describes this as the mud wrestlers and the chess players. The third paradigm should stick with fundamental cosmology and leave astrophysical cosmology, as interesting as it is, to the astrophysicists.

That is not to say that one branch cannot inform the other and probably will. Right now ΛCDM is a good enough framework for astrophysical cosmology; when more is learned about dark matter, inflation and dark energy, it may need to be upgraded to get the astrophysical story even more precisely correct. Conversely, the extraordinary cosmological datasets being produced may provide important observational clues, e.g., about the dark matter particle or evidence that dark energy changes with time, relevant to the cosmological framework.

How many numbers determine the Universe? Sandage had cosmology described by two numbers. We now know it is more interesting than that. The Planck fit to the ΛCDM cosmology has 6 numbers: the baryon and

---

[f]While there continues to be a steady stream of such claims — dating back to 1983 — none has yet to convince me that CDM is in trouble. Essentially all such claims involve discrepancies on small scales, where as-of-yet-not-understood hydrodynamics could plausibly resolve the problem.

matter densities; the dimensionless amplitude of the curvature fluctuations; the slight tilt from a scale-invariant spectrum of curvature fluctuations; the sound horizon at last scattering and an astrophysical parameter, the optical depth τ to the last-scattering surface (determined by the ionization history of the Universe once stars light up). A fundamental theory of dark matter, dark energy, baryogenesis and inflation would predict all the "physics" parameters; and a detailed account of the astrophysical evolution of structure formation would predict τ as well. Once "the theory of everything" is known, my aspiration is no additional parameters are needed to explain the Universe. That is, zero numbers!

I know of two conjectures that could realize this lofty goal. In the Hartle-Hawking approach, the Hamiltonian of the fundamental theory specifies the wavefunction of the Universe. In the very early days of string theory, Murray Gell-Mann once speculated that the theory of everything is unique. This would also answer Einstein's famous question: God didn't have a choice about the laws of physics.[g]

Initial conditions: relevant or not? For many years, Roger Penrose has taken a nearly opposite view; namely, that initial conditions are everything; in particular, the Weyl curvature.

I am advocating for the opposite, initial conditions are irrelevant. The Universe is automatic: the light-element abundances, the baryon asymmetry, the ratio of dark matter-to-baryons, smoothness, flatness, inhomogeneity, ... all arose due to early Universe microphysics.

Sadly, the axion may provide a counterexample to my aspiration. Here is the dilemma. The mass of the axion arises due to the explicit breaking of Peccei–Quinn (PQ) symmetry by small quark masses. When PQ symmetry spontaneously breaks, at a much larger energy scale, the axion was massless and hence its potential was flat, with no dynamics to determine its value. In general, the random value of the axion field will be misaligned with the ultimate minimum of its potential. After chiral symmetry breaking, the axion mass arises and the axion field begins to oscillate with an amplitude set by its misalignment. These oscillations, which correspond to a condensate of zero-momentum axions, are the dark matter. The amount of axionic dark matter is determined by the random initial misalignment, which is only coherent over the size of the horizon at the time of PQ SSB.

---

[g]At the other extreme is, God tried all the possibilities: The "marriage" of the multiverse and the infinity of string theory vacua with anthropic reasoning leads to a zoo of universes. We find ourselves in this one because it had laws of physics that permit life to evolve. Ugh.

If Peccei–Quinn symmetry breaking occurs after inflation, the axion mass density today is just the statistical average over the random misalignment angles of the many, many horizon-sized regions at the time of PQ SSB that today comprise our Universe. However, if PQ symmetry breaking occurs first, then our observable Universe resides within one such patch and the amount of axionic dark matter is in essence an initial condition for that patch.

That wouldn't be such a big deal except for the fact that its influence could be non-trivial: if the misalignment is small and the scale of inflation is high, isocurvature fluctuations in the axion would dominate over the usual inflation produced curvature fluctuations, qualitatively changing the nature of structure formation [12]. The same random misalignment angle determines the ratio of dark matter to baryonic matter, which can have a dramatic impact on the very existence of stars, galaxies and us [13]. This random variable — an initial condition if you will — could be important for our Universe if axions are the dark matter.

How big to think? The short answer is, don't think too small! ΛCDM provides a strong foundation to speculate from, there are fundamental connections between cosmology and particle physics, and particle physics too has a strong foundation, big aspirations and powerful ideas (David Gross treated us to his overview of them [14].) By the way, theorists have rarely thought too big or taken their ideas too seriously; it is often just the opposite.

In Einstein's big bang theory, the big bang was the singular origin of matter, energy, space and *time*, making the question of what happened before the big bang moot. It seems clear that Einstein did not get the last word on gravity, and if GR's successor (string theory?) cleans up the singularity, the question becomes addressable. Nonetheless, the *emergence* of space, time and the Universe is not only a solution worthy of the question, but also is at the very heart of the connection between particle physics and cosmology. Where else might one have a better opportunity to address the 400+ year-old question of the fundamental nature of space and time?

On the particle physics side, I see a growing sense that space and time are not fundamental but rather are emergent phenomena, a concept that is difficult to wrap one's head around. I was struck by David Gross' remark that went something like this, "space-time is not always the best way to think about things." As creatures of time, moving in the river of time with an arrow we don't fully understand, I feel better about not fully understanding his remark while also appreciating the depth of it. After David's talk, I viewed the ubiquitous WMAP history of the Universe, with its beginning, end and boundaries in a new way. A cosmic solution can be read in different ways, not just the simple flow in time that a creature of time is most comfortable doing.

Moving forward. As we have learned from cosmology, the past is hard to predict and the future is even harder. The shift from the mid-second paradigm inflation + CDM to ΛCDM involved discrepancies. Today there is the Hubble tension: direct measurements of the current expansion rate yield $H_0 = 74 \pm 1\,\mathrm{km/sec/Mpc}$ and "indirect" measurements of the expansion rate using CMB anisotropy and the *assumption* of ΛCDM to extrapolate from the early time expansion rate to the present yield $H_0 = 67.5 \pm 0.4\,\mathrm{km/sec/Mpc}$ [15]. The resolution could be a systematic error in one (or both) determinations of H_0 or the assumption of ΛCDM and an indicator of a missing ingredient!

A paradigm begins with its aspirations, is measured by its accomplishments, and the difference between the two defines how revolutionary it was. How and when we get to the third paradigm remains to be seen. I am confident that the shift from ΛCDM to the next paradigm will be at least as revolutionary as that from a cosmology described by two numbers to ΛCDM and that bold and unsettling new ideas will underpin it.

4. The Joy of Collaborating with Frank

I end on a personal note, discussing our collaborations over the years. Frank and I have written 8 papers together; all involved cosmology, and a few were influential. Some were written when we were together at the ITP in Santa Barbara (before it was the KITP); and two involved work that began at a Nobel Symposium in Graftavellens. Each was a joyful and insightful experience. What I remember most vividly was their intensity: whatever Frank was working on got his full attention, he saw the full possibilities, and that project was — at least for the moment — the most important thing he had going. Here is a quick run down:

- *Reheating an inflationary Universe* [16]. In December of 1981, Frank and I received a preprint from Andrei Linde entitled, *A new inflationary Universe scenario*, claiming to have cured the problems of Guth's original model of inflation. The paper looked important, and we worked over the holidays to figure out what was going on. We wrote down the evolution equation for the scalar field, including the friction effect of the expansion (neglected in Linde's paper), and focussed on how particle production would reheat the Universe. On a visit to Penn in January, I discovered that Paul Steinhardt was doing similar work as Linde, with his student

Andreas Albrecht, and a collaboration was born. Among other things, the first integration (to my knowledge) of the slow roll equation was done on my HP calculator.

- *Is our vacuum metastable* [17]? The different symmetry breaking patterns of the $SU(5)$ GUT and how we landed in $SU(3) \times SU(2) \times U(1)$ motivated us, and we explored the possibility that the $SU(3) \times SU(2) \times U(1)$ vacuum was not the ground state, but rather a metastable state with a very-long tunneling time. The possibility of a transition to a lower energy state has come up almost every time a new accelerator is turned on (Short answer, no. Cosmic rays have already done the experiment.).

- *Formation of structure in an axion-dominated Universe* [18]. The axion is the quintessential cold dark matter particle, and this is one of the first, if not the first, paper on CDM — and we have the erratum to prove it. Starting with the inflationary density-perturbation spectrum and axions, we discussed how structure would form. It was great fun working with Frank's long-time friend and collaborator, Tony Zee.

- *Positron-line radiation as a signature of particle dark matter in the halo* [19]. Frank had moved to the IAS by now and I can't remember the origin of this collaboration. In any case, this paper led to a new signature for dark matter in the halo and became one of the main physics motivations for Sam Ting's AMS experiment. For a while, AMS had a hint of the positron-line we were talking about.

- *Inflationary axion cosmology* [12]. Much of what I said earlier about axions was in this paper that began at the *Nobel Symposium on the Birth and Early Evolution of the Universe* in Graftavallens, Sweden during the summer of 1990.

- *Relic gravitational waves and extended inflation* [20]. This work also began (or was finished) at the Graftavallens symposium.

- *Cosmological implications of axinos* [21]. This was my delightful and productive introduction to Frank's then student and now MIT colleague, Krishna Rajagopal.

- *Astrophysics, cosmology and unification of forces.* [22]. This paper, written with two Nobel prizewinners (Frank and Barry Barish), was part of the Snowmass 1994 DPF Planning process. With that author list, it should have been a blockbuster; to date, it has never been cited!

Happy birthday Frank and thanks for such a stimulating meeting, one that reflects the breadth and depth of your interests in the big, important ideas in physics. It has been a joy and privilege to be your friend and colleague for more than 40 years.

References

[1] S. Weinberg, *Gravitation and Cosmology* (John Wiley & Sons, 1972).

[2] A. Sandage, *Physics Today*, **23**, 34 (1970).

[3] W.L. Freedman *et al.*, *Astrophys. J.* **553**, 47 (2001).

[4] A.R. Neben and M.S. Turner, *Astrophys. J.* **769**, 133 (2013)

[5] R.V. Wagoner, W.A. Fowler, and F. Hoyle, *Astrophys. J.* **148**, 3 (1967).

[6] R.H. Dicke, P.J.E. Peebles, P.G. Roll, and D.T. Wilkinson, *Astrophys. J.* **142**, 414 (1965).

[7] V. Rubin, *Science* **220**, 1339 (1983).

[8] S.D.M. White *et al.*, *Nature* **366**, 429 (1993).

[9] L.M. Krauss and M.S. Turner, *Gen. Rel. Grav.* **27**, 1137 (1995); see also, J.P. Ostriker and P.J. Steinhardt, *Nature* **377**, 600 (1995).

[10] A. Riess *et al.*, *Astron. J.* **116**, 1009 (1998); S. Perlmutter *et al.*, *Astrophys. J.* **517**, 565 (1999).

[11] M.S. Turner and M. White, *Phys. Rev. D* **56**, R4439 (1997).

[12] M.S. Turner and F. Wilczek, *Phys. Rev. Lett.* **66**, 5 (1991).

[13] M. Tegmark, A. Aguirre, M.J. Rees, and F. Wilczek, *Phys. Rev. D* **73**, 023505 (2006).

[14] David Gross, in this volume.

[15] E. Di Valentino *et al.*, arXiv:2103.01183v2 (2021).

[16] A. Albrecht, P.J. Steinhardt, M.S. Turner, and F. Wilczek, *Phys. Rev. Lett.* **48**, 1437 (1982).

[17] M.S. Turner and F. Wilczek, *Nature* **298**, 633 (1982).

[18] M.S. Turner, F. Wilczek, and A. Zee, *Phys. Lett. B* **125**, 35 (1983); *ibid*, 519 (E).

[19] M.S. Turner and F. Wilczek, *Phys. Rev. D* **42**, 1001 (1990).

[20] M.S. Turner and F. Wilczek, *Phys. Rev. Lett.* **65**, 3080 (1990).

[21] K. Rajagopal, M.S. Turner, and F. Wilczek, *Nucl. Phys. B* **358**, 447 (1991).

[22] B.C. Barish, M.S. Turner, and F. Wilczek, Astrophysics, cosmology and unification of physics, in *Particle Physics: Perspectives and Opportunities (Snowmass 1994)*, edited by R.D. Peccei *et al.*

https://doi.org/10.1142/9789811251948_0020

A Note on Complex Spacetime Metrics

Edward Witten

Institute for Advanced Study
Einstein Drive, Princeton, NJ 08540, USA
witten@ias.edu

For various reasons, it seems necessary to include complex saddle points in the "Euclidean" path integral of General Relativity. But some sort of restriction on the allowed complex saddle points is needed to avoid various unphysical examples. In this article, a speculative proposal is made concerning a possible restriction on the allowed saddle points in the gravitational path integral. The proposal is motivated by recent work of Kontsevich and Segal on complex metrics in quantum field theory, and earlier work of Louko and Sorkin on topology change from a real time point of view.

1. Introduction

In their original paper interpreting black hole entropy in terms of the gravitational action, Gibbons and Hawking [1], after analyzing the thermodynamics of a Schwarzschild black hole, went on to consider black holes with angular momentum. They pointed out that the Kerr metric, assuming that the angular momentum is real, becomes complex-valued when continued to imaginary time. While complex-valued, this metric is everywhere nondegenerate, like all complex metrics that will be considered in this article. Gibbons and Hawking showed that one can recover the expected results for the thermodynamics of the Kerr solution by assuming that this complex saddle point dominates the appropriate path integral.

Somewhat later, Gibbons, Hawking, and Perry [2], observing that the action of Euclidean quantum gravity is not positive-definite, argued that therefore the path integral of "Euclidean" quantum gravity should really be understood as a sort of infinite-dimensional version of a complex contour integral, with the integration running over a suitable family of nondegenerate complex metrics on spacetime.

Since then, other reasons have been put forward to consider complex spacetime metrics and complex saddle points. For example, it has been argued by Halliwell and Hartle [3] that to get sensible answers for the behavior of large, semiclassical spacetimes from the Hartle–Hawking no-boundary proposal for the wavefunction of the universe [4], one must consider complex solutions of Einstein's equations as saddle points. It has also been argued by Louko and Sorkin [5] that to get sensible answers for real time topology-changing processes, one must consider complex spacetime metrics that correspond roughly to tunneling trajectories. Various additional arguments have been given, some of which will be discussed later.

On the other hand, in considering complex saddle points of Einstein's equations, one is potentially opening Pandora's box. Many such saddle points, if included in a functional integral, will give results that are not physically sensible. This point was made in [5], and we will illustrate it further in section 2 with some additional examples. The examples of section 2 are all constructed by taking real submanifolds of simple complex manifolds, so perhaps we should point out that this method of constructing examples is useful but in a sense atypical. There typically is no canonical way to complexify a real manifold M or to analytically continue a complex metric g, and generically a complex metric on M is not related in any useful way to a complexification of M.

If some complex metrics are "bad," which ones are "good"? Consider a semiclassical theory of gravity coupled to matter, and assume that the matter is described by ordinary quantum fields. In that context, an important necessary condition for complex metrics, discussed for example in [3] and [5], is that the complex spacetime should be one in which the quantum field theory of the matter system can be defined. If the matter system is sufficiently generic, the complex spacetime should be one in which more or less any quantum field theory could be defined.

Recently, with a different motivation, Kontsevich and Segal [6] have made a proposal for what is the class of complex geometries in which a generic quantum field theory can be consistently coupled. Their proposal was not directly motivated by quantum gravity; their basic goal was to explore the extent to which traditional axiom sets of quantum field theory can be replaced by the assumption that a theory can be consistently coupled to a certain class of complex metrics. However, it is interesting, though speculative, to consider their class of "allowable" complex metrics in the context of quantum gravity.

In section 3 of this paper, we describe the class of metrics considered in [6] and show that the problematical examples of section 2 are not allowable in their sense. Then in section 4, we consider some of the cases in which apparently useful statements about quantum gravity have been made using complex solutions of Einstein's equations, and show that the metrics considered are allowable. This gives at least some support for the idea of restricting to "allowable" metrics as saddle points.

In section 5, we discuss from this point of view the integration cycle of the gravitational path integral. As originally discussed by Gibbons, Hawking, and Perry [2], the action of Euclidean quantum gravity is not bounded below. They proposed that the gravitational path integral should be understood as an integral over a real cycle in the space of complex metrics. In the context of perturbation theory around a given classical solution, their proposal is satisfactory, and, if the given solution is allowable, their construction stays in the class of allowable metrics. A satisfactory extension of their proposal beyond perturbation theory is not apparent.

Finally, in Appendix A, we analyze and generalize a question from [5]. The original question involved the Euler characteristic of a two-manifold M and the conditions under which it can be computed as $\int_M \mathrm{d}^2x\sqrt{\det g}R/4\pi$, where R is the Ricci scalar of a complex metric g.

It is a pleasure to submit this article to a volume in honor of the 70th birthday of Frank Wilczek, who was my colleague at Princeton in the early 1970s, and later on the IAS faculty. Frank has made many important contributions to different areas of physics, never shying away from bold speculation. So I hope it is not too inappropriate to submit to this volume a rather speculative article, which is largely motivated by a limited number of examples that are discussed in section 4.[a]

2. Some Examples of Complex Solutions of Einstein's Equations

The usual flat metric on $\mathbb{R}^D$ can be written

$$\mathrm{d}s^2 = \mathrm{d}r^2 + r^2\mathrm{d}\Omega^2, \tag{2.1}$$

where r is a non-negative real variable and $\mathrm{d}\Omega^2$ is the usual round metric on a sphere S^{D-1}. One simple way to generalize this to a complex invertible metric,[b] is to leave alone the real sphere S^{D-1} but relax the condition for r to be real. Instead, we specify that r runs over a curve in the complex

---

[a]An earlier version of part of this material was presented at a conference in honor of the 70th birthday of another distinguished colleague, Thibault Damour.
[b]In $D = 2$, this example was briefly described in footnote 5 of [5].

r-plane, for example a curve $r = r(u)$, where u is a real variable. The metric is then

$$ds^2 = r'(u)^2 du^2 + r(u)^2 d\Omega^2. \qquad (2.2)$$

This metric is nondegenerate as long as $r(u)$ and $r'(u)$ are both nonzero for all u. In that case, the metric is flat. Indeed, if $r(u)$ is real, the metric (2.2) just differs from the original flat metric (2.1) by a reparametrization, so it is certainly flat. But when one verifies this flatness, one never has to use the fact that $r(u)$ is real, so the metric remains flat even when $r(u)$ is complex-valued.

If we want a compact manifold without boundary, we should take u to run over a compact interval $u_0 \leq u \leq u_1$ and require $r(u_0) = r(u_1) = 0$, as in Fig. 1(a). Topologically this gives a sphere S^D. The complex metric on S^D that is obtained in this way certainly satisfies the Einstein equations with zero cosmological constant, since it is flat.

We get more options if we complexify the sphere S^{D-1}. A unit sphere defined by real variables $\vec{x}$ satisfying $\vec{x}^2 = 1$ can be complexified by simply taking the components of $\vec{x}$ to be complex variables satisfying the same equation. If we complexify S^{D-1} as well as the radial variable r, we get a complex manifold $M_{\mathbb{C}}$ that comes with a holomorphically varying, complex nondegenerate metric.The metric of a real sphere can be defined as $d\Omega^2 = d\vec{x} \cdot d\vec{x}$, with the constraint $\vec{x} \cdot \vec{x} = 1$, and, after complexification, the same formula and constraint define a nondegenerate and holomorphically varying complex metric on the complexification of the sphere. So a flat, holomorphic

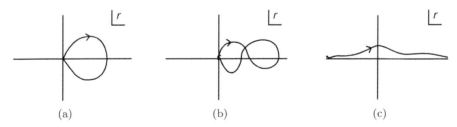

(a)   (b)   (c)

Fig. 1.   Some choices of curve $r(u)$ in the complex r-plane, leading to various complex flat metrics. (a) A loop that starts and ends at $r = 0$, leading to a complex flat metric on S^D. (b) A homotopically inequivalent immersed loop that starts and ends at $r = 0$, leading to another complex flat metric on S^D. This example is equivalent to the one in (a) if equivalence is based on homology rather than homotopy. (c) A path from $r = -\infty$ to $r = +\infty$, avoiding the origin in the complex plane. It leads to a flat "wormhole" metric, as sketched in Fig. 2(a).

metric on $M_{\mathbb{C}}$ can be written as[c] $dr^2 + r^2 d\Omega^2$. By picking a curve $r(u)$ while also keeping the angular variables real, we have described in the last paragraph an embedding of a real D-manifold $M \cong \mathsf{S}^D$ in $M_{\mathbb{C}}$. Of course, we can consider more general embeddings, or even immersions,[d] of M in $M_{\mathbb{C}}$, with the angular variables no longer real, and this will give more general complex metrics on the same M, though the condition that the metric should be everywhere nondegenerate puts a strong constraint on the immersion of M in $M_{\mathbb{C}}$.

What equivalence relation should we place on complex metrics derived from different immersions of a given M in the same $M_{\mathbb{C}}$? If has been proposed that two complex metrics on M obtained by different immersions in the same $M_{\mathbb{C}}$ should be considered equivalent if they differ by "complex diffeomorphisms." However, it appears difficult to define this notion precisely. It seems that at a minimum, we should insist that two metrics on M are equivalent if they come from homotopic immersions of M in the same $M_{\mathbb{C}}$. More optimistically, one might hope that two immersions of M in $M_{\mathbb{C}}$ give equivalent metrics if they are merely homologous. Going back to the case that the angular variables are real, in our examples, the first condition would say that two metrics are equivalent if they come from immersed curves $r(u)$ and $\tilde{r}(u)$ that are homotopic (keeping endpoints fixed) and the second condition would say that for equivalence of the metrics, the curves just have to be homologous. An equivalence relation based on homology is much stronger than one based on homotopy. This is illustrated in Fig. 1(b); there are many classes of curves $r(u)$ associated to complex flat metrics on S^D that are homologous but not homotopic. (It may be that some of these become homotopic once one allows the angular variables to become complex.)

To get exotic complex flat metrics on $\mathbb{R}^D$, we can simply use the same construction, but now with u ranging over the semi-infinite interval $[0, \infty)$. To get $\mathbb{R}^D$ topologically, we require $r(0) = 0$; to get a metric asymptotic to the standard Euclidean metric on $\mathbb{R}^D$, we require $r(u) \sim u$ for $u \to \infty$. If we take $r(u)$ to be identically equal to u for $u > c$ (for some constant c), we get a metric that coincides with the standard Euclidean metric outside a bounded region. Of course, the case $r(u) = u$ just gives back the standard

---

[c]As this formula suggests, $M_{\mathbb{C}}$ is closely related to the usual complexification $\mathbb{C}^D$ of $\mathbb{R}^D$, which we could have used, albeit less interestingly, in this discussion. It is more convenient to proceed as in the text.

[d]An immersion is a map that is locally an embedding. In the examples described previously, the curve $r(u)$ might be immersed rather than embedded in the complex r-plane; this will suffice to give a nondegenerate complex metric.

Euclidean metric. We can get other families of complex flat metrics on $\mathbb{R}^D$ by choosing the curve $r(u)$ to be immersed, rather than embedded, in the complex r plane. Provided that $r(u)$ approaches u sufficiently rapidly at infinity to avoid a boundary term in the Einstein action, all of these flat metrics on $\mathbb{R}^D$ have vanishing action, like the standard one.

However, these examples are all equivalent if the appropriate notion of equivalence is based on homology. More interesting are "wormhole" solutions, which we can get if u runs over the whole real line. We assume that $r(u) \to \pm\infty$ for $u \to \pm\infty$ and that $r(u) \neq 0$ for all u. A simple example is in Fig. 1(c). Such a construction gives a connected spacetime (Fig. 2(a)) with two "ends" each of which is asymptotic to a copy of $\mathbb{R}^D$; the ends are connected through a wormhole. So this construction gives complex wormhole solutions of Einstein's equations with zero action. For additional examples of the same type, we could have $r(u) \to +\infty$ at both ends $u \to \pm\infty$; the curve $r(u)$ could be immersed rather than embedded, and in particular it could wrap any integer number of times around the point $r = 0$.

Given a solution of Einstein's equations (possibly with matter fields) in which a wormhole connects two different asymptotically flat regions of spacetime, typically one can cut and paste to get an approximate solution in which a similar wormhole connects two distant regions of a spacetime that has only one asymptotically flat end (Fig. 2(b)). The ability to do this is based on the fact that far from a wormhole mouth, spacetime is approximately flat. Usually spacetime is only approximately flat far from a wormhole, in which case an exact solution in a world with two asymptotically flat ends leads only to an approximate solution in a world with a single asymptotically flat end. However, in the present context, we can assume that

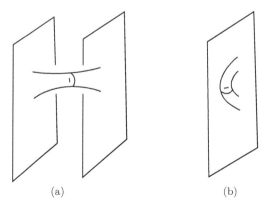

(a)   (b)

Fig. 2.   (a) Two copies of $\mathbb{R}^D$ have been connected via a "wormhole." (b) Two possibly distant regions of the same $\mathbb{R}^D$ are connected by a wormhole.

the function $r(u)$ in Fig. 1(c) is identically equal to u for $|u| > c$ (for some constant c); then the metric in Fig. 2(a) is identically equal to the standard Euclidean metric on $\mathbb{R}^D$ outside of a compact set on each branch. Given this, the cut and paste procedure required to get a wormhole metric of the sort sketched in Fig. 2(b) is exact. So we get complex solutions of Einstein's equations of wormhole type, with vanishing action, on a spacetime that at infinity reduces to $\mathbb{R}^D$ with its standard flat metric.

Finally, we can consider the case that the curve $r(u)$ is a circle embedded, or at least immersed, in the r-plane minus the point $r = 0$. In this case, we get a flat complex metric on $\mathsf{S}^1 \times \mathsf{S}^{D-1}$, again with zero action.

Somewhat similarly, we can make exotic complex solutions of Einstein's equations with a positive cosmological constant starting with the standard metric on a round sphere of radius ρ:

$$\mathrm{d}s^2 = \rho^2(\mathrm{d}\theta^2 + \cos^2\theta \mathrm{d}\Omega^2). \tag{2.3}$$

One important difference from the flat case is that the action I of a compact solution of Einstein's equation with cosmological constant does not vanish; it is a negative multiple of the volume V,

$$I = -\frac{2}{D-2}\Lambda V, \tag{2.4}$$

where Λ is the cosmological constant. After solving Einstein's equations to determine ρ and therefore V in terms of Newton's constant G and Λ, one finds that $\Lambda V \sim 1/G^{D/2}\Lambda^{(D-2)/2}$. Thus the action is large and negative if Λ is small and positive, a fact that has been offered as the reason that "the cosmological constant is probably zero" [7]. The de Sitter entropy is defined as $S = -I$.

Rather as before, we can construct complex metrics that solve the Einstein equations with a cosmological constant by considering curves in the complex θ plane. The resulting metric has the form $\mathrm{d}s^2 = \rho^2(\theta'(u)^2\mathrm{d}u^2 + \cos^2\theta(u)\mathrm{d}\Omega^2)$. First let us discuss compact solutions. The function $\cos^2\theta$ vanishes at $\theta = (n+1/2)\pi$, $n \in \mathbb{Z}$. A curve connecting two of these zeroes, and otherwise avoiding all zeroes, will give a manifold that is topologically S^D. Of course, there are many homotopy classes of such embedded or immersed curves, even after fixing the endpoints. The most basic example is a straight line on the real θ axis between two consecutive zeroes. This gives the standard real metric on a round sphere. Curves between nonconsecutive zeroes give exotic complex solutions of the Einstein equations. The volume is defined in Riemannian geometry as $\int \mathrm{d}^D x\sqrt{\det g}$. In the case of a complex invertible metric, it is not immediately obvious what sign one should take for $\sqrt{\det g}$, and on a manifold that is not simply-connected, in general there can be an inconsistency in defining this sign. For the allowable metrics of Kontsevich and Segal, which we discuss in section 3, there is a natural choice of sign. In the present section, we will not try to be precise about the sign of the volume.

For a metric derived from the round metric (2.3) by a choice of curve $\theta(u)$, the volume can be computed as the integral of the differential form $\Psi = \rho^D \cos^{D-1}\theta\,\mathrm{d}\theta\mathrm{d}\Omega$. (In this formulation, the sign ambiguity appears when one picks an orientation of the cycle on which one wishes to integrate this differential form.) Hence, letting v_D denote the volume of a standard D-sphere of unit radius, the volume for a solution based on a curve from $(m+1/2)\pi$ to $(n+1/2)\pi$ is

$$V_{m,n} = \rho^D v_{D-1} \int_{(m+1/2)\pi}^{(n+1/2)\pi} \mathrm{d}\theta\,\cos^{D-1}\theta. \tag{2.5}$$

By Cauchy's theorem, this integral depends only on the endpoints of the curve, not on the path taken between those endpoints. That happened because the differential form Ψ is closed, and means that the volume depends only on the homology class of the curve $\theta(u)$. For even D, $V_{m,n}$ vanishes if $n - m$ is even, and equals $v_D\mathrm{sign}(n - m)$ if $n - m$ is odd. For odd D, $V_{m,n} = (n - m)v_D$. Thus, for odd D, there exist complex solutions of Einstein's equations with topology S^D and action much more negative than the action of the standard real solution.

Another basic example is the curve $\theta = \mathrm{i}u$, with $-\infty < u < \infty$. The resulting line element

$$\mathrm{d}s^2 = \rho^2(-\mathrm{d}u^2 + \cosh^2 u\,\mathrm{d}\Omega^2) \tag{2.6}$$

describes de Sitter spacetime of Lorentz signature with radius of curvature ρ. An embedded or immersed curve from $\theta = -\mathrm{i}\infty$ to $\theta = +\mathrm{i}\infty$ that avoids the zeroes of $\cos\theta$ gives a complex metric that is asymptotic to de Sitter space in the far past and future.

Now suppose that we want a solution of the complex Einstein equations that has no boundary to the past, and coincides with de Sitter space in the future. Such solutions have been discussed in the context of the "no boundary" wavefunction of the universe [4]. We can get such a solution from a curve $\theta(u)$ with u running over the half-line $[0, \infty)$, provided $\theta(0)$ is one of the zeroes of $\cos\theta$, and $\theta(u) = \mathrm{i}u$ for large u. The case most often discussed is a curve that goes along the real axis from $\theta = -\pi/2$ (or $\theta = \pi/2$) to $\theta = 0$ and then continues along the imaginary axis from $\theta = 0$ to $\theta = \mathrm{i}\infty$ (or to some given point on the imaginary θ axis). This is usually described as follows. The path integral along the real axis from $\theta = \pm\pi/2$ to $\theta = 0$ is a Euclidean path integral that prepares an initial state; then the path integral along the imaginary θ axis up to a point $\theta = iu$ is a Lorentz signature path integral that propagates the state for an arbitrary real time ρu. The Euclidean part of the contour contributes an action $-S/2$ (where again S is the de Sitter entropy) and the Lorentz signature part of the contour makes an imaginary contribution

$$-i\mathcal{I}(u) = -i\frac{\rho^D c_D v_{D-1}}{G^{D/2}\Lambda^{(D-2)/2}} \int_0^u du'\, \cosh^{D-1} u'. \qquad (2.7)$$

In a classical approximation, the time-dependent state created by the path integral on this contour is described by the exponential of the action: $e^{-I} = e^{S/2}e^{i\mathcal{I}(u)}$. The real factor $e^{S/2}$ is the norm of the state. The oscillatory factor $e^{i\mathcal{I}(u)}$ describes the real time evolution of de Sitter space, as discussed for example in [3].

However, in the world of complex metrics, we can easily construct additional complex metrics that could conceivably represent the creation of de Sitter space from nothing, in the context of the no boundary wavefunction. With u still ranging over the half-line $[0,\infty)$, we can choose $\theta(0)$ to be a zero of $\cos r$ at $r = -(n+1/2)\pi$, for any n, while keeping $\theta(u) = iu$ for large u. For odd D, this multiplies the real part of the action by $2n+1$ and gives a wavefunction proportional to $e^{(n+1/2)S}e^{i\mathcal{I}(u)}$. Thus, naively, we can increase the amplitude to "create a universe from nothing" by increasing n.

By taking the curve $\theta(u)$ to be a circle, one can similarly get complex metrics on $\mathsf{S}^1 \times \mathsf{S}^{D-1}$ with zero volume that satisfy Einstein's equations with a cosmological constant.

What hopefully stands out from this discussion is that many or all of the exotic examples are going to give unphysical results if included in path integrals. One way or another, they must be excluded. With this in mind, after describing in section 3 the allowable metrics of Kontsevich and Segal, we will show that the exotic examples considered in this section are not allowable.

3. Allowable Metrics

On a spacetime M of dimension D with a complex invertible metric g, consider a p-form gauge field A with $p+1$-form field strength $F = dA$; set $q = p+1$. The usual action is

$$I_q = \frac{1}{2q!}\int_M d^D x \sqrt{\det g}\, g^{i_1 j_1}\cdots g^{i_q j_q} F_{i_1 i_2\cdots i_q} F_{j_1 j_2\cdots j_q}. \qquad (3.1)$$

The metric g is *allowable*, in the sense of Kontsevich and Segal, if I_q has positive real part for every nonzero (real) q-form F, for any $0 \leq q \leq D$. This amounts to a pointwise condition:[e]

$$\mathrm{Re}\left(\sqrt{\det g}\, g^{i_1 j_1} \cdots g^{i_q j_q} F_{i_1 i_2 \cdots i_q} F_{j_1 j_2 \cdots j_q}\right) > 0, \quad 0 \leq q \leq D, \qquad (3.2)$$

for any real, nonzero q-form F.

A motivation for imposing this positivity is that it makes the path integral of a p-form gauge field convergent, for any p. The idea in [6] is that quantum field theory in general — not just the free theory of a p-form field — is well-defined for a general allowable metric. More specifically, the hope is that this property can substitute for at least some of the standard axioms of quantum field theory. Some evidence in this direction is given in [6]. The condition (3.2) is imposed for all $0 \leq q \leq D$, although the motivation in terms of the field strength of a $q-1$-form field does not apply for $q = 0$. The $q = 0$ condition is just $\mathrm{Re}\,\sqrt{\det g} > 0$. One way to motivate the $q = 0$ case of the condition (3.2) is to observe that a zero-form field ϕ is a scalar field, which could have a bare mass m. Positivity for real ϕ of the real part of the corresponding action $\frac{m^2}{2} \int_M \mathrm{d}^D x \sqrt{\det g}\, \phi^2$ gives the $q = 0$ case of Eq. (3.2).

Many questions can be asked about whether the condition of allowability is either necessary or sufficient for well-definedness of quantum field theory. We will be rather brief with such questions, as it will not be possible to resolve them definitively. In terms of sufficiency, one can ask whether well-definedness of p-form theories for all p in a spacetime with a given complex metric is sufficient to ensure well-definedness of general quantum field theories in that spcaetime. Here it is worth noting that free field theories of massless bosonic fields[f] other than p-forms do exist, but those theories do not have gauge-invariant stress tensors [10] and therefore cannot be defined in curved spacetime. Moreover, non-free ultraviolet-complete theories of massless fields

---

[e] For $q \leq 2$, this condition was proposed by Louko and Sorkin in footnote 8 of [5] (see also their discussion of Eq. (2.20)). Note that the case $q \leq 2$ suffices in $D = 2$, which is the main case considered in [5]. One might think that one could weaken the condition (3.2) by taking advantage of the fact that $F = \mathrm{d}A$ obeys a Bianchi identity. This is actually not true, because every q-form F can be written as a sum $F_1 + \star F_2$, where F_1 is a closed q-form and F_2 is a closed $(D - q)$-form ($\star$ is the Hodge star). Condition (3.1) for closed F_1 and F_2 implies (3.2) for arbitrary F.

[f] Bare masses do not help; it is difficult to construct consistent couplings to gravity of massive fields other than p-form fields except via Kaluza-Klein theory or string theory [8, 9].

other than p-forms are not known, even in flat spacetime. So p-form theories are actually important examples of quantum field theories. For $p = 0, 1$, there are nonlinear versions of p-form theories — nonabelian gauge theory for $p = 1$ and nonlinear sigma-models for $p = 0$ — and for all p, there are mildly nonlinear theories in which, for example, the field strength of a p-form field A is not dA but $dA + B \wedge C$, where B, C are forms of degree r, s with $r + s = p + 1$. In any of these cases, the real part of the action is positive in an allowable metric. So it is plausible that known quantum field theories that are associated to underlying classical theories can all be consistently coupled to an allowable metric.

Concerning necessity, one might ask if the condition of allowability is unnecessarily strong. For example, let g be an allowable metric and let $g_\varphi = e^{i\varphi} g$ for some real φ. Replacing g by g_φ would multiply the action (3.1) by a factor $e^{i\varphi(D/2-q)}$, potentially spoiling the positivity of $\mathrm{Re}\, I_q$. Can we compensate by rotating the integration contour for the p-form path integral by a phase, $A \to Ae^{-i\varphi(D/4-q/2)}$? This might make sense for perturbative fluctuations, but as noted in [6], the partition function of a p-form field also involves a sum over quantized integer fluxes that cannot be rotated in the complex plane. So some condition along the lines of allowability is needed, though from this point of view a weaker condition might suffice. Another important point is that one may want the path integral for a quantum field theory in curved spacetime to have a Hilbert space interpretation. For this, the path integral of the matter fields has to be defined by local considerations, not by a completely general analytic continuation. Yet another issue is that the Wick rotation of the matter fields in general may multiply the path integral measure by an ill-defined phase.

In this article, we will not try to address such issues and instead will concentrate on the following two questions. Does a restriction to allowable metrics remove unwanted examples such as the solutions of Einstein's equations discussed in section 2? And where useful results have come from a consideration of complex solutions of Einstein's equations, have the metrics in question been allowable? We address the first question here, after summarizing some additional facts from [6], and we explore the second question in section 4.

A simple and useful characterization of allowable metrics was found in [6]. The $q = 1$ case of Eq. (3.2) tells us that the real part of the matrix $W = \sqrt{\det g}\, g^{ij}$ is positive definite. Writing $W = A + iB$, where A and B are real, it follows that A and B can be simultaneously diagonalized by a suitable choice of real basis. (First one picks a basis to put A in the form δ_{ij}; such a basis is unique up to an orthogonal transformation, which can be used to also diagonalize B.) In such a basis, W is diagonal, and therefore so is $W^{-1} = g/\sqrt{\det g}$. Multiplying by the scalar $\sqrt{\det g}$, it follows that g is diagonal in this basis:

$$g_{ij} = \lambda_i \delta_{ij}, \quad i,j = 1, \ldots, D. \tag{3.3}$$

Therefore $\sqrt{\det g} = \prod_i \sqrt{\lambda_i}$. Condition (3.2) for $q = 0$ tells us to pick the sign of the square root so that $\mathrm{Re}\,\sqrt{\det g} > 0$. Condition (3.2) now says that for any subset[g] S of the set $\{1, 2, \ldots, D\}$,

$$\mathrm{Re}\left(\sqrt{\det g} \prod_{i \in S} \lambda_i^{-1} \right) > 0. \tag{3.4}$$

This holds precisely if

$$\sum_{i=1}^{D} |\mathrm{Arg}\,\lambda_i| < \pi. \tag{3.5}$$

This statement is Theorem 2.2 in [6].

For example, a Lorentz signature metric $\mathrm{d}s^2 = -\mathrm{d}x_1^2 + \sum_{j=2}^{D} \mathrm{d}x_j^2$ is not allowable, since this corresponds to the case $\mathrm{Arg}\,\lambda_1 = \pi$. The inequality (3.5) is just barely violated, so a Lorentz signature metric is on the boundary of the space of allowable metrics. In fact, a Lorentz signature metric is on the boundary of the space of allowable metrics in two different ways, since for positive ϵ, either of the two metrics

$$\mathrm{d}s_{\pm}^2 = -(1 \mp \mathrm{i}\epsilon)\mathrm{d}x_1^2 + \sum_{j=2}^{D} \mathrm{d}x_j^2 \tag{3.6}$$

is allowable. The difference between the two cases involves the sign of $\sqrt{\det g}$. Since we are instructed in Eq. (3.2) to choose the sign of the square root such that $\mathrm{Re}\,\sqrt{\det g} > 0$, it follows that for $\epsilon \to 0$, $\sqrt{\det g}$ approaches the positive or negative imaginary axis depending on the sign in Eq. (3.6). Therefore, the sign of the Lorentz signature action $\int \mathrm{d}^D x \sqrt{g} \mathcal{L}$ (where $\mathcal{L}$ is the Lagrangian density) depends on the sign of the $\pm \mathrm{i}\epsilon$ term. The choice $\epsilon > 0$ leads to the standard Feynman integral computing real time propagation by $\exp(-\mathrm{i}Ht - \epsilon H)$, where H is the Hamiltonian and ϵ appears in the usual Feynman $\mathrm{i}\epsilon$,

---

[g]If x is a complex number, then $\mathrm{Re}\,x > 0$ if and only if $\mathrm{Re}\,1/x > 0$. Using this, one can see that condition (3.4) for a given set S is equivalent to the same condition for the complement of S. Hence it suffices to consider sets S of cardinality at most $D/2$. Equivalently, it suffices in this construction to consider p-form fields with $p \leq D/2 - 1$. This is related to the duality in D dimensions between a p-form field and a $(D - 2 - p)$-form field.

and the choice $\epsilon < 0$ leads to a complex conjugate Feynman integral that computes $\exp(+iHt - \epsilon H)$. In the Schwinger–Keldysh approach to thermal physics, one sign leads to propagation of the ket vector and the other sign leads to propagation of the bra. Which is which is a matter of convention. Clearly, the two metrics in Eq. (3.6) cannot be considered "close," even for small ϵ, and one is definitely not allowed to interpolate between them by letting ϵ change sign.

Perhaps it is worth stressing that the ability to regularize in this way a Lorentz signature metric as an allowable complex metric does not depend at all on the causal properties of the Lorentz signature metric. So from this point of view, it is perfectly sensible to consider Lorentz signature spacetimes with closed timelike curves.

The criterion (3.5) implies, as was explained in [6], that the space of allowable complex metrics is contractible onto the space of Euclidean metrics.[h] Indeed, Eq. (3.5) implies that for all i, λ_i is not on the negative real axis, so there is a canonical path to rotate λ_i to the positive real axis while always satisfying the condition (3.5): one rotates λ_i in the upper half plane if $\operatorname{Im} \lambda_i > 0$, and in the lower half plane if $\operatorname{Im} \lambda_i < 0$. It follows that any topological invariant that can be defined using an invertible metric, such as the integrals that define the Euler characteristic or the Pontryagin numbers of M, takes the same value for an allowable complex metric as for a Euclidean metric. It was shown in [5], with the example of the Gauss-Bonnet integral in two dimensions, that in general this is not true for complex invertible metrics. We return to this point in Appendix A.

The $q = 0$ case of Eq. (3.2) implies that if M is a manifold with allowable metric, then its volume $\int_M \mathrm{d}^D x \sqrt{g}$ has positive real part. In [6], it is shown that Eq. (3.5) implies that if M has an allowable complex metric, then the induced metric on any submanifold N of M is also allowable. Hence the volume of any such N has positive real part. One can take this as an indication that perturbative strings and branes make sense on a manifold with allowable complex metric. (In the case of perturbative string theory,

---

[h]The space of Euclidean metrics in turn is contractible to a point, by a standard argument. If g_0 is some chosen Euclidean signature metric on M and g is any other such metric, then for $0 \le t \le 1$, $g_t = (1 - t)g + t g_0$ is a Euclidean signature metric. Here we use the fact that the only constraint on a real symmetric tensor to make it a Euclidean signature metric is that it should be positive-definite; if g and g_0 have this property, then so does g_t. By letting t vary from 0 to 1, we contract the space of all Euclidean signature metrics on M onto the metric g_0, showing that the space of Euclidean signature metrics is contractible. Note that this argument is not valid (and the conclusion is not true) for real metrics of Lorentz signature, or any signature other than Euclidean signature.

one will need to impose worldsheet conformal invariance, as in the more familiar case of a Euclidean metric on M.)

Now we will use Eq. (3.5) to show that the problematic examples of section 2 are not allowable. First consider the flat metrics of the form $ds^2 = r'(u)^2 du^2 + r(u)^2 d\Omega^2$, where $r(u)$ is a curve in the complex plane. If there is any value of u for which $r(u)$ is imaginary, then at that value of u, $r(u)^2 d\Omega^2$ is negative-definite, so $D-1$ of the λ_i in Eq. (3.3) are negative and Eq. (3.5) is not satisfied at that value of u. If $r(u)$ is never imaginary, then (except for possible endpoints at $r(u) = 0$) the curve is contained in one of the half-planes $\operatorname{Re} r(u) > 0$ and $\operatorname{Re} r(u) < 0$. If the curve is homotopic to the positive or negative u axis, the corresponding metric is equivalent to the standard flat metric on $\mathbb{R}^D$. Otherwise, there is some value of u at which $\operatorname{Re} r(u)$ has a maximum or a minimum. At such a point, $\operatorname{Re} r'(u) = 0$ so $r'(u)$ is imaginary. Hence $r'(u)^2 du^2$ is negative definite and one of the λ_i in Eq. (3.3) is negative, contradicting Eq. (3.5). The behavior near a maximum or minimum of $\operatorname{Re} r(u)$ actually consists of a forbidden transition between the two choices of sign in Eq. (3.6).

Finally, consider the metrics $ds^2 = \rho^2(\theta'(u)^2 du^2 + \cos^2 \theta(u) d\Omega^2)$ that satisfy Einstein's equations with a cosmological constant. Here $\theta(u)$ is a curve that avoids the points $\theta = \pi(n + 1/2)$, $n \in \mathbb{Z}$, except at endpoints. For an allowable metric, $\operatorname{Re} \cos \theta(u)$ must be nonzero, except possibly at endpoints; otherwise $\cos^2 \theta(u) d\Omega^2$ is negative definite and Eq. (3.5) is violated. To avoid vanishing of $\operatorname{Re} \cos \theta(u)$, the curve $\theta(u)$ must be confined to a strip $(n - 1/2)\pi \leq \operatorname{Re} \theta \leq (n + 1/2)\pi$, for some $n \in \mathbb{Z}$. This excludes many of the exotic possibilities described in section 2, including the closed universes and the solutions describing "creation of a universe from nothing" that have action more negative than the standard values. The other exotic possibilities are excluded by the fact that $\operatorname{Re} \theta(u)$ cannot have a maximum or minimum along the curve, since at such a maximum or minimum, $\theta'(u)^2 du^2$ is negative definite.

4. Some Useful Complex Saddles

Our goal in this section is to examine some examples in which results that appear to be physically sensible have been obtained by considering complex metrics on spacetime. We will see in these examples that the metrics in question are allowable. However, we consider only a few examples and it is not clear what conclusions can be drawn.[i]

---

[i]There are also proposals in the literature for applications of some non-allowable metrics. See for example [11].

4.1. *Topology change in Lorentz signature*

The first example that we will consider is topology change in Lorentz signature, which was considered originally by Louko and Sorkin [5] from a similar point of view. See for example [12–15] for further discussion of topology change in real time.

For closed universes in two spacetime dimensions, the basic examples of topology change are the creation of a closed universe from nothing (Fig. 3(a)), the splitting of a closed universe in two (Fig. 3(b)), and the time reverses of these. Neither is possible with a smooth and everywhere nondegenerate Lorentz signature metric. However, it is possible to pick a Lorentz signature metric which is smooth, and is nondegenerate except at one point in spacetime, at which the topology change occurs. For example, on a spacetime that describes creation of a closed universe from nothing, we can take real coordinates x, y such that the creation event occurs at $x = y = 0$, and consider the line element

$$(x^2 + y^2)(\mathrm{d}x^2 + \mathrm{d}y^2) - \zeta(x\mathrm{d}x + y\mathrm{d}y)^2 \tag{4.1}$$

with a constant ζ. The metric (4.1) smooth, and is nondegenerate except at $x = y = 0$. At $x = y = 0$, the metric is degenerate — it vanishes. Provided that $\zeta > 1$, this metric has Lorentz signature except at $x = y = 0$; $t = x^2 + y^2$ can be viewed as a "time" coordinate, and the metric describes a circle that is "created" at $t = 0$ and grows in proportion to t.

Some regularization is required, since presumably the coupling of quantum fields to a degenerate metric is not well-defined. One way to regularize the metric is to replace the line element with[j]

$$(x^2 + y^2 + \widetilde{\epsilon}(x, y))(\mathrm{d}x^2 + \mathrm{d}y^2) - (\zeta \pm i\epsilon)(x\mathrm{d}x + y\mathrm{d}y)^2. \tag{4.2}$$

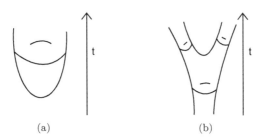

(a)   (b)

Fig. 3.   (a) Creation of a universe from nothing. (b) Splitting of a universe in two. In each case the time coordinate t runs vertically, as shown.

---

[j]Louko and Sorkin used a slightly different regulator that is also consistent with Eq. (3.5) in a suitable range of ζ.

In the framework discussed in the present paper, ϵ should be nonzero for all x, y because a Lorentz signature metric is regarded as a limiting case of a complex invertible metric that satisfies Eq. (3.5). The role of $\widetilde{\epsilon}$ is to make the metric nondegenerate for all x, y; for this, $\widetilde{\epsilon}$ should be positive at $x = y = 0$ but can vanish except very near that point. To see that the line element (4.2) corresponds to an allowable metric, let V be the one-form $x\mathrm{d}x + y\mathrm{d}y$, and let W be a one-form that is orthogonal to V. Then for $(x, y) \neq (0, 0)$, (4.2) has the general form

$$-(A \pm i\epsilon)V \otimes V + BW \otimes W, \quad A, B > 0. \tag{4.3}$$

This is manifestly consistent with Eq. (3.5). At $x = y = 0$, the metric has Euclidean signature and again Eq. (3.5) is satisfied.

Splitting of a closed universe into two can be treated similarly. One can pick a "time" coordinate t whose differential is nonzero except at an isolated saddle point, at which the topology change occurs (Fig. 3(b)). Near the saddle point, one can pick local coordinates x, y with $t = x^2 - y^2$. The line element $(x^2 + y^2)(\mathrm{d}x^2 + \mathrm{d}y^2) - \zeta(x\mathrm{d}x - y\mathrm{d}y)^2$, $\zeta > 1$ describes a smooth metric that has Lorentz, signature everywhere except at the saddle point, where it vanishes. This again can be regularized to give an allowable complex metric $(x^2 + y^2 + \widetilde{\epsilon}(x, y))(\mathrm{d}x^2 + \mathrm{d}y^2) - (\zeta \pm i\epsilon)(x\mathrm{d}x - y\mathrm{d}y)^2$.

Now consider the case that spacetime is a closed two-manifold Σ of genus g. The Gauss-Bonnet integral $I_\Sigma = \frac{1}{4\pi}\int_\Sigma \mathrm{d}^2x\sqrt{g}R$ appears in the action of "Euclidean" quantum gravity with a negative coefficient. If we pick on Σ a Euclidean signature metric h_{ab}, then the Gauss-Bonnet theorem gives $I_\Sigma = 2 - 2g$. On the other hand, it is possible to pick on Σ a Morse function t which has one local minimum, one local maximum, and $2g$ saddle points (Fig. 4). Together these points are called the critical points of t. As noted by Louko and Sorkin [5], given h_{ab} and t, one can construct the metric

$$g_{ab} = h_{ab}(h^{cd}\partial_c t\partial_d t) - \zeta\partial_a t\partial_b t, \tag{4.4}$$

which is everywhere smooth, and has Lorentz signature except at the critical points, where it vanishes. A simple regularization that gives an allowable complex metric is to replace g_{ab} with

$$\widetilde{g}_{ab} = h_{ab}(h^{cd}\partial_c t\partial_d t + \widetilde{\epsilon}) - (\zeta \pm i\epsilon)\partial_a t\partial_b t, \tag{4.5}$$

with $\widetilde{\epsilon} > 0$ near critical points (but potentially vanishing except near critical points) and $\epsilon > 0$. Now let us consider the Gauss-Bonnet integral I_Σ for this kind of metric. As noted by Louko and Sorkin, $\sqrt{g}R$ is imaginary for a Lorentz signature metric, and therefore in the limit $\epsilon, \widetilde{\epsilon} \to 0$, the expected real contribution $2 - 2g$ from I_Σ must be localized at the critical points of

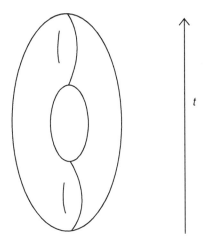

Fig. 4.   A torus embedded in $\mathbb{R}^3$ in such a way that the coordinate t, running verti-cally, has a maximum, a minimum, and two saddle points. An analogous embedding of a surface of genus g has a maximum, a minimum, and $2g$ saddle points.

the function t. Indeed, they showed that a local maximum or minimum of t contributes 1 to I_Σ, while a critical point contributes -1. As was explained in section 3, the Gauss-Bonnet integral has its standard value for an allowable complex metric. This is not so for a general complex metric, as observed by Louko and Sorkin and further discussed in Appendix A.

Topology change in Lorentz signature in any dimension D can be treated similarly. On any manifold M, one can choose a "Morse function" t that has only isolated, nondegenerate critical points. A metric of the form (4.5) is smooth and has Lorentz signature except at the critical points, where it vanishes. The regularization (4.5) makes sense in any dimension and gives a complex allowable metric.

4.2. The Hartle–Hawking wavefunction

An important application of complex spacetime metrics is to the Hartle–Hawking wavefunction of the universe [4]. In D dimensions, one considers a $D-1$-dimensional manifold Y with metric g_{D-1}. The Hartle–Hawking wavefunction $\Psi_{HH}(g_{D-1})$ is formally defined by a sum over all manifolds M with boundary Y, with the contribution of each M to the sum being the gravitational path integral over metrics on M that restrict on the boundary to g_{D-1}.

A saddle point in this context is a classical solution of the Einstein equations on M that restricts to g_{D-1} on Y. This problem makes sense for Euclidean metrics. If the Einstein-Hilbert action in Euclidean signature

were bounded below, one might hope that real saddle points would exist —
a metric that minimizes the action for given g_{D-1} would be an example.
Such a real saddle point might fail to exist if when we try to minimize the
action, M develops a singularity. The analog of this actually happens for
instantons in Yang-Mills theory with Higgs fields on $\mathbb{R}^4$; in an instanton
sector, there is no true classical solution, since the action can be reduced
by letting the instanton shrink to a point. Similar behavior can occur in
gravity; see for example [16]. Even if a classical minimizer does not exist,
if the action were bounded below, it would have a greatest lower bound
$\mathcal{J}(g_{D-1})$ and the asymptotic behavior of the Hartle–Hawking wavefunction,
near a classical limit or when g_{D-1} describes a manifold of large volume,
would be $\Psi_{HH}(g_{D-1}) \sim \exp(-\mathcal{J}(g_{D-1}))$. If the greatest lower bound on
the Euclidean classical action is not achieved by any smooth classical field
(because a singularity develops when one tries to minimize the action), but
can be approximated by a sequence of smooth classical fields, one could
describe this roughly by saying that there is no true saddle point but there
is a virtual saddle point at infinity in field space, analogous to a point instanton in Yang-Mills theory.

In many known examples, the gravitational path integral in the semiclassical limit is dominated by a critical point at infinity rather than a
conventional critical point; for one such example, see Fig. 5. In all cases
in which any candidate has been suggested for the semiclassical behavior
of a gravitational path integral, it is dominated by a conventional critical

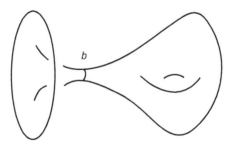

Fig. 5.   The genus 1 contribution to the one-boundary partition function in JT
gravity with a negative cosmological constant, as studied in [16]. There is no conventional critical point; in searching for one, one finds that the length b of the
indicated geodesic that separates the disc from the genus 1 surface tends to shrink
to 0, because of a contribution to the action proportional to b^2. Instead of a conventional critical point there is a critical point at infinity — or more precisely, at
$b = 0$. This critical point describes a hyperbolic disc with one cusp and a hyperbolic
torus with one cusp, with the cusp points identified. It controls the semiclassical
behavior of the path integral.

point or a critical point at infinity. The reason for this is just that if a critical point, possibly at infinity, has not been found, then the asymptotic behavior of the gravitational path integral is unknown. From the standpoint of a possible ultraviolet completion of Einstein gravity, there is potentially no fundamental difference between an ordinary critical point and a critical point at infinity. What looks in one description like a singular configuration might be perfectly smooth in a more complete description. Precisely this has happened to many types of singularity in gauge theory and gravity that have turned out to be perfectly smooth from the vantage point of string theory. In Morse theory, where topological meaning is given to the critical points of a function, it is a standard fact that on a non-compact manifold in general one has to include critical points at infinity. So their appearance in the gravitational path integral, where one deals with critical points of the action functional on the noncompact space of all real or complex metrics on a manifold M, should not be too much of a surprise.

In fact, however, the Euclidean action for gravity is unbounded below, and in general the boundary value problem associated to the Hartle–Hawking wavefunction is believed to have no classical solution of Euclidean signature (not even a virtual solution at infinity). For instance, consider Einstein's equations with positive cosmological constant Λ and choose Y to be a sphere with a round metric with a very large radius of curvature (compared to the length scale set by Λ). It is believed there is no real classical solution, not even in a limiting sense.

As is explained in [3], this phenomenon is actually a necessary condition for the Hartle–Hawking wavefunction of the universe to make sense in the context of cosmology. If the Einstein-Hilbert action in Euclidean signature were positive-definite like the action of a conventional scalar field, then the wavefunction $\Psi_{HH}(g_{D-1})$ would behave semiclassically as $\Psi_{HH}(g_{D-1}) \sim \exp(-\mathcal{J}(g_{D-1}))$, as noted earlier, where $\mathcal{J}$ is the greatest lower bound on the action. If gravity had similar positivity properties to scalar field theory, where the action is strictly positive unless the field is constant, we would expect $\mathcal{J}$ to be strictly positive except in very special cases. By a simple scaling argument, $\mathcal{J}$ would grow if the metric on Y is scaled up to large volume, and hence the Hartle–Hawking wavefunction would vanish exponentially when Y is large. This exponential decay of the wavefunction for large volumes would be analogous to the fact that, for a real scalar field ϕ, a wavefunction $\Psi(\phi_{D-1})$ defined similarly to the Hartle–Hawking wavefunction vanishes exponentially for large ϕ. The scalar analog of the Hartle–Hawking wavefunction is defined by choosing a particular M with boundary Y, and performing a path integral over ϕ fields on M that restrict to ϕ_{D-1} on Y. This wavefunction vanishes exponentially for large ϕ because the usual action of a scalar field is positive-definite, and grows when the boundary values are increased. In fact, the action grows quadratically with ϕ so the wavefunction vanishes as the exponential of ϕ^2.

In the case of gravity, the Hartle–Hawking wavefunction can behave differently because, as the Euclidean action is not bounded below, it is possible for there to be no real critical point (even at infinity), and the integral can potentially be dominated by complex critical points. For instance, in the example of the round sphere of large radius in a world with $\Lambda > 0$, though there is no real saddle point, there are complex saddle points that give an oscillatory contribution to the path integral. Moreover, this contribution can be large near a classical limit, because the real part of the "Euclidean" action can be negative. As explained in the discussion of Eq. (2.3), there are both conventional complex saddles, which involve trajectories from $\theta = \pm\pi/2$ to a point $\theta = iu$ on the imaginary axis, and unconventional ones, which start at $\theta = \pm(n + 1/2)\pi$, $n > 0$. The unconventional ones lead to apparently unphysical behavior, but we noted at the end of section 3 that they are not allowable. An equally important fact is that the conventional saddle points, starting at $\theta = \pm\pi/2$, are allowable. To get an allowable metric, we can start with the usual idea of a straight line from $\theta = \pi/2$ to $\theta = 0$ joined to a straight line from $\theta = 0$ to $\theta = iu$, and modify this slightly to get a smooth path along which $\mathrm{Re}\,\theta'(u)$ is everywhere nonzero. This gives the allowable metric $\mathrm{d}s^2 = \rho^2(\theta'(u)^2\mathrm{d}u^2 + \cos^2\theta(u)\mathrm{d}\Omega^2)$.

As many authors have pointed out, although the exponentially large amplitude for this allowable trajectory that "creates a universe from nothing" is interesting, it cannot be the whole story for cosmology, since this mechanism would tend to produce an empty universe with the smallest possible positive value of the cosmological constant. For an alternative treatment of these solutions, based on a different boundary condition in which the second fundamental form of the boundary is fixed, rather than the metric of the boundary, see [17].

4.3. Timefolds

In many contexts, for instance in real time thermal physics and in various analyses of gravitational entropy, such as [18–20], it is convenient to consider path integrals that in a sense zigzag back and forth in time. For example, given an initial state Ψ and an operator $\mathcal{O}$, one might want to calculate $\langle\Psi|\mathcal{O}(\tau)|\Psi\rangle = \langle\Psi|e^{iH\tau}\mathcal{O}e^{-iH\tau}|\Psi\rangle$. To describe this as a path integral, we need a path integral that propagates the state forwards in time by a time

τ to construct the factor $e^{-iH\tau}$, after which we insert the operator $\mathcal{O}$ and then apply a path integral that will propagate the state backwards in time to construct the factor $e^{iH\tau}$.

As explained in section 3, from the point of view of allowable complex metrics, the two cases of forwards and backwards propagation in time correspond to two possible regularizations of a Lorentz signature metric, in which, for example, $-dt^2 + d\vec{x}^2$ is replaced by $-(1 \mp i\epsilon)dt^2 + d\vec{x}^2$.

Thus, if we do not mind working with a discontinuous metric, we can describe the timefold with the discontinuous metric

$$ds^2 = -f(t)dt^2 + d\vec{x}^2, \tag{4.6}$$

with

$$f(t) = \begin{cases} 1 - i\epsilon & t < 0 \\ 1 + i\epsilon & t > 0. \end{cases} \tag{4.7}$$

However, to couple quantum fields to a discontinuous metric is likely to be problematical. To get something better behaved, we should replace $f(t)$ with a smooth function that equals $1 - i\epsilon$ for (say) $t < -\delta$, for some small δ, and $1 + i\epsilon$ for $t > \delta$. The only subtlety is that $f(t)$ is not allowed to pass through the positive real axis, as this would violate the condition (3.5) for an allowable metric. So $f(t)$ has to go "the long way around" from $1 - i\epsilon$ in the lower half plane through the negative real axis and finally to $1 + i\epsilon$ in the upper half plane (Fig. 6). The portion of this path in which $\operatorname{Re} f(t) < 0$ gives some imaginary time propagation that regularizes the real time path integral that we would naively compute using the real but discontinuous function $f(t)$ in Eq. (4.7).

4.4. *The double cone*

Somewhat similar to a timefold is the double cone, which has been used [21] to study the spectral form factor $\langle \operatorname{Tr} e^{iHT} \operatorname{Tr} e^{-iHT} \rangle$ in a holographic theory.

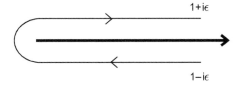

Fig. 6. The long way around from $1 - i\epsilon$ to $1 + i\epsilon$, avoiding the positive real axis.

A simple version of the double cone metric in two dimensions is

$$ds^2 = -\sinh^2 r \, dt^2 + dr^2. \tag{4.8}$$

If t is a real variable with an identification $t \cong t + T$, and r is real and nonnegative, then this metric describes a cone, with Lorentz signature and with a singularity at $r = 0$ (where one identifies points with different values of t). However, in the application to $\langle \text{Tr} \, e^{iHT} \, \text{Tr} \, e^{-iHT} \rangle$, one wishes to allow negative as well as positive values of r. In this case, still identifying $t \cong t+T$, one has a pair of cones, meeting at their common apex. In a holographic interpretation, the conformal boundaries of the two cones are related to the two traces in the spectral form factor.

This rather singular spacetime has a rather simple regularization, essentially discussed in [21], in which we avoid letting r pass through the origin in the complex plane. We simply take, for example,

$$r = u - i\epsilon, \quad u \in \mathbb{R}, \tag{4.9}$$

leading to the metric

$$ds^2 = -\sinh^2(u - i\epsilon)dt^2 + du^2. \tag{4.10}$$

Here ϵ is a small nonzero real number, whose sign is not important, in the sense that one can compensate for changing the sign of ϵ by $u \to -u$, $r \to -r$. As will be clear in a moment, this would have the effect of reversing which of the two cones computes $\text{Tr} \, e^{-iHT}$ in a holographic context and which computes $\text{Tr} \, e^{iHT}$.

The function $\sinh(u - i\epsilon) = \cos \epsilon \sinh u - i \sin \epsilon \cosh u$ is never positive for real u, so $-\sinh^2(u - i\epsilon)$ is never negative, and therefore the line element in Eq. (4.10) corresponds to an allowable complex metric. For positive u, $\sqrt{\det g}$ is close to the positive imaginary axis, and for negative u, it is close to the negative imaginary axis. Accordingly, with standard conventions, the positive u cone is related in a holographic description to $\text{Tr} \, e^{-iHT}$, and the negative u cone is related to $\text{Tr} \, e^{iHT}$.

Also analyzed in [21] is a regularized version of the double cone that is related to $\langle \text{Tr} \, e^{-H(\beta - iT)} \, \text{Tr} \, e^{-H(\beta + iT)} \rangle$. The line element is

$$ds^2 = -\left(\sinh r + \frac{i\beta}{T} \cosh r \right)^2 dt^2 + dr^2, \tag{4.11}$$

Again this is an allowable complex metric.

4.5. *Rotating black holes*

The last example that we will consider is a rotating black hole.

Gibbons and Hawking [1] computed the thermodynamic properties of a Schwarzschild black hole by computing the action of a smooth Euclidean signature solution of Einstein's equations obtained by continuing the Schwarzschild solution to imaginary time. They then considered a rotating or Kerr black hole, and observed that in this case continuation to imaginary time gives a complex metric,[k] which they called quasi-Euclidean. It turned out that the thermodynamic properties of a Kerr black hole can be computed from the action of the quasi-Euclidean solution, with physically sensible results that are in accord with other approaches.

From the perspective of the present article, it is natural to ask if the quasi-Euclidean metric is an allowable complex metric. In general, the answer to this question is "no." For example, let us consider the case of a black hole in an asymptotically flat spacetime. In the field of a stationary, rotating black hole, a quantum field has at least two conserved quantities — the energy H and angular momentum J. (Above $3 + 1$ dimensions, there might be more than one conserved angular momentum component.) The partition function of a quantum field propagating in the black hole spacetime is a contribution to Tr $\exp(-\beta(H - \Omega J))$, where β and Ω are the inverse temperature and the angular velocity of the black hole. In the case of a black hole in asymptotically flat spacetime, a particle of given energy can have arbitrarily large J if it is located far from the black hole. Hence such a particle can make an arbitrarily large contribution to Tr $\exp(-\beta(H - \Omega J))$, and one should not expect to get a sensible answer for a quantum contribution to Tr $\exp(-\beta(H - \Omega J))$. Hence it is natural that the coupling of quantum fields to the quasi-Euclidean metric would be ill-defined, and that this metric would not be allowable.

---

[k]This statement assumes that one continues to imaginary time while keeping the angular momentum real. If one also takes the angular momentum to be imaginary, then there is a real solution in Euclidean signature. One approach to black hole thermodynamics is to compute for imaginary angular momentum using a real Euclidean metric and then continue back to real angular momentum. This seems to give sensible results. However, it is natural to ask what happens if we keep the angular momentum real. The physical meaning of the imaginary angular momentum "ensemble" based on $e^{-\beta(H-i|\Omega|J)}$ is not very transparent. We put the word "ensemble" in quotes because the operator $e^{-\beta(H-i|\Omega|J)}$ is not positive, so in taking its trace, we are not counting states with positive weights. It is not clear what states dominate this trace, or even whether this question has a clear answer.

In Minkowski space, for example, if J corresponds to the rotation generator $x\partial_y - y\partial x$, then $H - \Omega J$ corresponds to the vector field

$$V = \frac{\partial}{\partial t} - \Omega \left(x\frac{\partial}{\partial y} - y\frac{\partial}{\partial x} \right). \qquad (4.12)$$

This vector field is spacelike for $\Omega^2(x^2+y^2) > 1$, and hence a particle localized at $\Omega^2(x^2 + y^2) > 1$ can have an arbitrarily negative value of $H - \Omega J$. The same is true in an asymptotically flat Kerr spacetime.

It was observed in the early days of the AdS/CFT correspondence that matters are better in an asymptotically Anti de Sitter (AAdS) spacetime [22–24]. In conformal field theory on a unit sphere, the operator $H - \Omega J$ is bounded below if $|\Omega| < 1$, and the trace Tr $\exp(-\beta(H-\Omega J))$ converges under that restriction on Ω. Therefore, in the bulk dual to a boundary conformal field theory, one expects the partition function Tr $\exp(-\beta(H-\Omega J))$ to make sense for $|\Omega|$ small enough.

In AAdS space, pick a rotating black hole solution with the property that outside the black hole horizon, the Killing vector field V that corresponds to $H - \Omega J$ is everywhere timelike. One expects that to be the condition that makes the quantum operator $H - \Omega J$ bounded below for perturbations outside the horizon, ensuring that the trace Tr $\exp(-\beta(H - \Omega J))$, taken over quantum fluctuations outside the horizon, is well-defined. The path integral on the quasi-Euclidean metric is supposed to be a way to compute that trace. So under these conditions, we may hope that the quasi-Euclidean metric might be allowable. In fact, as we will explain, the quasi-Euclidean metric is allowable if and only if the vector field V is everywhere timelike outside the horizon.

In four dimensions, a rotating black hole is conveniently parametrized by coordinates t, ϕ, r, θ, where H and J are generated by $\partial_t|_{\phi,r,\theta}$ and $\partial_\phi|_{t,r,\theta}$, respectively ($\phi$ is an angular variable with $\phi \cong \phi + 2\pi$), and in the asymptotic region, r is a radial coordinate and θ, ϕ are polar angles. In three dimensions, one can omit θ from this discussion; above four dimensions, some additional coordinates are needed but the essence of the following argument is not changed, as we will explain at the end. A general form of the metric of a rotating black hole is

$$\mathrm{d}s^2 = -N^2\mathrm{d}t^2 + \rho^2(N^\phi\mathrm{d}t + \mathrm{d}\phi)^2 + g_{rr}\mathrm{d}r^2 + g_{\theta\theta}\mathrm{d}\theta^2. \qquad (4.13)$$

All functions N, N^ϕ, ρ, g_{rr}, and $g_{\theta\theta}$ depend on r, θ only. This form is partly constrained by the fact that a rotating black hole has a symmetry under $t, \phi \to -t, -\phi$. We have assumed a coordinate choice such that $g_{r\theta} = 0$, though this will not be important. The function N^ϕ vanishes at $r = \infty$; this is part of the AAdS condition. On the horizon, N^ϕ has a constant value N_h^ϕ; this fact is important in constructing the quasi-Euclidean spacetime. Indeed, the constant N_h^ϕ is the quantity Ω that appears in the black hole thermodynamics. It is convenient in constructing the quasi-Euclidean spacetime to define a new angular coordinate $\widetilde{\phi} = \phi + \Omega t$. The line element is then

$$ds^2 = -N^2 dt^2 + \rho^2((N^\phi - \Omega)dt + d\widetilde{\phi})^2 + g_{rr}dr^2 + g_{\theta\theta}d\theta^2. \qquad (4.14)$$

In this coordinate system, the vector field that generates $H - \Omega J$ is just $V = \partial_t|_{\widetilde{\phi}, r, \theta}$. The condition for V to be everywhere timelike outside the horizon is therefore simply $g_{tt} < 0$ or

$$N^2 - \rho^2(N^\phi - \Omega)^2 > 0. \qquad (4.15)$$

This function vanishes on the black hole horizon, where V becomes null.

In the coordinate system $t, \widetilde{\phi}, r, \theta$, the quasi-Euclidean metric is constructed by discarding the region behind the horizon, setting $t = i\tau$, and identifying points on the horizon that differ only in the value of τ. The quasi-Euclidean metric is thus

$$ds^2 = N^2 d\tau^2 + \rho^2(i(N^\phi - \Omega)d\tau + d\widetilde{\phi})^2 + g_{rr}dr^2 + g_{\theta\theta}d\theta^2. \qquad (4.16)$$

In showing that this is smooth, one uses the vanishing of $N^\phi - \Omega$ on the horizon.

It is rather immediate from the definitions that a metric of this form is allowable if and only if, treating r and θ as constants, the purely two-dimensional metric $g_{(2)}$ that corresponds to the line element

$$ds_{(2)}^2 = N^2 d\tau^2 + \rho^2(i(N^\phi - \Omega)d\tau + d\widetilde{\phi})^2 \qquad (4.17)$$

is allowable. This condition is trivial on the horizon, where $g_{(2)}$ is Euclidean. Away from the horizon, we have a line element of the general form

$$ds_{(2)}^2 = A d\tau^2 + B d\widetilde{\phi}^2 + 2iC d\tau d\widetilde{\phi}, \qquad (4.18)$$

with real A, B, C. Such a metric is allowable if and only if $A, B > 0$. To see necessity, observe that such a metric has $\det g_{(2)} > 0$, so the necessary condition $\mathrm{Re}\,(g_{(2)}/\sqrt{\det g_{(2)}}) > 0$ for allowability reduces to $\mathrm{Re}\,g_{(2)} > 0$, that is, $A, B > 0$. Sufficiency of $A, B > 0$ can be seen by observing that for $A, B > 0$, $g_{(2)}$ can be put in the form (3.3) with $|\mathrm{Arg}\,\lambda_1| = |\mathrm{Arg}\,\lambda_2| < \pi/2$.

The condition $A > 0$ is equivalent to Eq. (4.15), and it is also true that $B > 0$ outside the horizon, since the black hole metric would fail to have Lorentz signature if $B = \rho^2$ is not positive outside the horizon. Thus we have shown that the quasi-Euclidean metric is allowable if and only if the vector field V that generates $H - \Omega J$ is everywhere timelike outside the horizon.

Above four dimensions, rotating black holes are more complicated [25]. However, the complications do not really affect the preceding analysis. Consider a black hole solution that has a Killing vector field that is everywhere timelike outside the horizon, and pick coordinates so that this Killing vector field is just $\partial/\partial t$; denote the other coordinates as $x^1, x^2, \ldots, x^{D-1}$. The metric then has the general form

$$ds^2 = g_{tt}dt^2 + dt \sum_i \alpha_i dx^i + h_{ij}dx^i dx^j, \qquad (4.19)$$

where g_{tt}, α_i, and h_{ij} depend only on $x^1, x^2, \ldots, x^{D-1}$. The function g_{tt} vanishes on the horizon and is negative outside, and h_{ij} is positive-definite outside the horizon. The quasi-Euclidean solution is obtained as before by substituting $t \to i\tau$, omitting the region behind the horizon, and identifying points on the horizon that differ only in the value of τ. Alowability is a pointwise criterion, and in checking this criterion at a given point, only one linear combination of the dx^i is relevant, namely $\sum_i \alpha_i dx^i$. Therefore, allowability of the quasi-Euclidean metric again comes down to the fact that a two-dimensional metric of the form (4.18) is allowable for $A, B > 0$.

A simple example of a rotating black hole with a Killing vector field that is everywhere timelike outside the horizon is the BTZ black hole in three dimensions. Consider a BTZ black hole of mass M and angular momentum J in a world of radius of curvature l. Black hole solutions exist for $|J| < Ml$, with

$$N^2 = \left(\frac{r}{l\rho}\right)^2 (r^2 - r_+^2)$$

$$N^\phi = -\frac{4GJ}{\rho^2}$$

$$\rho^2 = r^2 + 4GMl^2 - \frac{1}{2}r_+^2 \qquad (4.20)$$

$$r_+^2 = 8Gl\sqrt{M^2l^2 - J^2}.$$

The horizon is at $r = r_+$, so $\Omega = -8GJ/(r_+^2 + 8GMl^2)$. A short calculation reveals that

$$N^2 - \rho^2(N^\phi - \Omega)^2 = \frac{(r^2 - r_+^2)}{\rho^2}\left(\frac{r^2}{l^2} + \frac{(4GJ)^2(r^2 - r_+^2)}{(\frac{1}{2}r_+^2 + 4GMl)^2}\right), \qquad (4.21)$$

which is positive outside the horizon, that is for $r > r_+$.

5. Searching for the Integration Cycle of the Gravitational Path Integral

In [2], Gibbons, Hawking, and Perry (GHP) observed that the Einstein action in Euclidean signature is unbounded below. In fact, if one makes a Weyl transformation of the metric by $g \to e^{2\phi}g$, the action picks up a negative term proportional to $\int_M d^D x \sqrt{\det g}\, e^{(D-2)\phi} g^{ab} \partial_a \phi \partial_b \phi$. To deal with this, GHP proposed to Wick rotate the integration contour for the scale factor of the metric tensor, setting $\phi = i\varphi$ with φ real. They considered the path integral for asymptotically flat metrics on a space that is asymptotic to $\mathbb{R}^D$ at infinity, and argued that every such metric can be uniquely written[1] as $g = e^{2\phi}g_0$, where g_0 is a metric of zero scalar curvature. GHP formulated a "positive action conjecture," according to which the Einstein action is nonnegative for an asymptotically flat metric g_0 of zero scalar curvature. The combination of the positive action conjecture for g_0 and the contour rotation for ϕ was supposed to make the gravitational path integral convergent. The positive action conjecture was later proved by Schoen and Yau [26].

At least in the context of perturbation theory around a classical solution, the GHP procedure does make sense of the gravitational path integral, modulo the usual problems concerning ultraviolet divergences. In the Gaussian approximation, setting $\phi = i\varphi$, with real φ, makes the action positive and the path integral convergent. In perturbation theory, one is always integrating the product of a polynomial times a Gaussian function, and, provided that the Gaussian is convergent, such an integral is well-defined. So there are no further difficulties in perturbation theory, except for the usual ultraviolet divergences of quantum gravity.

Should one do better? One possible point of view is that the gravitational path integral only makes sense in perturbation theory around a classical solution, and to do better requires a better theory. However, it is also imaginable that extending the GHP recipe to make sense beyond perturbation theory would be a step towards a better theory. To go beyond perturbation theory, one would want an integration cycle Γ in the space of complex-valued metrics such that the real part of the Einstein action grows at infinity along Γ — ensuring at least formally that the gravitational path integral converges as an integral on Γ. Extrapolating from [2], an obvious guess might be to define Γ by saying $g = e^{2i\varphi}g_0$ where φ is an angle-valued field and g_0 is a real metric of zero scalar curvature. This is not satisfactory because with this choice, the

---

[1] In situations other than asymptotically flat metrics on $\mathbb{R}^D$, one needs to somewhat modify the GHP proposal. Some issues concerning this proposal were discussed in [3].

gravitational action $\int \mathrm{d}^D x \sqrt{g} R$ has no useful positivity property; it changes by an arbitrary phase when φ is shifted by a constant.

From the perspective of the present paper, one would like Γ to be contained within the space of allowable complex metrics. One can attempt to use gradient flow to construct the integration cycle Γ, as described in detail for three-dimensional Chern–Simons theory in [27]. In perturbation theory, this procedure will be equivalent to that of [2], but it might extend beyond perturbation theory. The general procedure is as follows. Let Φ^I, $I = 1, \ldots, N$ be a set of fields or integration variables, with an action $I(\Phi^I)$, so that the integral of interest is formally $Z_U = \int_U \mathrm{d}\Phi^1 \ldots \mathrm{d}\Phi^N \exp(-I(\Phi))$. The goal is to generalize this integral, which may not converge, to a convergent complex contour integral. As a first step, analytically continue the Φ^I to complex variables $\varPhi^I$, and analytically continue the action $I(\Phi)$ to a holomorphic function $\mathcal{I}(\varPhi)$. The Φ^I are functions on a space U and the $\varPhi^I$ are holomorphic functions on a complexification $\mathcal{U}$ of U. The goal is now to find a middle-dimensional integration cycle $\Gamma \subset \mathcal{U}$, such that the integral $Z_\Gamma = \int_\Gamma \mathrm{d}\varPhi^1 \ldots \mathrm{d}\varPhi^N \exp(-I(\varPhi))$, which formally reduces to the original Z_U if $\Gamma = U$, converges.

This may formally be done as follows.[m] Pick a positive-definite metric G on $\mathcal{U}$. In the previously mentioned application of this formalism to Chern-Simons theory, a simple choice of G leads to a relation with renormalizable gauge theory in four dimensions. In gravity, since we are dealing anyway with a highly nonlinear low energy effective field theory, we can contemplate a rather general choice of G. We will, however, assume that G is a Kahler metric $G_{I\bar{J}} \mathrm{d}\varPhi^I \mathrm{d}\bar{\varPhi}^{\bar{J}}$, as this leads to some simplifications. Introduce a "flow variable," a real variable s, and view the $\varPhi^I$ as functions of s. Now consider the gradient flow equation

$$\frac{\mathrm{d}\varPhi^I}{\mathrm{d}s} = G^{I\bar{J}} \frac{\partial \mathrm{Re}\,\mathcal{I}}{\partial \bar{\varPhi}^{\bar{J}}}. \tag{5.1}$$

In an application to D-dimensional field theory on a D-manifold M, this equation is really a differential equation on a $D+1$-manifold $M \times \mathbb{R}$, where $\mathbb{R}$ is parametrized by s. The solutions of the gradient flow equation in which

---

[m] See [28] for a discussion of this formalism in the context of gravity (and an introduction to the formalism). The perspective taken there is that the Lorentz signature path integral is the basic definition, and analytic continuation to complex metrics is used only as a procedure to more precisely define and evaluate it and deal with any ambiguities. A consequence is that complex critical points can only make exponentially small contributions, not exponentially large ones. So in particular the $e^{S/2}$ enhancement in the "creation of a universe from nothing," discussed in section 4.2, is replaced by an $e^{-S/2}$ suppression.

Φ is independent of s correspond to critical points of the action function $\mathcal{I}$ or in other words to classical solutions of the equations of motion. In any nonconstant solution, $\mathrm{Re}\,\mathcal{I}$ is a strictly increasing function of s.

Let p be a critical point of the action,[n] which for simplicity we will assume to be isolated and nondegenerate. (The discussion can be generalized to include other cases.) Because the function $\mathrm{Re}\,\mathcal{I}$ is the real part of a holomorphic function, the matrix of second derivatives of $\mathrm{Re}\,\mathcal{I}$ at p, which is known as the Hessian matrix, has equally many positive and negative eigenvalues.[o] Now consider solutions of the gradient flow equation on a semi-infinite interval $-\infty < s \leq 0$ that start at p at $s = -\infty$. Because half the eigenvalues of the Hessian at p are positive and half are negative, the values of such a solution at $s = 0$ comprise a middle-dimensional submanifold $\Gamma_p \subset \mathcal{U}$. In a finite-dimensional context, under mild assumptions,[p] the function $\mathrm{Re}\,I$ grows at infinity along Γ_p and the integral $\int_{\Gamma_p} D\Phi^1 \dots D\Phi^N \exp(-\mathcal{I}(\Phi))$ converges. Moreover, again under some mild assumptions, any integration cycle Γ such that the integral $\int_\Gamma D\Phi^1 \cdots D\Phi^N \exp(-\mathcal{I}(\Phi))$ converges is an integer linear combination of the Γ_p.

In gravity, U would be the space of all metrics on a manifold M and $\mathcal{U}$ is the space of complex-valued metrics on M. The diffeomorphism group $\mathrm{Diff}(M)$ of M acts on U, and the path integral is really an integral over $U/\mathrm{Diff}(M)$. Upon complexification, U is replaced by $\mathcal{U}$. One might naively think that $\mathrm{Diff}(M)$ would have a complexification $\mathrm{Diff}_{\mathbb{C}}(M)$ and that one would really want to define a cycle in $\mathcal{U}/\mathrm{Diff}_{\mathbb{C}}(M)$. This is wrong for two reasons. First, although the Lie algebra $\mathrm{diff}(M)$ of $\mathrm{Diff}(M)$ can be complexified to a complex Lie algebra $\mathrm{diff}_{\mathbb{C}}(M)$, there is no corresponding complexification of the group $\mathrm{Diff}_{\mathbb{C}}(M)$, so there is no way to define a quotient $\mathcal{U}/\mathrm{Diff}_{\mathbb{C}}(M)$. Second, even in gauge theory, where a complexification of the gauge group does exist, the gradient flow equation is not invariant under this complexification. The appropriate procedure to deal with gauge symmetries

---

[n]In all of the following statements, one has to allow critical points at infinity as well as ordinary critical points. Critical points at infinity were discussed in section 4.2.
[o]For example, if $\mathcal{U}$ has complex dimension 1, we can pick a local holomorphic coordinate $z = x + iy$ on $\mathcal{U}$ near a critical point so that $\mathcal{I} = z^2$. Then $\mathrm{Re}\,\mathcal{I} = x^2 - y^2$, and clearly the Hessian matrix of this function has one positive and one negative eigenvalue.
[p]The main assumption needed is that there is no solution of the flow equation on the whole real line $-\infty < s < \infty$ that flows from one critical point p at $s = -\infty$ to another one p' at $s = +\infty$. A sufficient condition to ensure that no such flow exists is that the different critical points have different values of $\mathrm{Im}\,\mathcal{I}$. This statement depends on the metric G being Kähler. If there is a flow between two distinct critical points p and p', one says that one is sitting on a Stokes line (in the space of all possible actions $\mathcal{I}$), and the statements in the text require some modification.

was described in [27]. One replaces the action $\mathcal{I}(\Phi)$ with an extended action $\mathcal{I}(\Phi) + \int_M \phi\mu$, where ϕ is a Lagrange multiplier and μ is a moment map for the imaginary part of $\mathrm{diff}_{\mathbb{C}}(M)$. Roughly, $\mu = 0$ is a partial gauge-fixing condition that reduces invariance under $\mathrm{diff}_{\mathbb{C}}(M)$ to invariance under $\mathrm{diff}(M)$. Then one proceeds as before, studying the flow equation of this extended action.

Unfortunately, it seems doubtful that this procedure will really accomplish what we want in the case of gravity. With a simple choice of the metric G, there is no obvious reason for Γ to remain in the space of allowable metrics. We could choose G to be a complete Kahler metric on the space of allowable metrics. This will force Γ to remain in the space of allowable metrics, but the real part of the action might not go to $+\infty$ along Γ.

An alternative to this discussion — and to the framework of the present article — would be to use gradient descent to define an integration cycle not for gravity alone but for the combined system of gravity plus matter fields. One would simply follow the above-described procedure, but taking $\mathcal{I}$ to be the combined action of gravity plus matter. In this case, all critical points are potentially allowed; one simply Wick rotates all gravitational or matter field variables to make any integral converge. Another mechanism has to be found to exclude undesirable examples such as those of section 2. As remarked in section 3, the sum over discrete fluxes for matter fields may be a problem in such an approach, and one also would have to accept that in expanding around a critical point, the matter path integral does not have a Hilbert space interpretation. The reason for the last statement is for a path integral on a manifold M to have a Hilbert space interpretation, the field variables and integration cycle have to be defined by local conditions on M; an integration cycle produced by gradient descent (or in perturbation theory by Wick rotating any mode whose kinetic energy has a real part with the wrong sign) does not have the appropriate locality. Still another issue is that Wick rotating the matter fields multiplies the path integral measure by a potentially ill-defined phase.

One last comment concerns the positive action theorem. Consider instanton solutions of Einstein's equations with zero cosmological constant that are asymptotic to $\mathbb{R}^D$ at spatial infinity. It is not difficult to prove that such a solution has zero action.[q] It would presumably not be physically sensible

---

[q]The bulk term $\int \mathrm{d}^D x \sqrt{g} R$ in the action vanishes for a Ricci flat metric, and the linearized Einstein's equations imply that a solution that is asymptotic to flat $\mathbb{R}^D$ at spatial infinity approaches the flat metric on $\mathbb{R}^D$ fast enough that the Gibbons-Hawking-York surface term in the action also vanishes.

to include in the gravitational path integral an instanton with zero action, since its contribution to the path integral would be too large, so one is led to hope that such solutions do not exist. Indeed, a special case of the positive action conjecture of [2], proved in [26], says that the Einstein equations in Euclidean signature with zero cosmological constant have no solution asymptotic to $\mathbb{R}^D$ other than $\mathbb{R}^D$ itself. With complex metrics, this is not so, as we saw in an example in section 2. Optimistically, an extension of the positive action theorem might say that the real part of the action is always positive for an allowable classical solution that is asymptotic to $\mathbb{R}^D$ at infinity. Alternatively, perhaps allowability is not the right condition or not a sufficient condition.

Acknowledgments

I thank R. Bousso, J.-L. Lehners, L. Iliesiu, J. Maldacena, S. Murthy, H. Reall, G. Segal, S. Shenker, R. Sorkin, M. Taylor, and J. Turiaci for helpful discussions. Research supported in part by NSF Grant PHY-1911298.

A. Pontryagin Classes, Euler Classes, and Volumes

Here we discuss topological aspects of the strange world of nondegenerate but possibly nonallowable complex metrics.

The Chern classes of a rank N complex vector bundle V over a manifold X can be described in de Rham cohomology by familiar expressions involving the curvature F of any connection A on V. For example, the second Chern class is associated to the four-form $\mathrm{Tr}\, F \wedge F / 8\pi^2$. Depending on the dimension of X, Chern numbers of V can be defined as integrals over X of products of Chern classes.

This construction is probably most familiar in the case that the structure group of A is $U(N)$, but it is valid more generally if A is a connection with structure group $GL(N, \mathbb{C})$.

If instead V is a rank N real vector bundle over X, then its Pontryagin classes are defined as the Chern classes of the complexification $V_{\mathbb{C}}$ of X. The Pontryagin classes of a manifold X are defined as the Pontryagin classes of its tangent bundle TX. So in other words, they are by definition the Chern classes of the complexification $T_{\mathbb{C}}X = TX \otimes_{\mathbb{R}} \mathbb{C}$ of TX, and they can be computed using any connection, in general of structure group $GL(N, \mathbb{C})$, on $T_{\mathbb{C}}X$. So given any connection A on $T_{\mathbb{C}}X$ with curvature F, the Pontryagin classes of X can be defined by the usual polynomials in F.

In particular, suppose we are given a nondegenerate complex metric g on X, not necessarily allowable. The standard formulas defining the Levi-Civita connection on the tangent bundle of X make sense in this situation, but if g is not real, they give a complex-valued connection. In other words, the Levi-Civita connection associated to a complex metric is a connection on $T_{\mathbb{C}}X$. The structure group of this connection is in general $O(N, \mathbb{C})$, a subgroup of $GL(N, \mathbb{C})$. But as we have just noted, Pontryagin classes can be defined using the curvature of any connection on $T_{\mathbb{C}}X$. So in particular, Pontryagin numbers of X can be computed using the Riemann curvature tensor R of any complex-valued metric. For example, if X is a four-manifold, the integral $-\int_X \operatorname{Tr} R \wedge R / 8\pi^2$ associated to the first Pontryagin class will always have its standard value.

One way to understand this statement is the following. If g is a non-allowable complex metric on X, it may not be possible to interpolate continuously in the space of invertible complex metrics between g and a Euclidean metric g_0. But it is always possible to continuously interpolate between the Levi-Civita connection ω derived from g and the Levi-Civita connection ω_0 derived from g_0: one just considers the family of connections on $T_{\mathbb{C}}X$ defined by $(1-t)\omega + t\omega_0$, $0 \leq t \leq 1$. (The interpolating connections in general have structure group $GL(N, \mathbb{C})$.) So they give the same results for Pontryagin classes.

In dimension $N = 2k$, another interesting curvature integral is the integral that appears in the Gauss-Bonnet formula for the Euler characteristic of X. As was noted by Louko and Sorkin[r] [5] in the case $k = 1$, it is not true that in general the Gauss-Bonnet integral computed using the curvature of a nondegenerate complex metric takes its standard value. In the case of the curvature formula for the Euler characteristic, the underlying invariant is the Euler class of an oriented real vector bundle. The differential form that represents the Euler class of a real vector bundle is a multiple of $\epsilon^{a_1 a_2 \cdots a_{2k}} F_{a_1 a_2} F_{a_3 a_4} \cdots F_{a_{2k-1} a_{2k}}$, where we view F as a two-form valued in antisymmetric $2k \times 2k$ matrices (generators of the Lie algebra of $SO(2k)$). Thus the definition uses the fact that there is a symmetric k^{th} order invariant on the Lie algebra of $SO(2k)$, namely the tensor $\epsilon^{a_1 a_2 \cdots a_{2k}}$ (in a different language, the invariant is the Pfaffian of an antisymmetric matrix). There is no such invariant on the Lie algebra of $GL(2k, \mathbb{C})$ (or even $SL(2k, \mathbb{C})$). But there is such an invariant in $SO(2k, \mathbb{C})$. So without more structure, a rank $2k$ complex vector bundle $V \to X$ does not have an Euler class. However,

---

[r]They illustrated the point with a nondegenerate complex metric on S^2 whose curvature vanishes, so the usual Gauss-Bonnet integral gives the value 0, not the standard Euler characteristic 2 of S^2. Their example of the complex flat metric on S^2 was described in section 2.

if we are are given a reduction of the structure group of V to $SO(2k,\mathbb{C})$, then one can define a Euler class of V. It is not a topological invariant of V but depends on the topological choice of the reduction of structure group to $SO(2k,\mathbb{C})$.

Applying this to complex metrics on X, we observe that a complex non-degenerate metric determines a reduction of the structure group of $T_{\mathbb{C}}X$ to $O(2k,\mathbb{C})$. If the structure group can be further reduced to $SO(2k,\mathbb{C})$ (which is the case if the Levi-Civita connection derived from g has holonomy in $SO(2k,\mathbb{C}) \subset O(2k,\mathbb{C}))$, then this enables one to define an Euler class of $T_{\mathbb{C}}X$. This Euler class can be represented by the standard curvature polynomial. However, the Euler class of $T_{\mathbb{C}}X$ defined this way in general really will depend on the topological class of the chosen complex metric, and will not agree with the standard Euler class.

A simple case in which X is orientable but a complex metric g on X reduces the structure group of $T_{\mathbb{C}}X$ to $O(2k,\mathbb{C})$ but not to $SO(2k,\mathbb{C})$ is as follows. Let X be a two-torus with angular coordinates α, β ($0 \leq \alpha, \beta \leq 2\pi$) and consider the metric $ds^2 = d\alpha^2 + e^{i\beta}d\beta^2$. A simple computation shows that this metric is flat, and that the holonomy under $\beta \to \beta + 2\pi$ is $\mathrm{diag}(1,-1)$, which is valued in $O(2,\mathbb{C})$ but not in $SO(2,\mathbb{C})$. Accordingly, it is not possible to define an Euler class with this metric. We note as well that $\sqrt{\det g} = e^{i\beta/2}$ likewise changes sign under $\beta \to \beta + 2\pi$, so that with this metric it is not possible to define the volume of X.

The general situation concerning the obstruction to defining $\sqrt{\det g}$ for a complex nondegenerate metric is as follows. A complex vector bundle such as $T_{\mathbb{C}}X$ does not have a first Stieffel-Whitney class. However, a reduction of its structure group to $O(N,\mathbb{C})$, such as that which is provided by a complex invertible metric g, enables one to define a first Stieffel-Whitney class $w_1^g(T_{\mathbb{C}}X)$. If and only if this coincides with the usual $w_1(X)$ (the class that measures the obstruction to the orientability of X), $\sqrt{\det g}$ can be consistently defined. In the preceding example with X a two-torus, $w_1(T_{\mathbb{C}}X) = 0$ but $w_1^g(T_{\mathbb{C}}X) \neq 0$, and there is an obstruction to globally defining $\sqrt{\det g}$.

One way to see that the obstruction to defining $\sqrt{\det g}$ and the obstruction to defining the Euler class must be the same is the following. The integrand in the Gauss-Bonnet formula for the Euler characteristic is $\sqrt{\det g}$ times an invariant polynomial in the Riemann tensor R. R is well-defined for any invertible complex metric, as is any invariant polynomial in R. So the obstruction to making sense of the Gauss-Bonnet formula is the obstruction to defining $\sqrt{\det g}$.

The Euler class in dimension 2 can be analyzed in more detail as follows. For simplicity we consider the case of an orientable two-manifold X.

The tangent bundle TX of X is in general nontrivial as a real vector bundle; the obstruction to its triviality is the Euler class. But the complexification $T_{\mathbb{C}}X$ of TX is trivial and in particular its first Chern class is 0, $c_1(T_{\mathbb{C}}X) = 0$. Now suppose we are given a complex invertible metric g on X. This determines two null directions in $T_{\mathbb{C}}X$ and hence locally it determines a decomposition of $T_{\mathbb{C}}X$ as a direct sum of line bundles. The exchange of the two line bundles under monodromy by the Levi-Civita connection would involve an element of $O(2, \mathbb{C})$ with determinant -1. So if the metric g actually leads to a reduction of the structure group to $SO(2, \mathbb{C})$, which is the case that an Euler characteristic can be defined, the decomposition of $T_{\mathbb{C}}X$ as a sum of two null line bundles can be made globally. (In the example given earlier of the metric $\mathrm{d}s^2 = \mathrm{d}\alpha^2 + e^{\mathrm{i}\beta}\mathrm{d}\beta^2$, the two null directions correspond to the null 1-forms $\mathrm{d}\alpha \pm \mathrm{i}e^{\mathrm{i}\beta/2}\mathrm{d}\beta$, which are exchanged under $\beta \to \beta + 2\pi$, so the decomposition cannot be made globally.) Since $c_1(T_{\mathbb{C}}X) = 0$, if $T_{\mathbb{C}}X$ is decomposed as the direct sum of two line bundles, then the form of the decomposition is $T_{\mathbb{C}}X = \mathcal{L} \oplus \mathcal{L}^{-1}$, for some $\mathcal{L}$. The complex line bundle $\mathcal{L} \to X$ is classified topologically by its first Chern class, which can be an arbitrary integer n. For any n, $\mathcal{L} \oplus \mathcal{L}^{-1}$ is trivial, and it is possible to pick a complex metric on X such that the decomposition in null directions is $T_{\mathbb{C}}X = \mathcal{L} \oplus \mathcal{L}^{-1}$. The Levi-Civita connection of X in this situation has structure group $\mathbb{C}^*$ (the complexification of the usual $SO(2) = U(1)$) and concretely it can be viewed as a connection on $\mathcal{L}$. The usual Gauss-Bonnet integral computes the first Chern class of $\mathcal{L}$. So, generalizing the observation of Louko and Sorkin, the Gauss-Bonnet integral can have any integer value.

References

[1] G. W. Gibbons and S. W. Hawking, Action Integrals and Partition Functions in Quantum Gravity, *Phys. Rev.* **D15**, 2752–6 (1977).

[2] G. W. Gibbons, S. W. Hawking, and M. J. Perry, Path Integrals and the Indefiniteness of the Gravitational Action, *Nucl. Phys.* **B138**, 141–50 (1978).

[3] J. J. Haliwell and J. B. Hartle, Integration Contours for the No-Boundary Wave Function of the Universe, *Phys. Rev.* **D41**, 1815–34 (1990).

[4] J. B. Hartle and S. W. Hawking, Wave Function of the Universe, *Phys. Rev.* **D28**, 2960–75 (1983).

[5] J. Louko and R. Sorkin, Complex Actions In Two-Dimensional Topology Change, *Class. Quant. Grav.* **14**, 179–204 (1997), arXiv:gr-qc/9511023.

[6] M. Kontsevich and G. B. Segal, Wick Rotation and the Positivity of Energy in Quantum Field Theory, *Quart. J. Math.* **72**, 673–99 (2021), arXiv::2105.10161.

[7] S. W. Hawking, The Cosmological Constant is Probably Zero, *Phys. Lett.* **B134**, 403–4 (1984).

[8] P. C. Argyres and C. R. Nappi, Massive Spin-2 Bosonic String States in an Electromagnetic Background, *Phys. Lett.* **B224**, 89–96 (1989).

[9] C. R. Nappi and L. Witten, Interacting Lagrangian For Massive Spin Two Field, *Phys. Rev.* **D40**, 1095 (1989).

[10] S. Weinberg and E. Witten, Limits on Massless Particles, *Phys. Lett.* **B96**, 59–62 (1980).

[11] J. Maldacena, J. Turiaci, and Z. Yang, Two-Dimensional Nearly de Sitter Gravity, arXiv:1904.01911.

[12] F. Dowker and S. Surya, Topology Change and Causal Continuity, arXiv: gr-qc/9711070.

[13] F. Dowker, "Topology Change in Quantum Gravity," in G. W. Gibbons *et al.*, eds., *The Future of Theoretical Physics and Cosmology*, pp. 436–50 (Cambridge University Press, 2003), arXiv:gr-qc/0206020.

[14] A. Borde, H. F. Dowker, R. S. Garcia, R. D. Sorkin and S. Surya, Causal Continuity in Degenerate Spacetimes, *Class. Quant. Grav.* **16**, 3457–3481 (1999), gr-qc/9901063.

[15] R. Sorkin, Is The Spacetime Metric Euclidean Rather Than Lorentzian? arXiv:0911.1479.

[16] P. Saad, S. H. Shenker, and D. Stanford, JT Gravity as a Matrix Integral, arXiv:1903.11115.

[17] R. Bousso and S. Hawking, Lorentzian Condition in Quantum Gravity, *Phys, Rev.* **D59**, 103501 (1999), arXiv:hep-th/9807148.

[18] X. Dong, A. Lewkowycz, and M. Rangamani, Deriving Covariant Holographic Entanglement, *JHEP* **11**, 028 (2016), arXiv:1607.07506.

[19] D. Marolf and H. Maxfield, Observations of Hawking Radiation: The Page Curve and Baby Universes, *JHEP* **04**, 272 (2021), arXiv:2010.06602.

[20] S. Colin-Ellerin, X. Dong, D. Marolf, M. Rangamani, and Z. Wang, Real-time Gravitational Replicas: Formalism and a Variational Principle, arXiv:2012.00828.

[21] P. Saad, S. H. Shenker, and D. Stanford, A Semiclassical Ramp in SYK and in Gravity, arXiv:1806.06840.

[22] S. W. Hawking and H. S. Reall, Charged and Rotating AdS Black Holes and Their CFT Duals, arXiv:hep-th/9908109.

[23] S. W. Hawking, Stability of AdS and Phase Transitions, *Class. Quantum Grav.* **17**, 1093–99 (2000).

[24] S. W. Hawking, C. J. Hunter, and M. M. Taylor-Robinson, Rotation and the AdS/CFT Correspondence, arXiv:hep-th/9811056.

[25] R. Myers and M. Perry, Black Holes in Higher Dimensional Spacetimes, *Ann. Phys.* **172**, 304–47 (1986).

[26] R. Schoen and S.-T. Yau, Proof of the Postive-Action Conjecture in Quantum Relativity, *Phys. Rev. Lett.* **42**, 547 (1979).

[27] E. Witten, Analytic Continuation of Chern-Simons Theory, in J. E. Andersen *et al.*, eds., *Chern-Simons Gauge Theory: 20 Years After* (American Mathematical Society, 2011), arXiv:1001.2933.

[28] J. Feldbrugge, J.-L. Lehner, and N. Turok, Lorentzian Quantum Cosmology, arXiv:1703.02076.

Classical Computer, Quantum Computer, and the Gödel's Theorem

Biao Wu

International Center for Quantum Materials
School of Physics, Peking University, Beijing 100871, China
Wilczek Quantum Center, School of Physics and Astronomy
Shanghai Jiao Tong University, Shanghai 200240, China and
Collaborative Innovation Center of Quantum Matter
Beijing 100871, China
wubiao@pku.edu.cn

Galileo wrote in 1623, "*Philosophy is written in this grand book — I mean the universe — which stands continually open to our gaze, but it cannot be understood unless one first learns to comprehend the language in which it is written. It is written in the language of mathematics, and its characters are triangles, circles, and other geometric figures, without which it is humanly impossible to understand a single word of it; without these, one is wandering about in a dark labyrinth.*" [1] This was a remarkably bold and visionary statement at the time when there were only a few accurate mathematical descriptions of physical phenomena, such as free fall and pendulum. Currently, there is no doubt that the universe is written in the language of mathematics. A physical process is literally a demonstration of a mathematical solution. As computation is a process of finding mathematical solutions, a physical process can be regarded as a computation of a mathematical equation. Or simply, physics is computational. How about the reverse, is computation physical? The answer had been "No" until the discovery of quantum computers [2–5]. It is now widely accepted that computation is physical. Different models of computation correspond to different physical laws. Classical physics underlies Turing machine and other models of classical computers, quantum physics is behind quantum computers.

However, it is not obvious at all why a classical computer is classical and a quantum computer is quantum. The models of classical computers do not operate according to the Newton's equations of motion; neither do the models of quantum computers run according to the Schrödinger equation. There is even no Planck constant $\hbar$ in theoretical models of quantum computers. It turns out that being classical and being quantum are concepts more

fundamental than equations of motion. The nature of a computer is determined by the cloneability of the information processed by the computer. If
the information is cloneable, the computer is classical; if it is uncloneable, the
computer is quantum. As the information processed in neurons are cloneable,
brains (human or non-human) are classical computers. Penrose argued that
the Gödel theorem implies that human brains (not all brains) are not classical [6]. I shall show that this is due to his misunderstanding of the theorem.
The Gödel theorem in fact implies that there are innumerable mathematical
statements so that human mathematicians, who have only finite physical
resources, cannot prove all of them to be true or false. An example is constructed to demonstrate it. In the end, I shall give an example on how to
construct theoretical models of computing that are more powerful than quantum computers [7]. To do this, the information processed by the computers
has to be different from both classical computers and quantum computers.

1. Classical Computer and Quantum Computer

There are many different models of classical computers, such as the famed
Turing machine and the conventional digital computer. They are all equivalent in terms of theoretical computing power [8]. I shall use the reversible
classical computer to illustrate the essential features of a classical computer.
The primary reason is that quantum computers can be viewed as a straightforward extension or quantization of reversible classical computers, which
makes the comparison between classical computer and quantum computer
more transparent.

A reversible classical computer has one universal logic gate, the Tofolli
gate, along with an array of bits. Each bit has only two values, 0 and 1. The
Tofolli gate, as shown in Fig. 1(b), has two control bits and one target bit.
Only when both control bits are 1, the target bit switches between 0 and 1 [8].

On top of the reversible classical computer, if we add two more logic
gates and replace bits with qubits, we have the standard circuit model of a
quantum computer. The two additional gates are the Hadamard gate H and

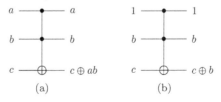

Fig. 1.   (a) The Toffoli gate; (b) CNOT gate constructed from the Tofolli gate. The
inputs a, b, c are Boolean variables.

$\pi/8$ gate T [8],

$$H = \frac{1}{\sqrt{2}} \begin{pmatrix} 1 & 1 \\ 1 & -1 \end{pmatrix}, \quad T = \begin{pmatrix} 1 & 0 \\ 0 & e^{i\pi/4} \end{pmatrix}. \tag{1}$$

The usual universal quantum gate, CNOT gate, can be easily constructed from the Tofolli gate as shown in Fig. 1(B). The key difference between qubit and bit is that a qubit can be in a superposition state

$$|\psi\rangle = \alpha |0\rangle + \beta |1\rangle. \tag{2}$$

The states of a bit correspond to two special cases, $\alpha = 1, \beta = 0$ and $\alpha = 0, \beta = 1$.

The Hadamard gate is the key in a quantum computer. It is the only universal gate that is capable of generating a superposition state out of a non-superposition state, for example,

$$H |0\rangle = \frac{1}{\sqrt{2}}(|0\rangle + |1\rangle). \tag{3}$$

Only with Hadamard gates will we be able to generate more superposition terms, change the superposition amplitudes, and facilitate interference in the course of computation. This shows that quantum computers can be viewed as a quantization of reversible classical computers. The quantization is achieved primarily with the Hadamard gate and additionally with $\pi/8$ gate T, but remarkably without Planck constant. A classical computer with n bits have exactly 2^n states,

$$|J\rangle = |J_1, J_2, \dots, J_k, \dots, J_n\rangle \tag{4}$$

where J_k is the kth binary digit of J ($J = 0, 1, 2, \dots, 2^n - 1$). In contrast, a quantum computer with n qubits has infinite states that live in a Hilbert space spanned by $|J\rangle$'s. In general, a quantum computer is in a superposition state

$$|\Psi\rangle = \sum_{J=0}^{2^n-1} a_J |J\rangle. \tag{5}$$

2. Cloneable States and Uncloneable States

The reversible classical computer is clearly not quantum as it does not allow generation of superposition. But why is it classical? Why is Turing machine classical? The conventional digital computer is also as regarded as classical even it is irreversible. What do these models of classical computers have in common with classical mechanics? Similarly, why is the model of quantum computers described above quantal? There is even no Planck constant in the model.

To answer these questions, let us review dynamical systems in general. A dynamical system has a configuration space and an evolution rule (or a set of evolution rules). Its state is a point in the configuration space. The system can start at any point in the configuration space. The evolution rule dictates it to evolve deterministically from one state to another. Classical mechanics is a dynamical system. The configuration space is the phase space and the evolution rule is the Newton's equations of motion. Quantum mechanics is a dynamical system. The configuration space is the Hilbert space and the evolution rule is the Schrödinger equation. Mathematically, classical mechanics and quantum mechanics are essentially the same type of dynamical systems. Koopman and von Neumann formulated classical mechanics mathematically as quantum systems [9, 10]. And Heslot converted the Schrödinger equation mathematically into a set of Newton's equations of motion [11].

This shows that the equations of motion are not what makes classical mechanics classical and quantum mechanics quantal. The key difference is how their states, the points in their configuration spaces, are related to physical reality. The coordinates of a point in the phase space are momenta and positions, which can be directly measured and cloned. In contrast, a point in a Hilbert space, usually called wave function, is not directly observable and can not be cloned in general. To relate a wave function to physical reality, one has to first select a complete set of orthonormal basis, which are usually the eigenfunctions of a physical quantity such as momentum, position or angular momentum. This selection of basis is outside of the configuration space and the equations of motion, and is done independently. When the wave function is expanded in this basis, the expansion coefficients (or the coordinates) are not measurable, and thus not cloneable. Upon measurement, the basis vector is observed along with its corresponding eigenvalue, not the coefficients (or the coordinates). To distinguish this crucial difference, we call classical state (a point in phase space) *cloneable* and quantum state (a vector in Hilbert space) *uncloneable*. It is this cloneability of their states that separates a classical system from a quantum system, not its equations of motion. This cloneability is related to the well-known no-cloning theorem for quantum states [12, 13]. According to this theorem, all the states $|J\rangle$ of bits can be cloned but not their superpositions, such as the states in Eq. (5).

The states of a classical particle are cloneable. Its position and momentum can be measured and recorded directly, ultimately cloned faithfully with negligible errors. The states $|J\rangle$ of bits are cloneable not only theoretically but also in practice: the two states, 0 or 1, of a bit, often represented by different voltages, can be measured and observed directly, and cloned faithfully. It is this common feature with a classical particle that makes bits classical. This is the key reason that any computer with bits, such as the Turing machine, the conventional digital computer, and the reversible computer are classical. In contrast, the states of qubits are vectors in the Hilbert space just like the wave functions in quantum mechanics. Upon measurement, only partial information of these states can be recorded; they can not be cloned faithfully with negligible errors. As a result, computers with qubits are quantum computers. It is now clear. Classical computer is classical because its states (or information) are cloneable. Quantum computer is quantal because its states (or information) are uncloneable. One can force the quantum states to be cloneable. This is exactly what happens when we simulate a quantum system on a classical computer. The price to pay is that the memory size of a classical computer would have to grow exponentially with the size of the quantum system. It is precisely what motivated the concept of quantum computers [2, 3]. Note that one can also repeat measurements on a given quantum state and ultimately clone it faithfully. Unfortunately, the number of measurements needed grows exponentially with the system size [14].

3. Brain and the Gödel's Theorem

The brain (human or non-human) is clearly a classical computer because the states of each neuron are cloneable. A neuron state is marked by electrical pulses (usually called action potential) passing through the axon, opening of ion channels, sodium and potassium concentrations, activation of chemical or electric signals at synapses. These physical and chemical states can be measured and recorded directly and cloned faithfully, at least in principle. Technically, it is challenging to clone faithfully the functions of a single neuron, not to mention a network of neurons (brain). But it is an issue of technology, not an issue of theoretical principles. Technically, we are still far away from building a machine that moves in a jungle as adeptly as monkeys. Nevertheless, the monkey's brain, muscle, and other body parts function classically.

That human brain is a classical computer is also evident in the process of a mathematician proving a theorem. When a mathematician proves a theorem, axioms or assumptions are inputs, mathematical inductions are logical gates, known theorems or lemmas are subroutines. A completed proof is essentially a classical algorithm because all the symbols and induction rules can be written down without any ambiguity, and be cloned faithfully from mathematician to mathematician. In other words, they are cloneable just like the states of bits.

However, Penrose argued that the human brain is not a classical computer and may be of quantum nature [6]. He believes that this is implied in Gödel's incompleteness theorem, which states that there are statements in any consistent formal system F which can neither be proved nor disproved in F. Let me first summarize Penrose's arguments or proof [6]. He listed all the computations $C_q(n)$ that take a natural number n as its input. $C_q(n)$ is the qth algorithm that computes on the input n. $A(q, n)$ of two inputs q and n is an algorithm that intends to ascertain whether $C_q(n)$ will stop: if $A(q, n)$ stops, $C_q(n)$ does not stop. With Cantor's diagonalization argument, Penrose arrives at the statement (M): if $C_k(k)$ stops, $C_k(k)$ does not stop. This leads him to conclude that

> Human mathematicians are not using a knowably sound algorithm in order to ascertain mathematical truths.

This means that the human brain is not a classical computer. For me, (M) is simply a self-contradictory statement and means that at least one of the assumptions made at the start of Penrose's proof is wrong. In fact, Penrose implicitly assumed that all the algorithms $C_q(n)$ are countable and therefore can be listed. This assumption is certainly wrong. In Cantor's proof that the real numbers are innumerable, he first assumed that the real numbers are countable and can be listed. With the diagonalization argument, he found a real number outside of the list. A contradiction so that the assumption that the real numbers are countable is wrong. Cantor's proof also implies that irrational numbers can not be exhausted by a finite number of different operations with finite symbols. In contrast, all rational numbers can be obtained by one operation (division) with 10 symbols (0,1,2,3,4,5,6,7,8,9).

Similarly, it is wrong to assume that algorithms are countable. Here is an example that demonstrates there are innumerable algorithms. A number is said to be embedded in π if its decimal digits can be found in π in sequential order. For example, 1.23456 is embedded in the first 50 decimal digits of π,

$$3.\underline{1}4159\underline{2}653\underline{5}89793238\underline{4}626433832795\underline{0}288419716\underline{6}939937510... \quad (6)$$

$R^{(n)}(x)$ is an operation that repeats n times for each decimal digit of x. For example, $R^{(1)}(1.23456) = 1.23456$ and $R^{(3)}(1.23456) = 111.222333444555666$. For every real number x, we construct a list of mathematical statements $E^{(n)}(x)$: $R^{(n)}(x)$ is embedded in π. The statement $E^{(1)}(\sqrt{2})$ is probably true. Its first twelve decimal digits are embedded in the first 100 digits of π.

3.**141**59265358979323384**6**2643383279502884**1**97169**3**9937**5**10

5820974944592307816**4**06**2**862089986280**3**48253421**1**70679...   (7)

Its thirteenth digit is 3 and will be found in the rest of the digits of π, similarly its fourteenth digit 0, and so on. The statement $E^{(2)}(\sqrt{2})$ is no longer as obvious. Here is the situation for the first 200 digits of π.

3.141592653589793233846264338327950288419716939937510

58209749445923078164062862089986280348253421**1**170679

82148086513282306647093**44**609550582231725359408128

48**11**174502841027019385211055596**44**6**22**94895493038196...   (8)

But still it is hard to believe that the next two digits 11 never appear in the rest digits of π, similarly 33, and so on. $E^{(2)}(\sqrt{2})$ is probably true. As n increases, we become less confident that the statement $E^{(n)}(\sqrt{2})$ is true. Consider $n = 6$. The first string of six or more consecutive identical digits is six 9's starting at the 762nd decimal place of π, the next is again six 9's starting at position 193034, and the next is six 8's starting at position 222,299 [15].

To verify whether $E^{(n)}(x)$'s are true or not, one can set up algorithms that simply compute every decimal digit of x and π and check them one by one. This method can show that some statements, such as $E^{(6)}(9)$, are true. When x is irrational, this method fails. It can not even show with 100% certainty whether $E^{(1)}(\sqrt{2})$ is true because mathematicians (including machines) have only finite resources and they can not compute an infinite number of digits. However, sometimes one does not need to compute all the digits of an irrational number to verify whether a statement is true or false. For example, one can show that $\sqrt{2}$ is irrational and $E^{(1)}(\pi)$ is true without computing all the digits. So, it is possible that mathematicians can figure out a "clever" way or algorithm to verify that $E^{(1)}(\sqrt{2})$ is true. However, it is hard to imagine that "clever" algorithms can be found for all irrational numbers and any n.

As the real numbers are innumerable, we have innumerable mathematical statements $E^{(n)}(x)$. Each statement $E^{(n)}(x)$ is clearly also an algorithm with two inputs n and x, and can be identified with Penrose's $C_q(n)$ via $q = x$. This example shows Penrose's assumption that $C_q(n)$'s are countable is wrong.

We now face two realities: (1) there are innumerable number of mathematical statements; (2) human mathematicians are only capable of using a finite number of symbols, finite sets of induction rules, and doing finite steps of deductions (similar to a finite number of logical gates in an algorithm). The latter means the mathematical statements that can be verified by human mathematicians are countable and can be listed. Therefore, it is clear that mathematicians can not prove all the mathematical statements, which are innumerable, true or false. This is the essence of the Gödel's theorem. Therefore, Gödel's theorem has nothing to do with whether the human brain is classical or not. The theorem just shows with mathematical rigor a common sense: it is impossible for any thinking machine (including the human brain) with finite resources to solve innumerable problems.

Gödel's theorem is often explained with self-referencing examples, for example, this statement is not true. This self-referencing is made rigorous in its proof with the diagonalization argument. It gives the theorem a mysterious appearance that obscures its essence and true implication: innumerable problems can not be solved with finite physical resources.

There are obvious differences between the brain and a conventional digital computer. It is a mundane task for many animals, including humans, to walk or run on difficult terrains; it is declared a major achievement whenever a robot's walking abilities have been improved in one or another aspect. It takes a long time for a human to add two large numbers; it takes almost no time for a digital computer to do it. This does not imply that the human brain may be a quantum computer. It is simply that we do not understand the networking of neurons inside a human brain. Just as we do not need to know every technical details of a digital computer to know for sure that it is classical, we can be absolutely sure that the human brain is classical before we understand it completely.

Galileo said that physics is written in the language of mathematics; Gödel proved that mathematics is limited by physics. After all, human is physical. All human products, including mathematical theorems, are limited by the physical laws. What we know and will know is negligible relative to what we will never know. This is in a sense good as we will never run out of truths to discover.

4. Beyond Quantum Computing

Is it possible to go beyond a quantum computer? According to the analysis in Sec. 2, it is impossible in practice since we do not have any experimentally tested theory that goes beyond quantum mechanics. Theoretically, it is certainly possible. We only need a dynamical system whose states in its configuration space are related to physical reality in a different way from both classical mechanics and quantum mechanics.

One such system was discussed a long time ago by Pauli [16] who was inspired by Dirac [17]. It was considered independently many years later as a generalization of Bogoliubov–de Gennes equation [18]. It was named Lorentz quantum mechanics because its dynamical evolution is generalized Lorentz transformation. The key features of the Lorentz mechanics are: (1) its states are vectors in a complex linear space with an indefinite metric; (2) its dynamics is generalized Lorentz transformation; (3) there are two sets of states, ones with positive inner products and the other with negative products. The third feature is crucial: the positive states are regarded as physical and can be measured; the negative ones are regarded unphysical. This means that the states in the configuration space, an inner product space with indefinite metric, are not only uncloneable but half of them are also unphysical. This is different from both classical states and quantum states.

We have proposed a new theoretical model of computing based on this Lorentz quantum mechanics [7]. We find that the search algorithm designed for this new computer model is exponentially faster than Grover's algorithm [19]. It shows explicitly that one can go beyond conventional quantum computers. In a new theory that unifies quantum theory and gravity, if its states are different from both classical states and quantum states, we would also expect to have a more powerful model of computing.

There are two computer models that were shown to be more powerful than quantum computers [20, 21]. Both add nonlinearity to quantum mechanics and claim that nonlinearity is behind the enhancement of computing power. It is a suspicious argument. Classical mechanics is inherently nonlinear and no one has been able to exploit its nonlinearity to enhance computing power. It is no surprise that both models were critically questioned from the theoretical point of view [22].

Note: I started looking seriously into quantum computing around 2015. As usual for a newcomer in the field, I soon had a "breakthrough", a constant-time search algorithm; as an experienced researcher, I also felt uncomfortable. Something may be wrong, but I was not sure what it was. In the summer of 2015, I visited Stockholm, where I discussed this work with Frank. Soon it was clear what the mistake was. What was inspiring was that Frank kept discussing this problem with me, suggesting various ways to amend the mistake. The discussion continued even after I left Stockholm. The eventual conclusion was that my original proposal was hopeless. Nevertheless, I was encouraged and started to try new approaches. I discussed them with Frank when he visited Hangzhou in the fall of 2015. Again they were flawed. But this time Frank came up with a beautiful idea, using resonance to do Grover search. About one month later, Frank sent me a note where he had worked out all the details of this idea with an additional interesting ingredient, monitor qubit. It eventually led to a joint paper [23]. More collaboration between Frank and my group followed. Recently, we had a wonderful quantum algorithm, which significantly outperforms its classical counterpart, for approximating maximum independent sets [24, 25]. It has been a wonderful and inspiring experience. I learned from Frank this life lesson: *mistakes may be embarrassing, but often they are opportunities for progress.*

References

[1] G. Galilei, *The Assayer* (University of Pennsylvania Press, 1960).

[2] Y. I. Manin, *Computable and Noncomputable* (*Sov. Radio.*, 1980).

[3] R. P. Feynman, *Int. J. Theor. Phys.* **21**, 467 (1982).

[4] D. Deutsch, *Proc. Roy. Soc. Lond. A* **400**, 97 (1985).

[5] D. Deutsch, *Proc. R. Soc. Lond. A* **425**, 73 (1989).

[6] R. Penrose, *Shadows of the Mind* (Oxford University Press, New York, 1994).

[7] W. He, Z. Wang, and B. Wu, arXiv:2103.10315 (2021).

[8] M. A. Nielson and I. L. Chuang, *Quantum Computing and Quantum Information* (Cambridge University Press, Cambridge, 2000).

[9] B. O. Koopman, *Proc. Natl. Acad. Sci. USA* **17**, 315 (1931).

[10] J. von Neumann, *Ann. Math.* **33**, 587 (1932).

[11] A. Heslot, *Phys. Rev. D* **31**, 1341 (1985).

[12] J. L. Park, *Found. Phys.* **1**, 23 (1970).

[13] W. K. Wootters and W. H. Zurek, *Nature* **299**, 802 (1982).

[14] H.-Y. Hu and Y.-Z. You, arXiv:2102.10132 (2021).

[15] D. Andersen, *The pi searcher*, URL https://www.angio.net/pi/bigpi.cgi.

[16] W. Pauli, *Rev. Mod. Phys.* **15**, 175 (1943).

[17] P. A. M. Dirac, *Proc. R. Soc. Lond. A* **180**, 1 (1942).

[18] Q. Zhang and B. Wu, *New J. Phys.* **20**, 013024 (2018).

[19] L. K. Grover, *Phys. Rev. Lett.* **79**, 325 (1997).

[20] D. S. Abrams and S. Lloyd, *Phys. Rev. Lett.* **81**, 3992 (1998).

[21] D. Bacon, *Phys. Rev. A* **70**, 032309 (2004).

[22] C. H. Bennett, D. Leung, G. Smith, and J. A. Smolin, *Phys. Rev. Lett.* **103**, 170502 (2009).

[23] F. Wilczek, H.-Y. Hu, and B. Wu, *Chin. Phys. Lett.* **37**, 050304 (2020).

[24] B. Wu, H. Yu, and F. Wilczek, *Phys. Rev. A* **101**, 012318 (2020).

[25] H. Yu, F. Wilczek, and B. Wu, *Chin. Phys. Lett.* **38**, 030304 (2021).

Thermodynamics of Small Systems
and Time-Scale Separation

Xiangjun Xing

Wilczek Quantum Center, School of Physics and Astronomy
Shanghai Jiao Tong University, Shanghai 200240, China
xxing@sjtu.edu.cn

It is my great pleasure to present this article as a gift for Prof. Frank Wilczek's seventieth birthday. For the past four years, I had the privilege of working with Frank and his friends on the establishment and growth of Wilczek Quantum Center at Shanghai Jiao Tong University, which turns out to be not only intellectually enlightening, but also emotionally fulfilling.

Assuming time-scale separation, a simple and unified theory of thermodynamics and stochastic thermodynamics is constructed for small classical systems strongly interacting with its environment in a controllable fashion. The total Hamiltonian is decomposed into a bath part and a system part, the latter being the *Hamiltonian of mean force*. Both the conditional equilibrium of bath and the reduced equilibrium of the system are described by canonical ensemble theories with respect to their own Hamiltonians. The bath free energy is independent of the system variables and the control parameter. Furthermore, the weak coupling theory of stochastic thermodynamics becomes applicable almost verbatim, even if the interaction and correlation between the system and its environment are strong and varied externally. Finally, this TSS-based approach also leads to some new insights about the origin of the second law of thermodynamics.

1. Introduction

One of the most significant discoveries of non-equilibrium statistical physics in the past few decades is that thermodynamic variables can be defined on the level of dynamic trajectory [1–3]. Consider, for example, a small classical system with Hamiltonian $H(\boldsymbol{x}, \lambda)$ weakly coupled with its bath. Here weak coupling means the interaction energy and statistical correlation between the system and the bath are negligibly small. The differential work and heat at trajectory level are defined as $đ\mathcal{W} \equiv d_\lambda H(\boldsymbol{x}, \lambda)$ and $đ\mathcal{Q} \equiv d_{\boldsymbol{x}} H(\boldsymbol{x}, \lambda)$ where $\boldsymbol{x} = (\boldsymbol{q}, \boldsymbol{p})$ are the canonical variables, and λ the external control parameter; $d_{\boldsymbol{x}} H_{\mathbf{X}}$ and $d_\lambda H_{\mathbf{X}}$ are variations of H due to $d\boldsymbol{x}$ and $d\lambda$

respectively. With $H(\boldsymbol{x}, \lambda)$ identified as the fluctuating internal energy, the first law at trajectory level then follows directly: $dH = d_\lambda H_\mathbf{X} + d_{\boldsymbol{x}} H_\mathbf{X} = đW + đQ$. Studies of these fluctuating quantities in NEQ processes have led to significant results such as Fluctuation Theorems [2], Jarzynski equality [3], as well as a much better understanding of the second law of thermodynamics.

Most small open systems, however, interact strongly with their environments, hence the weak coupling assumption can not be justified. There have been significant recent interests [4–25] in generalizing equilibrium (EQ) and non-equilibrium (NEQ) thermodynamics to the *strong coupling regime*[a]. Srong interactions and correlations with the bath, however, cause serious ambiguities in construction of system thermodynamic quantities, such as entropy and internal energy [5,7]. Many different approaches have been tried to construct a reduced thermodynamic theory for strongly coupled small systems, both classical [5–14], and quantum [17–25], and there has been no sign of convergence yet on the opinions. Jarzynski [5] proposed to remove these ambiguities for the classical case by fixing the definition of *system volume*, and developed a theory encompassing both the classical thermodynamics and stochastic thermodynamics. However, in the majority of small systems being studied experimentally, volume either can not be experimentally controlled, or does not play a significant role. Some authors [6,7,11,26] tried to decompose total thermodynamic quantities into a system part and a bath part. The most popular choice [6, 7], which works only for EQ states, is to let the bath part correspond to an isolated bath. There is no general understating about proper decompositions in NEQ situations. Furthermore, the previous theories not only are substantially more complicated than the weak coupling theory, but also assume that the interactions between the system and bath are fixed. Hence they are not applicable to a large class of systems where experimental control of interactions is an important part of the problems. Given the conceptual and practical importance of strongly coupled small thermodynamic systems, it is highly desirable to search for a simpler theory without the above mentioned limitations. Here we will show that such a theory can indeed be developed, with the additional assumption of time-scale separation (TSS).

We identify all slow variables as the "system" and all other modes as the "bath". TSS means that there is a large gap between the fast and slow time-scales, so that in intermediate time-scales, the fast variables (the bath)

---

[a]Note that the term strong coupling is often also used to denote systems were interactions among particles inside the system is strong comparing with temperature. This is not what we mean in the present work.

achieve thermal EQ conditioned on the slow variables (the system). Such an assumption was often invoked heuristically to justify adiabatic approximation [27,28], Markov modeling [29], or dimensional reduction of dynamic theories [14,30,31]. Here we show that, in the setting of small system thermodynamics, TSS leads to huge simplification of the strongly coupled regime. More specifically, by identifying the *Hamiltonian of Mean Force* (HMF) as the system Hamiltonian, and relegating the remaining part of the total Hamiltonian to the bath, we find that both the EQ of system and the conditional EQ of the bath can be fully described by familiar canonical ensemble theories with respect to their own Hamiltonians. Furthermore, the bath free energy remains fixed even if the interaction between the system and bath is externally varied. This makes possible a reduced thermodynamic theory in terms of system variables only for essentially all possible thermodynamic processes.

More remarkably, with TSS and identification of HMF as the system Hamiltonian, the weak coupling theory of stochastic thermodynamics becomes applicable almost verbatim in the strong coupling regime. Work and heat retain the same definitions and the same physical meanings, as long as the bath entropy understood as conditioned on the system state. Furthermore, thermodynamic quantities at trajectory level can be measured at the intermediate time-scales, whereas those at ensemble level, in longer time-scales. Fluctuation Theorem, Jarzynski equality, and Clausius inequality can all be proved using nonlinear Langevin dynamics [35], whose validity relies on TSS but not on strength of coupling. Finally, using the conditional EQ nature of bath, it can be rigorously demonstrated that $dS - \beta dQ$ equals to the entropy change of the universe, which establishes the meaning of Clausius inequality as increasing total entropy. Summarizing, TSS leads to a natural and elegant unification of thermodynamics and stochastic thermodynamics at weak and strong couplings.

2. Conditional EQ of Bath

Let the total Hamiltonian of the system and the bath be

$$H_{\mathbf{XY}}(\boldsymbol{x}, \boldsymbol{y}; \lambda) = H_{\mathbf{X}}(\boldsymbol{x}; \lambda, \beta) + H_{\mathbf{Y}}(\boldsymbol{y}) + H_I(\boldsymbol{x}, \boldsymbol{y}; \lambda, \beta)$$

$$\equiv H_{\mathbf{X}}(\boldsymbol{x}; \lambda, \beta) + H_{\mathrm{Bath}}(\boldsymbol{y}; \boldsymbol{x}, \lambda, \beta), \qquad (1)$$

where $\mathbf{X}, \mathbf{Y}$ denote respectively the slow and fast variables, $\boldsymbol{x}, \boldsymbol{y}$ their values, and λ the external parameter, which appear in $H_{\mathbf{X}}, H_I$ but not in $H_{\mathbf{Y}}$. This Hamiltonian describes a large class of small systems where both the system Hamiltonian and its coupling to the bath can be controlled. Note that, unlike all previous theories, we have included the entire interacting Hamiltonian $H_I(\boldsymbol{x}, \boldsymbol{y}; \lambda, \beta)$ in H_{Bath}. The β dependence of $H_I, H_{\mathbf{X}}$ will be explained below.

Assume that $\mathbf{XY}$ is weakly interacting with a much larger super-bath whose dynamics is at least as fast as $\mathbf{Y}$. Because of TSS, in an intermediate time-scale, $\mathbf{Y}$ achieves EQ *conditioned on* $\mathbf{X} = \boldsymbol{x}$, which is described by the usual canonical ensemble theory:

$$p_{\mathbf{Y}}^{\text{EQ}}(\boldsymbol{y}|\boldsymbol{x}) = \frac{1}{Z_{\mathbf{Y}}(\beta)} e^{-\beta H_{\text{Bath}}(\boldsymbol{y}; \boldsymbol{x}, \lambda, \beta)}, \tag{2a}$$

$$Z_{\mathbf{Y}}(\beta) = e^{-\beta F_{\mathbf{Y}}(\beta)} \equiv \int_{\boldsymbol{y}} e^{-\beta H_{\text{Bath}}(\boldsymbol{y}; \boldsymbol{x}, \lambda, \beta)}. \tag{2b}$$

Note that $Z_{\mathbf{Y}}(\beta), F_{\mathbf{Y}}(\beta)$ as defined above generically depend on $\boldsymbol{x}$ and λ. However, we can always redistribute $H_{\mathbf{X}}$ and H_I in Eq. (1) without changing $H_{\mathbf{XY}}$, such that $Z_{\mathbf{Y}}(\beta), F_{\mathbf{Y}}(\beta)$ become independent of $\boldsymbol{x}$ and λ[b]:

$$\frac{\partial Z_{\mathbf{Y}}(\beta)}{\partial \boldsymbol{x}} = \frac{\partial F_{\mathbf{Y}}(\beta)}{\partial \boldsymbol{x}} = 0, \quad \frac{\partial Z_{\mathbf{Y}}(\beta)}{\partial \lambda} = \frac{\partial F_{\mathbf{Y}}(\beta)}{\partial \lambda} = 0. \tag{3}$$

Such a repartitioning of the total Hamiltonian has no experimental consequence, but will greatly simplify the thermodynamic theory, as we will demonstrate below. Note also this generally leads to dependence of $H_I, H_{\mathbf{X}}$ on β, even though the total Hamiltonian $H_{\mathbf{XY}}$ is independent of β. We comment that it is possible to define the conditional EQ state of bath without TSS [10]. It however would not be measurable experimentally in a specific range of time-scales.

The internal energy and entropy of the bath in the conditional EQ state are given respectively by

$$E_{\mathbf{Y}}(\boldsymbol{x}) = \int_{\boldsymbol{y}} p_{\mathbf{Y}}^{\text{EQ}}(\boldsymbol{y}|\boldsymbol{x}) H_{\text{Bath}}(\boldsymbol{y}; \boldsymbol{x}, \lambda, \beta), \tag{4a}$$

$$S_{\mathbf{Y}|\mathbf{X}=\boldsymbol{x}} = - \int_{\boldsymbol{y}} p_{\mathbf{Y}}^{\text{EQ}}(\boldsymbol{y}|\boldsymbol{x}) \log p_{\mathbf{Y}}^{\text{EQ}}(\boldsymbol{y}|\boldsymbol{x}), \tag{4b}$$

$$F_{\mathbf{Y}}(\beta) = E_{\mathbf{Y}}(\boldsymbol{x}) - T S_{\mathbf{Y}|\mathbf{X}=\boldsymbol{x}}. \tag{4c}$$

$S_{\mathbf{Y}|\mathbf{X}=\boldsymbol{x}}$ is known as *the conditional Shannon entropy of* $\mathbf{Y}$ *given* $\mathbf{X} = \boldsymbol{x}$ [32]. Note that even though both $E_{\mathbf{Y}}(\boldsymbol{x})$ and $S_{\mathbf{Y}|\mathbf{X}=\boldsymbol{x}}$ depend on $\boldsymbol{x}$ and λ, $F_{\mathbf{Y}}(\beta)$ does not.

---

[b]Note also that even now $H_{\mathbf{X}}, H_I$ are determined only up to an additive constant. We shall not need to fix these constants in our theory, except that we require that in the limit the bath size goes to infinity, $H_{\mathbf{XY}}(\boldsymbol{x}, \boldsymbol{y}; \lambda)$ has a finite limit.

3. Joint EQ of System and Bath

In long time-scales, $\mathbf{XY}$ achieves a joint EQ canonical distribution:

$$p_{\mathbf{XY}}^{\mathrm{EQ}}(\boldsymbol{x}, \boldsymbol{y}) = \frac{e^{-\beta H_{\mathbf{XY}}(\boldsymbol{x}, \boldsymbol{y}; \lambda)}}{Z_{\mathbf{XY}}(\beta, \lambda)}. \tag{5}$$

Various thermodynamic quantities of $\mathbf{XY}$ are again given by the canonical ensemble theory:

$$Z_{\mathbf{XY}}(\beta, \lambda) = \int_{\boldsymbol{xy}} e^{-\beta H_{\mathbf{XY}}} = \int_{\boldsymbol{x}} e^{-\beta H_{\mathbf{X}}} Z_{\mathbf{Y}}(\beta) \tag{6a}$$

$$F_{\mathbf{XY}}(\beta, \lambda) = -T \log Z_{\mathbf{XY}}(\beta, \lambda), \tag{6b}$$

$$E_{\mathbf{XY}}(\beta, \lambda) = \int_{\boldsymbol{xy}} p_{\mathbf{XY}}^{\mathrm{EQ}}(\boldsymbol{x}, \boldsymbol{y}) H_{\mathbf{XY}}(\boldsymbol{x}, \boldsymbol{y}; \lambda), \tag{6c}$$

$$S_{\mathbf{XY}}(\beta, \lambda) = -\int_{\boldsymbol{xy}} p_{\mathbf{XY}}^{\mathrm{EQ}}(\boldsymbol{x}, \boldsymbol{y}) \log p_{\mathbf{XY}}^{\mathrm{EQ}}(\boldsymbol{x}, \boldsymbol{y}), \tag{6d}$$

$$F_{\mathbf{XY}}(\beta, \lambda) = E_{\mathbf{XY}} - T S_{\mathbf{XY}}. \tag{6e}$$

Reduced EQ of System.   Because $Z_{\mathbf{Y}}(\beta)$ is independent of $\boldsymbol{x}$, $Z_{\mathbf{XY}}(\beta, \lambda)$ in Eq. (6a) can be factorized:

$$Z_{\mathbf{XY}}(\beta, \lambda) = Z_{\mathbf{X}}(\beta, \lambda) Z_{\mathbf{Y}}(\beta), \tag{7a}$$

where $Z_{\mathbf{X}}(\beta, \lambda)$ is the partition function of the system:

$$Z_{\mathbf{X}}(\beta, \lambda) \equiv \int_{\boldsymbol{x}} e^{-\beta H_{\mathbf{X}}(\boldsymbol{x}; \lambda, \beta)}. \tag{7b}$$

The joint distribution (5) can also be factorized as:

$$p_{\mathbf{XY}}^{\mathrm{EQ}} = p_{\mathbf{X}}^{\mathrm{EQ}}(\boldsymbol{x}) p_{\mathbf{Y}}^{\mathrm{EQ}}(\boldsymbol{y}|\boldsymbol{x}), \tag{7c}$$

where $p_{\mathbf{X}}^{\mathrm{EQ}}(\boldsymbol{x})$ is canonical with respect to $H_{\mathbf{X}}(\boldsymbol{x}, \lambda)$:

$$p_{\mathbf{X}}^{\mathrm{EQ}}(\boldsymbol{x}) = \int_{\boldsymbol{y}} p_{\mathbf{XY}}^{\mathrm{EQ}}(\boldsymbol{x}, \boldsymbol{y}) = \frac{e^{-\beta H_{\mathbf{X}}(\boldsymbol{x}; \lambda, \beta)}}{Z_{\mathbf{X}}(\beta, \lambda)}. \tag{7d}$$

Hence $H_{\mathbf{X}}(\boldsymbol{x}; \lambda)$ is actually the *Hamiltonian of mean force* (HMF) [4–7,33]. Equation (7d) prompts us to construct a canonical ensemble theory for the system, with free energy, internal energy, and entropy given by

$$F_{\mathbf{X}} = -T \log Z_{\mathbf{X}}(\beta, \lambda), \tag{8a}$$

$$E_{\mathbf{X}} = \int_{\boldsymbol{x}} p_{\mathbf{X}}^{\mathrm{EQ}}(\boldsymbol{x}) H_{\mathbf{X}}(\boldsymbol{x}; \lambda), \tag{8b}$$

$$S_{\mathbf{X}} = -\int_{\boldsymbol{x}} p_{\mathbf{X}}^{\mathrm{EQ}}(\boldsymbol{x}) \log p_{\mathbf{X}}^{\mathrm{EQ}}(\boldsymbol{x}), \tag{8c}$$

$$F_{\mathbf{X}} = E_{\mathbf{X}} - T S_{\mathbf{X}}. \tag{8d}$$

Comparing Eqs. (8) with Eqs. (4) and (6), we find the following decomposition of total thermodynamic quantities into system parts and bath parts:

$$F_{\mathbf{XY}}(\beta, \lambda) = F_{\mathbf{X}}(\beta, \lambda) + F_{\mathbf{Y}}(\beta), \tag{9a}$$

$$E_{\mathbf{XY}} = E_{\mathbf{X}} + \langle E_{\mathbf{Y}}(\boldsymbol{x}) \rangle_{\mathbf{X}}, \tag{9b}$$

$$S_{\mathbf{XY}} = S_{\mathbf{X}} + S_{\mathbf{Y}|\mathbf{X}}, \tag{9c}$$

where $\langle E_{\mathbf{Y}}(\boldsymbol{x}) \rangle_{\mathbf{X}}, S_{\mathbf{Y}|\mathbf{X}}$ are averages of the conditional bath variables $E_{\mathbf{Y}}(\boldsymbol{x})$, $S_{\mathbf{Y}|\mathbf{X}=\boldsymbol{x}}$ over fluctuations of $\mathbf{X}$:

$$\langle E_{\mathbf{Y}}(\boldsymbol{x}) \rangle_{\mathbf{X}} = \int_{\boldsymbol{x}} p_{\mathbf{X}}^{\mathrm{EQ}}(\boldsymbol{x}) E_{\mathbf{Y}}(\boldsymbol{x}), \tag{10a}$$

$$S_{\mathbf{Y}|\mathbf{X}} = \langle S_{\mathbf{Y}|\mathbf{X}=\boldsymbol{x}} \rangle_{\mathbf{X}} = \int_{\boldsymbol{x}} p_{\mathbf{X}}^{\mathrm{EQ}}(\boldsymbol{x}) S_{\mathbf{Y}|\mathbf{X}=\boldsymbol{x}}. \tag{10b}$$

That fact that each part in Eqs. (9) derives from canonical ensemble theory leads to the following two pleasing features: (i) all entropies are Gibbs-Shannon entropy, and (ii) all equilibrium distributions are Gibbs-Boltzmann. The independence of bath free energy $F_{\mathbf{Y}}(\beta)$ on $\lambda, \boldsymbol{x}$ is another convenient feature. Consider, for example we stretch a DNA immersed in an aqueous solvent, or tune the interaction between a nano-engine and its environment. There is no need to worry about the environment in our theory, because its free energy stays constant. This feature is not shared by any of the previous theories.

The temperature dependence of the system Hamiltonian $H_{\mathbf{X}}(\boldsymbol{x}; \lambda, \beta)$ has some peculiar consequences. The usual thermodynamic relations $E_{\mathbf{X}} = -\partial \log Z_{\mathbf{X}}/\partial \beta$ and $S_\alpha = \partial F_{\mathbf{X}}/\partial T$ no longer hold, even though they are valid in the theory of Refs. [6, 7]. The usual fluctuation-response relation $\partial E_{\mathbf{X}}/\partial T = \beta^2 \langle \delta H_{\mathbf{X}}^2 \rangle$ also break down, and the specific heat of the system is no longer necessarily positive. Since H_{Bath} also depend on β, similar things can be said about the bath. These features do not imply violation of detailed balance or stability conditions.

4. NEQ Work and Heat

Let us now study the consequences of TSS for NEQ processes, assuming that $\mathbf{XY}$ is in weak coupling with a super-bath $\mathbf{Z}$. We consider an infinitesimal process where $\boldsymbol{x}, \boldsymbol{y}, \mathbf{z}$ and λ change by $d\boldsymbol{x}, d\boldsymbol{y}, d\mathbf{z}$ and $d\lambda$. As in the weak coupling theory of stochastic thermodynamics, work is defined as the change of total energy:

$$d\!W = d_x H_{\mathbf{XYZ}} + d_y H_{\mathbf{XYZ}} + d_z H_{\mathbf{XYZ}} + d_\lambda H_{\mathbf{XYZ}}$$
$$= d_\lambda H_{\mathbf{XY}} = d_\lambda H_{\mathbf{X}} + d_\lambda H_I. \tag{11}$$

The second equality follows because for fixed λ, $H_{\mathbf{XYZ}}$ is conserved. We are interested in the intermediate time-scale where the system dynamics is monitored at trajectory level, whereas the bath achieves equilibrium. For this purpose we average Eq. (11) over the conditional EQ in Eq. (2a). Now, the second condition of Eq. (3) implies:

$$\int_{\mathbf{y}} p_{\mathbf{Y}}^{\mathrm{EQ}}(\mathbf{y}|\mathbf{x}) d_\lambda H_I = 0, \tag{12}$$

which leads to the definition for *work at trajectory level* of system variables:

$$d\!W = d_\lambda H_{\mathbf{X}} = \frac{\partial H_{\mathbf{X}}}{\partial \lambda} d\lambda. \tag{13}$$

Note that Eq. (11) can also be written as

$$d\!W = dH_{\mathbf{X}} + d\left(H_B + H_{\mathbf{Z}}\right). \tag{14}$$

As usual, we define $H_{\mathbf{X}}$ as the fluctuating internal energy and $-d\left(H_B + H_{\mathbf{Z}}\right)$ as the heat at the trajectory level. Equation (14) can then be rewritten into the first law at the trajectory level:

$$dH_{\mathbf{X}} = d\!W + d\!Q, \tag{15}$$

From this we obtain an alternative expression for $d\!Q$:

$$d\!Q \equiv dH_{\mathbf{X}} - d\!W = dH_{\mathbf{X}} - d_\lambda H_{\mathbf{X}} = d_x H_{\mathbf{X}}. \tag{16}$$

Now if we average Eq. (15) over distribution of $\mathbf{X}$, we obtain the first law at the ensemble level:

$$dE_{\mathbf{X}} = d\!W + d\!Q, \tag{17}$$

where $E_{\mathbf{X}}, d\!W$ are ensemble averages of $H_{\mathbf{X}}, d\!W$:

$$E_{\mathbf{X}} = \int_{\mathbf{x}} p_{\mathbf{X}} H_{\mathbf{X}}, \tag{18}$$

$$d\!W = \int_{\mathbf{x}} p_{\mathbf{X}} d_\lambda H_{\mathbf{X}}. \tag{19}$$

Now we can take differential of Eq. (18):

$$dE_{\mathbf{X}} = d \int_{\mathbf{x}} p_{\mathbf{X}} H_{\mathbf{X}} = d\!W + \int_{\mathbf{x}} H_{\mathbf{X}} dp_{\mathbf{X}}, \tag{20}$$

where x must be treated as dummy variables, and $dp_\mathbf{X}$ is understood as due to the coarse-grained dynamics of the system variables. Comparing this with Eq. (17) we obtain the definition of heat at ensemble level:

$$dQ = \int_x H_\mathbf{X} dp_\mathbf{X} = \langle đQ \rangle, \tag{21}$$

where $\langle \cdot \rangle$ means averaging over slow variables. In Ref. [35] it was explicitly proved that Eq. (21) is the ensemble average of Eq. (16) using Ito-Langevin theory.

5. Meanings of Heat

We use the remaining space to clarify the physical meaning of heat. It is more convenient to assume that $\mathbf{XY}$ is thermally closed with fixed total energy. We define Boltzmann entropy of bath as:

$$S_\mathbf{Y}(E_\mathbf{Y}) \equiv \log \Omega_\mathbf{Y}(E_\mathbf{Y})$$
$$\equiv \log \int_y \delta(H_{\text{Bath}}(\boldsymbol{y}; \boldsymbol{x}, \lambda, \beta) - E_\mathbf{Y}), \tag{22}$$

where H_{Bath} is defined in Eq. (1). The rationale behind this is again TSS, i.e., the bath achieves an equal probability distribution conditioned on energy $E_\mathbf{Y}$ and $\mathbf{X} = \boldsymbol{x}$. Note that $S_\mathbf{Y}(E_\mathbf{Y})$ generally also depends on $\boldsymbol{x}, \lambda, \beta$.

We consider an infinitesimal process where $\boldsymbol{x}$ and λ change by $d\boldsymbol{x}$ and $d\lambda$, whereas the total energy changes from $E_\mathbf{XY}$ to $E_\mathbf{XY} + đW$. The Boltzmann entropies of the bath in the initial and final states are respectively:

$$S_\mathbf{Y} = S_\mathbf{Y}(E_\mathbf{XY} - H_\mathbf{X}), \tag{23a}$$

$$S'_\mathbf{Y} = S_\mathbf{Y}\left(E_\mathbf{XY} + đW - H_\mathbf{X} - dH_\mathbf{X}\right), \tag{23b}$$

where $dH_\mathbf{X}$ and $đW$ are respectively given by Eqs. (15) and (13). Expanding Eq. (23b) in terms of $đW$ and $dH_\mathbf{X}$ and subtracting Eq. (23a), we obtain:

$$dS_\mathbf{Y} = S'_\mathbf{Y} - S_\mathbf{Y} = \beta \left(đW - dH_\mathbf{X}\right) = -\beta đQ, \tag{24}$$

where $\beta = \partial S_\mathbf{Y}/\partial E_\mathbf{Y}$ is the inverse temperature of bath, and was used Eq. (16) in the last step. Hence heat at the trajectory level, $đQ$, is the variation of Boltzmann entropy of the bath multiplied by $-T$. This interpretation, which is often taken for granted in the weak coupling theory, is valid only with TSS.

Let us now go to the ensemble level. For technical convenience, we assume that the total energy has a small uncertainty ϵ, and the slow variables $\mathbf{X}$

are distributed as $p_{\mathbf{X}}(\boldsymbol{x})$. The fast variables $\mathbf{Y}$ of course are in conditional equilibrium. The joint distribution of $\mathbf{XY}$ is then

$$p_{\mathbf{XY}}(\boldsymbol{x}, \boldsymbol{y}) = p_{\mathbf{X}}(\boldsymbol{x}) \frac{\delta_\epsilon(H_{\mathbf{XY}} - E_{\mathbf{XY}})}{\Omega_{\mathbf{Y}}(E_{\mathbf{XY}} - H_{\mathbf{X}})}, \tag{25}$$

where $\Omega_{\mathbf{Y}}$ is defined in Eq. (22), and $\delta_\epsilon(s)$ is defined as:

$$\delta_\epsilon(s) = \begin{cases} 1/\epsilon, & 0 < s < \epsilon, \\ 0, & \text{otherwise}, \end{cases} \tag{26}$$

which converges to the Dirac delta function as $\epsilon \to 0$. For sufficiently small ϵ, integration of $\delta_\epsilon(H_{\mathbf{XY}} - E_{\mathbf{XY}})$ over $\boldsymbol{y}$ yields $\Omega_{\mathbf{Y}}(E_{\mathbf{XY}} - H_{\mathbf{X}})$, hence Eq. (25) is properly normalized. The total entropy of Eq. (25) can be easily calculated:

$$\begin{aligned} S_{\mathbf{XY}}[p_{\mathbf{XY}}] &= - \int_{xy} p_{\mathbf{XY}}(\boldsymbol{x}, \boldsymbol{y}) \log p_{\mathbf{XY}}(\boldsymbol{x}, \boldsymbol{y}) \\ &= \int_{xy} p_{\mathbf{X}} \left[-\log p_{\mathbf{X}} + S_{\mathbf{Y}}(E_{\mathbf{XY}} - H_{\mathbf{X}}) \right] + \log \epsilon \\ &= S_{\mathbf{X}}[p_{\mathbf{X}}] + \langle S_{\mathbf{Y}}(E_{\mathbf{XY}} - H_{\mathbf{X}}) \rangle + \log \epsilon. \end{aligned} \tag{27}$$

Let us now take the differential of both sides:

$$\begin{aligned} dS_{\mathbf{XY}}[p_{\mathbf{XY}}] &= dS_{\mathbf{X}}[p_{\mathbf{X}}] + \langle dS_{\mathbf{Y}}(E_{\mathbf{XY}} - H_{\mathbf{X}}) \rangle \\ &= dS_{\mathbf{X}}[p_{\mathbf{X}}] - \beta \langle đQ \rangle \\ &= dS_{\mathbf{X}}[p_{\mathbf{X}}] - \beta đQ, \end{aligned} \tag{28}$$

where we have used consecutively Eq. (24) and the fact that ensemble average of $đQ$ is $đQ$. But the combined system $\mathbf{XY}$ is thermally closed. Hence $dS_{\mathbf{XY}}$ is the variation of the total entropy. This establishes the physical meaning of the Clausius inequality $dS_{\mathbf{X}} - đQ \geq 0$ as the monotonic increase of the total entropy. Finally, using Eq. (9c), decomposition of joint entropy in terms of marginal entropy and conditional entropy, Eq. (28) can also rewritten as $đQ = -T dS_{\mathbf{Y}|\mathbf{X}}$, which establishes the physical meaning of heat at ensemble level in terms of *the bath entropy conditioned on the system state*. For the weak coupling case, the correlation between $\mathbf{X}$ and $\mathbf{Y}$ is negligible, and the conditioning can be removed, which leads to the familiar result $đQ = -T dS_{\mathbf{Y}}$, which is well accepted in the weak coupling theory of stochastic thermodynamics.

6. Conclusion

With time-scale separation and with HMF identified as system Hamiltonian, we have constructed a simple and unified theory for thermodynamics and stochastic thermodynamics of small systems that is in strong and variable interaction with its environment. Equilibrium properties are fully described by usual canonical ensemble theory, whereas non-equilibrium work and heat retain the same definitions and physical meanings as in the weak coupling regime. These definitions of work and heat also agree with the covariant theory of nonlinear Langevin dynamics [34, 35], with $\beta H_{\mathbf{X}}$ understood as the generalized potential. Crooks Fluctuation Theorem, Jarzynski equality, as well as Clausius inequality were also proved in Refs. [34, 35] using Langevin theory, which itself can be understood as a consequence of TSS. It then follows that all results obtain in Refs. [34, 35] can be applied to the strong coupling regime, as claimed there.

It is well-known that the Gibbs-Shannon entropy of a thermally closed Hamiltonian is a constant of motion. This seems in contradiction with the Clausius inequality $dS - \beta dQ \geq 0$ from Langevin dynamics. In fact, starting from a NEQ state, an exact expression of the joint pdf $p_{\mathbf{XY}}(\boldsymbol{x}, \boldsymbol{y})$ must contain extra correlations between $\mathbf{X}, \mathbf{Y}$ and also among $\mathbf{Y}$ themselves, as envisaged by Gibbs long ago, and also as shown in Refs. [23, 24]. These correlations never go away, but are not expected to contribute to the statistical properties of the slow variables. In another word, the conditional EQ nature of the bath, Eq. (2a), strictly speaking can never be valid. What we can say is that two sides of Eq. (2a) are "macroscopically equivalent". Study of microscopic details, i.e., the fast variables, will reveal their differences. In this sense, the validity of the second law can be traced back to the ubiquity of time-scale separations, and to our incapability, as macroscopic creatures, of resolving the fast-scale details.

I acknowledge support from NSFC grants 11674217 as well as Shanghai Municipal Science and Technology Major Project (Grant No. 2019SHZDZX01). I am also thankful to additional support from Shanghai Talent Program.

References

[1] Seifert, Udo, Entropy production along a stochastic trajectory and an integral fluctuation theorem, *Phys. Rev. Lett.* **95**(4), 040602 (2005).

[2] Seifert, Udo, Stochastic thermodynamics, fluctuation theorems and molecular machines, *Reports on Progress in Physics* **75**(12), 126001 (2012).

[3] Jarzynski, Christopher, Equalities and inequalities: Irreversibility and the second law of thermodynamics at the nanoscale, *Annu. Rev. Condens. Matter Phys.* **2**(1), 329–351 (2011).

[4] Jarzynski, Chris, NonEQ work theorem for a system strongly coupled to a thermal environment, *J. Stat. Mech.: Theory and Experiment* **2004**(09), P09005 (2004).

 [5] Jarzynski, Christopher, Stochastic and macroscopic thermodynamics of strongly coupled systems, *Phys. Rev. X* **7**(1), 011008 (2017).

 [6] Seifert, Udo, First and second law of thermodynamics at strong coupling, *Phys. Rev. Lett.* **116**(2), 020601 (2016).

 [7] Talkner, Peter, and Peter Hänggi, *Colloquium:* Statistical Mechanics and Thermodynamics at Strong Coupling: Quantum and Classical, *Rev. Mod. Phys.* **92**, 041002 (2020).

 [8] Strasberg, P., Schaller, G., Lambert, N., & Brandes, T, Nonequilibrium thermodynamics in the strong coupling and non-Markovian regime based on a reaction coordinate mapping, *New J. Phys.* **18**(7), 073007 (2016).

 [9] Aurell, Erik. Unified picture of strong-coupling stochastic thermodynamics and time reversals, *Phys. Rev. E* **97**(4), 042112 (2018).

[10] Miller, Harry JD, and Janet Anders, Entropy production and time asymmetry in the presence of strong interactions, *Phys. Rev. E* **95**(6), 062123 (2017).

[11] Gelin, Maxim F., and Michael Thoss, Thermodynamics of a sub-ensemble of a canonical ensemble, *Phys. Rev. E* **79**(5), 051121 (2009).

[12] Huang, Wei-Ming, and Wei-Min Zhang, Strong Coupling Quantum Thermodynamics with Renormalized Hamiltonian and Temperature, arXiv preprint arXiv:2010.01828 (2020).

[13] de Miguel, Rodrigo, and J. Miguel Rubí, Strong Coupling and Nonextensive Thermodynamics, *Entropy* **22**(9), 975 (2020).

[14] Strasberg, Philipp, and Massimiliano Esposito, Stochastic thermodynamics in the strong coupling regime: An unambiguous approach based on coarse graining, *Phys. Rev. E* **95**(6), 062101 (2017).

[15] Hsiang, Jen-Tsung, and Bei-Lok Hu, Zeroth law in quantum thermodynamics at strong coupling: In equilibrium, not at equal temperature, *Phys. Rev. D* **103**(8), 085004 (2021).

[16] Carrega, Matteo, *et al.*, Energy exchange in driven open quantum systems at strong coupling, *Phys. Rev. Lett.* **116**(24), 240403 (2016).

[17] Rivas, Angel, Strong coupling thermodynamics of open quantum systems, *Phys. Rev. Lett.* **124**(16), 160601 (2020).

[18] Perarnau-Llobet, Martí, *et al.*, Strong coupling corrections in quantum thermodynamics, *Phys. Rev. Lett.* **120**(12), 120602 (2018).

[19] Strasberg, Philipp, Repeated interactions and quantum stochastic thermodynamics at strong coupling, *Phys. Rev. Lett.* **123**(18), 180604 (2019).

[20] Pucci, Lorenzo, Massimiliano Esposito, and Luca Peliti, Entropy production in quantum Brownian motion, *J. Stat. Mech.: Theory and Experiment* **2013**(04), P04005 (2013).

[21] Esposito, Massimiliano, Maicol A. Ochoa, and Michael Galperin, Nature of heat in strongly coupled open quantum systems, *Phys. Rev. B* **92**(23), 235440 (2015).

[22] Abe, Sumiyoshi, and A. K. Rajagopal, Validity of the second law in nonextensive quantum thermodynamics, *Phys. Rev. Lett.* **91**(12), 120601 (2003).

[23] Ptaszyski, Krzysztof, and Massimiliano Esposito, Entropy production in open systems: The predominant role of intraenvironment correlations, *Phys. Rev. Lett.* **123**(20), 200603 (2019).

[24] Esposito, Massimiliano, Katja Lindenberg, and Christian Van den Broeck, Entropy production as correlation between system and reservoir, *New J. Phys.* **12**(1), 013013 (2010).

[25] de Miguel, Rodrigo, and J. Miguel Rubí, Statistical Mechanics at Strong Coupling: A Bridge between Landsberg's Energy Levels and Hill's Nanothermodynamics, *Nanomaterials* **10**(12), 2471 (2020).

[26] Roux, Benot, and Thomas Simonson, Implicit solvent models, *Biophys. Chem.* **78**(1-2), 1–20 (1999).

[27] Born, M., and V. Fock, Proof of the adiabatic theorem, *Z. Phys* **51**, 165–169 (1928).

[28] Max Born, J. Robert Oppenheimer, Zur Quantentheorie der Molekeln [On the Quantum Theory of Molecules], *Annalen der Physik (in German)*, **389**(20), 457–484 (1927).

[29] Gardiner, Crispin W., *Handbook of Stochastic Methods,* 3rd ed., Berlin: Springer, 2004.

[30] Michaelis, L., and Menten, M., Die kinetik der Invertinwirkung, *Biochem Z* **49**, 333–369 (1913).

[31] Pavliotis, Grigoris, and Andrew Stuart, Multiscale methods: averaging and homogenization, Springer Science & Business Media, 2008.

[32] Cover, Thomas M., and Joy A. Thomas, *Elements of Information Theory*, John Wiley & Sons, 2012.

[33] Kirkwood, John G., Statistical mechanics of fluid mixtures, *J. Chem. Phys.* **3**(5), 300–313 (1935).

[34] Ding, Mingnan, Zhanchun Tu, and Xiangjun Xing, Covariant formulation of nonlinear Langevin theory with multiplicative Gaussian white noises, *Phys. Rev. Res.* **2**(3), 033381 (2020).

[35] Ding, Mingnan and Xiangjun Xing, Covariant Non-EQ Thermodynamics for Small Systems, 2021. Submitted to *Phys. Rev. Res.*

https://doi.org/10.1142/9789811251948_0023

To be Frank in Shanghai

A Physicist's Journey of Driving Aspirations Forward

Yu Zhao,[*] Li Fu,[†] and Wei Ku,[‡] on behalf of the TDLI staff, faculty, and students

[*] *zhao.yu@sjtu.edu.cn*
[†] *li.fu@sjtu.edu.cn*
[‡] *weiku@sjtu.edu.cn*

Five years may seem a short time to complete a construction project of a 56,000 square meter laboratory building, but it is long enough for Frank Wilczek to drive a string of events forward from scratch in Tsung-Dao Lee Institute (TDLI)'s research coordination, disciplinary development, talent recruitment, and public outreach.

Arduous, Whirlwind Visit, and More

When asked about when Frank has started a new front in Shanghai, for many, one might consider it to be 3 to 5 years ago. In fall 2018, it was the first time he mentioned Shanghai on social media for his "arduous, whirlwind visit to break ground on … T. D. Lee Institute", initiated by the great Chinese-American physicist Tsung-Dao Lee. One year earlier, he was "installed" as

Visit to the construction site of TDLI laboratory building, 2019.

Director Appointment Ceremony of TDLI, 2017.

the Institute's Founding Director. At the Institute's founding ceremony in late 2016, Frank joined TDLI, which takes upon particle and nuclear physics, astronomy and astrophysics, and quantum science as its initial focus.

But this relationship might well be traced back much further. Frank's doctoral advisor, David Gross, was awarded in 2010 the Honorary Professor of Shanghai Jiao Tong University (SJTU), with whom TDLI is partnering. Furthermore, according to young Frank in his graduate student days, the Institute's Honorary Director, Nobel laureate Tsung-Dao Lee, was among the 20 greatest physicists whose papers he had read completely. Quoted from Steve Jobs, the dots can only be connected looking backward.

Beyond a Nobel Laureate

Even after multiple rounds of communication and meeting, few people at the Institute or the University, have had experience working under the leadership of a Nobel laureate, not to mention that the director-to-be doesn't know any Chinese at all. How will he be like in everyday work? What role will he play? Will the cultural difference be an issue? Will he be easy to work with? Will he be realistic? ... So many uncertainties lingered on.

Frank surprises many people with his candid and approachable style. He's always been casual and friendly to everyone, physicist or not. There were of course difficult moments, but he handled them wisely and kindly to make sure everyone's opinion is respected, and the playground is fair and just.

Like many other work and activities he has committed to, Frank takes it seriously in building the Institute and shouldering his responsibilities as the founding director. He was actively involved in a series of business, varying from the Institute's vision, mission, and value, to management mechanism, research directions, talent recruitment, scientific coordination, outreach activities, etc.

Actions are Louder than Words

Since 2017, Frank has invited a group of world experts from leading universities and institutes, as TDLI International Advisory Committee (IAC) members, to advise on subjects from vision on scientific opportunities, operational infrastructure, talent incubation, to better service for the science community. Today, the IAC meeting has become an important annual event in which new scientific directions are highlighted, and fundamental improvements on daily operations are implemented.

In addition to that, a number of high-level scientific activities have been rolled out, such as the TDLI International Conference on Emerging Frontier of Physics, where 5 Nobel laureates and dozens of academicians attended, and hundreds of scientists gathered together. Furthermore, he actively promoted the participation of Chinese young researchers in multiple annual Quantum Connections events in Sweden, to increase their international exposure.

TDLI International Advisory Committee Meeting, 2018.

TDLI International Conference on Emerging Frontiers of Physics, 2019.

For more effective incubation of young talents, Frank initiated a joint post-doctoral fellowships between TDLI and NORDITA in Sweden, granting promising researchers wider international exposure, making foreign academic connections, and accessing additional career opportunities. (A similar program has been discussed actively with the physics department of MIT.) None of these could be made possible without Frank's worldwide connections.

To better guide government efforts in strengthening scientific activation, Frank took part in influencing scientific policies in Shanghai. In 2018, he delivered a keynote speech to Shanghai government leaders and higher education institution management team, on how to better promote young scientists and how to deliver an international top research institute including merging the strength of international and Chinese management systems.

Frank also shows strong interest in public outreach and branching out to the realm of art. He is an active member of the World Laureates Forum. Through such a platform, he shares many visions in a way easily accessible to the general public regarding the latest research progress, the prediction and planning of cutting-edge scientific areas, the application of modern scientific findings, and the cultivation of young talents. In 2018, he gave a lecture entitled "Crossroads of Science and Art at Shanghai Library" and donated his book, *A Beautiful Question: Finding Nature's Deep Design*, of which the Chinese version is one of the most outstanding popular science books awarded by the National Library of China. He has also identified the main themes for Tsung-Dao Lee Science and Art Activities in the past four consecutive

World Laureates Forum, 2018.

years. In a related event, he delivered a lecture on "spin" in 2020, attracting more than 4000 audiences to explore the mysteries of science and art.

Leading by example, Frank has been a true inspiration to many of our young researchers through his passion for science and his amazing productivity. With board interests, Frank is naturally curious about everything, especially emerging topics, for which he would organize talks and workshops, like Tsung-Dao Lee Frontier Lecture. Sometimes one would wonder how he managed to fit so many activities into his 24-hour schedule, in addition to being the author of so many quality papers every year.

Being Frank Means a Lot

No matter how occupied he is by the above events, Frank manages to make time to exchange ideas with students, postdocs, and faculty. Despite being thousands of miles apart and a large difference in time zone, Frank is heavily involved in the Institute's development and management. For example, he led the Science Policy Committee of TDLI which meets regularly for institutional business. In addition, he assembled a working group on a Five-year Plan to map out the Institute's scientific strategies for comprehensive development. Even more, he invested a significant amount of effort in recruitment, identifying, and assessing a large number of candidates.

Frank's active presence in TDLI operation and outreach activities is a true inspiration, not only to the students and junior researchers but to the general public in Shanghai. He enjoyed interacting with young generations in many different ways, such as lunch meetings, one-on-one meetings, and public lectures. He induces a sense of encouragement and motivation many

Frank and TDLI PhD students, 2019.

of our members have never encountered before. His words of wisdom are highly appreciated.

Hereby, we sincerely wish Director Frank Wilczek a very happy 70th birthday. May his future stay be equally joyful and meaningful, such that he may consider Shanghai his second home and grant our young members more opportunities to access his wisdom and kind personality. We are confident that, under Frank's leadership, TDLI will march forward and become a top international institute that would make Tsung-Dao Lee proud.

Publications by Frank Wilczek

Nothing better illustrates the scope and impact of Frank Wilczek's contributions to physics than a list of his publications. Beginning with his 1973 paper "Ultraviolet Behavior of Non-Abelian Gauge Theories", the 530 entries in this list include some of the most significant developments in particle physics, cosmology, and condensed matter physics of the last half century, as well as many gems that defy classification and an extensive body of essays aimed at a wider audience.

The list below includes publications through May 2021. An updated version, with links to most of the original papers, is available at frankawilczek.com/publications.

1. Ultraviolet Behavior of Non-Abelian Gauge Theories (with D. Gross), *Phys. Rev. Lett.* **30**, 1343 (1973).
2. Asymptotically Free Gauge Theories, I (with D. Gross), *Phys. Rev. D* **8**, 3633 (1973).
3. Asymptotically Free Gauge Theories, II (with D. Gross), *Phys. Rev. D* **9**, 980 (1974).
4. Gauge Dependence of Renormalization Group Parameters (with W. Caswell), *Phys. Lett.* **49B**, 291 (1974).
5. Possible Non-Regge Behavior of Electroproduction Structure Functions (with A. DeRujula, S.L. Glashow, H.D. Politzer, S.B. Treiman and A. Zee), *Phys. Rev. D* **10**, 1649 (1974).
6. Scaling Deviations for Neutrino Reactions in Asymptotically Free Field Theories (with S. Treiman and A. Zee), *Phys. Rev. D* **10**, 2881 (1974).
7. Implications of Anomalous Lorentz Structure in Neutral Weak Processes (with R. Kingsley and A. Zee), *Phys. Rev. D* **10**, 2216 (1974).
8. Scaling Properties of a Gauge Theory with Han-Nambu Quarks and Charged Vector Gluons (with T.P. Cheng), *Phys. Lett.* **53B**, 269 (1974).
9. Some Experimental Consequences of Asymptotic Freedom, Proceedings: *AIP Conference* #**23**, 596, AIP Press (1975).
10. Tests of Coupling Types in Weak Muonless Reactions (with R.L. Kingsley, R. Shrock and S.B. Treiman), *Phys. Rev. D* **11**, 1043 (1975).
11. Remarks on the New Resonances at 3.1 GeV and 3.7 GeV (with C.G. Callan, R.L. Kingsley, S.B. Treiman and A. Zee), *Phys. Rev. Lett.* **34**, 52 (1975).

12. Weak Decays of Charmed Hadrons (with R.L. Kingsley, S.B. Treiman and A. Zee), *Phys. Rev. D* **11**, 1919 (1975).

13. Weak Decays of Charmed Hadrons, II: Soft Meson Theorems (with R.L. Kingsley, S. Treiman and A. Zee), *Phys. Rev. D* **12**, 106 (1975).

14. Possible Degeneracy of Heavy Quarks, *Phys. Lett.* **59B**, 179 (1975).

15. Weak Interactions with New Quarks and Right-Handed Currents (with R.L. Kingsley, S.B. Treiman and A. Zee), *Phys. Rev. D* **12**, 2768 (1975).

16. Weak Interactions of Heavy Quarks (with R.L. Kingsley and A. Zee), *Phys. Lett.* **61B**, 259 (1976).

17. New Leptons and Old Lepton Numbers (with A. Zee), *Nucl. Phys.* **B106**, 461 (1976).

18. Non-Uniqueness of Gauge Field Potentials (with S. Deser), *Phys. Lett.* **65B**, 391 (1976).

19. Inequivalent Embeddings of SU(2) and Instanton Interactions, *Phys. Lett.* **65B**, 160 (1976).

20. Rare Muon Decays, Natural Lepton Models, and Doubly Charged Leptons (with A. Zee), *Phys. Rev. Lett.* **38**, 531 (1977).

21. Mass Corrections in Deep-Inelastic Scattering (with D. Gross and S. Treiman), *Phys. Rev. D* **15**, 2486 (1977).

22. $\Delta I = 1/2$ Rule and Right-Handed Currents: Heavy-Quark Expansion and Limitations in Zweig's Rule (with A. Zee), *Phys. Rev. D* **15**, 2660 (1977).

23. A Model for Weak Trimuon Production (with A. Zee and S. Treiman), *Phys. Lett.* **68B**, 369 (1977).

24. Orientation of the Weak Interaction with Respect to the Strong Interaction (with A. Zee), *Phys. Rev. D* **15**, 3701 (1977).

25. Rare Muon Decays, Heavy Leptons and CP Violation (with S. Treiman and A. Zee), *Phys. Rev. D* **16**, 152 (1977).

26. Geometry and Interaction of Instantons, *Quark Confinement and Field Theory: Proceedings of a Conference at the University of Rochester*, Rochester, NY, June 14–18, 1976, D.R. Stump and D.H. Weingarten, eds. (Wiley-Interscience, NY, 1977), pp. 211–219.

27. Possible New Species of Quarks and Hadrons (with A. Zee), *Phys. Rev. D* **16**, 860 (1977).

28. Asymptotic Freedom: A Status Report, *Proceedings of Brookhaven APS Meeting*, Brookhaven National Lab., Upton, NY, pp. C79–C87.

29. Sum Rules for Spin-Dependent Electroproduction — Test of Relativistic Constituent Quarks (with S. Wandzura), *Phys. Lett.* **72B**, 195 (1977).

30. Decay of Heavy Vector Mesons into Higgs Particles, *Phys. Rev. Lett.* **39**, 1304 (1977).

31. Discrete Flavor Symmetries and a Formula for the Cabibbo Angle (with A. Zee), *Phys. Lett.* **70B**, 418 (1977).

32. Instantons and Spin Forces Between Massive Quarks (with A. Zee), *Phys. Rev. Lett.* **40**, 83 (1977).

33. Problems of Strong P and T Invariance in the Presence of Instantons, *Phys. Rev. Lett.* **40**, 279 (1977).

34. Some Problems in Gauge Field Theories, *The Unification of Elementary Forces and Gauge Theories: Proceedings of the Ben Lee Memorial International Conference on Parity Nonconservation, Weak Neutral Currents and Gauge Theories*, Fermi National Accelerator Laboratory, Batavia, 1977 (N.Y., Harwood Academic Press, 1978), pp. 607–621.

35. Axion Emission in Decay of Nuclear Excited States (with S. Treiman), *Phys. Lett.* **B74**, 381 (1978).

36. Low Energy Manifestations of Heavy Particles: Application to the Neutral Current (with J. Collins and A. Zee), *Phys. Rev. D* **18**, 242 (1978).

37. Effect of Instantons on the Heavy Quark Potential (with C. Callan, R. Dashen, D. Gross and A. Zee), *Phys. Rev. D* **18**, 4684 (1978).

38. Steps Toward the Heavy Quark Potential, "50 Years of the Dirac Equation," in *AIP Conference Proceedings* (48), pp. 30–37 (APS Press, 1979).

39. Matter-Antimatter Accounting, Thermodynamics, and Black Hole Radiation (with D. Toussaint, S. Treiman and A. Zee), *Phys. Rev. D* **19**, 1036 (1979).

40. Elementary Examples of Baryon Number Generation (with D. Toussaint), *Phys. Lett.* **81B**, 238 (1979).

41. Horizontal Interactions and Weak Mixing Angles (with A. Zee), *Phys. Rev. Lett.* **42**, 421 (1979).

42. Light Quark Masses and Isospin Violation (with D. Gross and S. Treiman), *Phys. Rev. D* **19**, 2188 (1979).

43. SU(3) Predictions for Charmed Meson Decays (with S. Treiman), *Phys. Rev. Lett.* **43**, 816 (1979).

44. Interference Effects in Charmed Meson Decays (with S. Treiman), *Phys. Rev. Lett.* **43**, 1059 (1979).

45. Operator Analysis of Nucleon Decay (with A. Zee), *Phys. Rev. Lett.* **43**, 1571 (1979).

46. Unification of Fundamental Forces, *Proceedings of 9th Lepton and Photon Interactions at High Energies Conference*, (eds. T.W.B. Kirk and H.D.I. Abarbanel, pp. 437–445 (Batavia, IL, 1979).

47. Conservation or Violation of $B - L$ in Proton Decay (with A. Zee), *Phys. Lett.* **88B**, 311 (1979).

48. Possibility and Consequences of T Violation in Nucleon Decay (with A. Hurlbert), *Phys. Lett.* **B93**, 274 (1980).

49. Symmetry Relations in Nucleon Decay (with A. Hurlbert), *Phys. Lett.* **B92**, 95 (1980).

50. Thermalization of Baryon Asymmetry (with S. Treiman), *Phys. Lett.* **B95**, 222 (1980).

51. Hyperweak Interactions, *Proceedings: "Particles and Fields" Conference*, Montreal (APS Press, 1980).

52. Cosmic Asymmetry Between Matter and Antimatter, *Scientific American*, December 1980, p. 82.

53. Constraints on Neutrinos (with D. Toussaint), *Nature* **289**, 777 (1981).

54. Price of Fractional Charge in Unified Theories (with L.F. Li), *Phys. Lett.* **B107**, 64 (1981).

55. Families from Spinors (with A. Zee), *Phys. Rev. D* **25**, 553 (1982).

56. Supersymmetry and the Scale of Unification (with S. Dimopoulos and S. Raby), *Phys. Rev. D* **24**, 1681 (1981).

57. Fractional Charge on Solitons (with J. Goldstone), *Phys. Rev. Lett.* **47**, 986 (1981).

58. Supersymmetric Unified Models (with S. Dimopoulos), in *The Unity of the Fundamental Interactions*, ed. A. Zichichi (Plenum, New York, 1983).

59. Physical Processes Involving Majorana Neutrinos (with L.F. Li), *Phys. Rev. D* **25**, 143 (1982).

60. *Prospects at Higher Energy*, Isabelle Summer Study, 1981 (BNL Press, 1981).

61. Coming Attractions in SUMS and Cosmology, *Comments on Nuclear and Particle Physics* X175 (1981).

62. Erice Lectures on Cosmology, in *The Unity of the Fundamental Interactions*, ed. A. Zichichi (Plenum, New York, 1983).

63. Naturality Problems, *APS Particles and Fields*, Santa Cruz (1981), (APS Press).

64. Magnetic Flux, Angular Momentum, and Statistics, *Phys. Rev. Lett.* **48**, 1144 (1982).

65. Remarks on Dyons, *Phys. Rev. Lett.* **48**, 1146 (1982).

66. Proton Decay in Supersymmetric Models (with S. Dimopoulos and S. Raby), *Phys. Lett.* **112B**, 133 (1982).

67. Old and New Relics in Cosmology, *Proceedings NAS* **79**, 33376 (1982).

68. QCD — The Modern Theory of Strong Interactions, *Ann. Rev. Nucl. Sci.* **V32**, 177 (1982).

69. Some Recent Ideas Related to Supersymmetry, *Unified Theories and Their Experimental Tests*, CLEUP, Padova (1983).

70. Reheating an Inflationary Universe (with A. Albrecht, P. Steinhart and M. Turner), *Phys. Rev. Lett.* **48**, 1437 (1982).

71. Might Our Vacuum be Metastable? (with M. Turner), *Nature* **298**, 633 (1982).

72. Monopole-Flux Tube Repulsion in Strong Coupling (with R. Zacher), *Phys. Rev. D* **26**, 3685 (1982).

73. Boundness from below of the SU(5) Higgs Potential (with R. MacKenzie), *Phys. Rev. D* **26**, 3679 (1982).

74. Magnetic Monopoles: A Local Source? (with S. Dimopoulos, S. Glashow and E. Purcell), *Nature* **298**, 824 (1982).

75. Quantum Mechanics of Fractional Spin Particles, *Phys. Rev. Lett.* **49**, 957 (1982).

76. Catalyzed Nucleon Decay in Neutron Stars (with S. Dimopoulos and J. Preskill), *Phys. Lett.* **119B**, 320 (1982).

77. Cosmology of Invisible Axions (with J. Preskill and M. Wise), *Phys. Lett.* **B120**, 127 (1983).

78. Axions and Family Symmetry Breaking, *Phys. Rev. Lett.* **49**, 1549 (1982).

79. Particle Physics and Cosmology: Foundations and Working Pictures, in *The Very Early Universe*, eds. G.W. Gibbons, S.W. Hawking, S. Siklos, p. 2 (Cambridge University Press, 1983).

80. Fun with Monopoles and Axions, in *The Very Early Universe*, eds. G.W. Gibbons, S. Hawking, S. Siklos, pp. 383–392 (Cambridge University Press, 1983).

81. Conference Summary, in *The Very Early Universe*, eds. G.W. Gibbons, S.W. Hawking, S. Siklos. p. 484 (Cambridge University Press, 1983).

82. Review of "Quantum Physics" by J. Glimm and A. Jaffe, *Phys. Today*, October 1982.

83. Family Symmetries, *AIP Conference Proceedings No.* 102, p. 68 (AIP Press, 1983).

84. Thoughts on Family Symmetries, *AIP Conference Proceedings* No. 96 (AIP Press, 1982).

85. Microphysical Cosmology, XVIII Solvay Conference, *Phys. Reports* **C104**, 143 (1984).

86. Formation of Structure in an Axion-Dominated Universe (with M. Turner and A. Zee), *Phys. Lett.* **125B**, 35, 519(E) (1983).

87. Particle-Antiparticle Annihilation in Diffuse Motion (with D. Toussaint), *J. Chem. Phys.* **78**, 2642 (1983).

88. Linking Numbers, Spin, and Statistics of Solitons (with A. Zee), *Phys. Rev. Lett.* 51, 2250 (1983).

89. Remarks on the Chiral Phase Transition in Chromodynamics (with R. Pisarski), *Phys. Rev. D* **29**, 338 (1984).

90. New Macroscopic Forces? (with J.E. Moody), *Phys. Rev. D* **30**, 130 (1984).

91. The U(1) Problem: Instanton, Axions, and Familons, in *How Far Are We from the Gauge Forces?* ed. A. Zichichi (Plenum, 1985).

92. Statistical Mechanics of Anyons (with D. Arovas, J.R. Schrieffer and A. Zee), *Nucl. Phys.* **B251** [FS13], 917 (1985).

93. Solitons in Superfluid ^{3}He-A: Bound States on Domain Walls (with J.L. Ho, J.R. Fulco and J.R. Schrieffer), *Phys. Rev. Lett.* **52**, 1524 (1984).

94. Reflections on Mirror Fermions (with G. Senjanovic and A. Zee), *Phys. Lett.* **B141**, 389 (1984).

95. llustrations of Vacuum Polarization by Solitons (with R. MacKenzie), *Phys. Rev. D* **30**, 2194 (1984).

96. Examples of Vacuum Polarization by Solitons (with R. MacKenzie), *Phys. Rev. D* **30**, 2260 (1984).

97. Appearance of Gauge Structures in Simple Dynamical Systems (with A. Zee), *Phys. Rev. Lett.* **52**, 2111 (1984).

98. Fractional Statistics and the Quantum Hall Effect (with D. Arovas and J.R. Schrieffer), *Phys. Rev. Lett.* **53**, 722 (1984).

99. A Stellar Loss Mechanism Involving Axions (with L. Krauss and J. Moody), *Phys. Lett.* **B144**, 391 (1984).

100. Possible Form of Vacuum Deformation by Heavy Particles (with R. MacKenzie and A. Zee), *Phys. Rev. Lett.* **53**, 2203 (1983).

101. Possible Interpretation of a New Resonance at 8.3 GeV (with K. Lane and S. Meshkov), *Phys. Rev. Lett.* **53**, 1718 (1984).

102. Adiabatic Methods in Field Theory, in *TASI Lectures in Elementary Particle Physics*, ed. D.N. Williams (TASI Publications, Ann Arbor, MI, 1984, pp. 520–535).

103. Inhomogeneous Cosmology and Microphysics, in *TASI Lectures in Elementary Particle Physics*, ed. D.N. Williams (TASI Publications, Ann Arbor, MI, 1984).

104. Bolometric Detection of Neutrinos (with B. Cabrera and L. Krauss), *Phys. Rev. Lett.* **55**, 25 (1985).

105. Solar Neutrino Oscillations (with L. Krauss), *Phys. Rev. Lett.* **55**, 122 (1985).

106. Fundamental Physics, Mathematics, and Astronomy, in *Emerging Syntheses in Science*, ed. D. Pines (Santa Fe Institute, 1985).

107. Solar System Constraints and Signatures for Dark Matter Candidates (with L. Krauss and M. Srednicki), *Phys. Rev. D* **33**, 2079 (1986).

108. Calculations for Cosmic Axion Detection (with L. Krauss, J. Moody and D. Morris), *Phys. Rev. Lett.* **55**, 1797 (1985).

109. Resonant Production and Charm Showers in Ultra-High Energy Neutrino Interactions, *Phys. Rev. Lett.* **55**, 1252 (1985).

110. Simple Realizations of Magnetic Monopole Gauge Fields: Diatoms and Spin Procession (with J. Moody and A. Shapere), *Phys. Rev. Lett.* **56**, 893 (1986).

111. A Short-Lived Axion Variant (with L. Krauss), *Phys. Lett.* **B173**, 189 (1986).

112. Macroscopic T-Violation: Prospects for a New Experiment (with W. Bialek and J. Moody), *Phys. Rev. Lett.* **56**, 1623 (1986).

113. *Longing for the Harmonies* (with Betsy Devine) (W.W. Norton, 1988).

114. "Virtual Particles" (sonnet), Norton Anthology of Light Verse, ed. R. Baker, 1986.

115. Artificial Vacuum for T-Violation Experiment (with C. Pryor), *Phys. Lett.* **B194**, 137 (1987).

116. New Quarks and Neutrino Counting Below the Z Threshold (with L. Krauss), *Phys. Lett.* **181B**, 380 (1986).

117. Compactification of the Twisted Heterotic String (with V. Nair, A. Shapere and A. Strominger), *Nucl. Phys.* **B287**, 402 (1987).

118. Geometry of Self-Propulsion at Low Reynolds Number (with A. Shapere), *J. Fluid Mech.* **198**, 557 (1989).

119. Internal Representations for Associative Memory (with E. Baum and J. Moody), NSF-ITP-86-138, *Biol. Cybernetics* **59**, 217 (1988).

120. Two Applications of Axion Electrodynamics, *Phys. Rev. Lett.* **58**, 1799 (1987).

121. Efficiencies of Self-Propulsion at Low Reynolds Number (with A. Shapere), *J. Fluid Mech.* **198**, 587 (1989).

122. Self-Propulsion at Low Reynolds Number (with A. Shapere), *Phys. Rev. Lett.* **58**, 2051 (1987).

123. Lattice Fermions, *Phys. Rev. Lett.* **59**, 2397 (1987).

124. Supervised Learning of Probability Distributions by Neutral Networks (with E. Baum), *Neural Information Processing*, ed. D. Anderson, AIP Press, pp. 52–61 (1988).

125. A Modern Look at Newton's Final Queries, in *Action and Reaction: Proceedings of a Symposium to Commemorate the Tercentary of Newton's Principia*, eds. P. Theerman, A. Seeff (University of Deleware Press, 1993).

126. Gauge Kinematics of Deformable Bodies (with A. Shapere), *Am. J. Phys.* **57**, 514 (1989).

127. Peculiar Spin and Statistics in 2+1 Dimensions (with R. MacKenzie), *Int. J. Mod. Phys.* **A3**, 2827 (1988).

128. *Geometric Phases in Physics* (a text and reprint volume, edited with A. Shapere) (World Scientific, 1989).

129. Self-Dual Models with θ Terms (with A. Shapere), *Nucl. Phys. B* **320**, 669 (1989).

130. Field Corrections to Induced Statistics (with A. Goldhaber, R. MacKenzie), *Mod. Phys. Lett.* **A4**, 21 (1989).

131. Possible New Form of Spontaneous T Violation (with J. March-Russell), *Phys. Rev. Lett.* **61**, 2066 (1988).

132. Induced Quantum Numbers in Some $2 + 1$ Dimensional Models (with Y.-H. Chen), *Int. J. Mod. Phys.* **A4**, 493 (1989).

133. Aharonov-Bohm Interaction of Cosmic Strings with Matter (with M. G. Alford), *Phys. Rev. Lett.* **62**, 1071 (1989).

134. Chiral Spin States and Superconductivity (with X.G. Wen, A. Zee), *Phys. Rev.* **B39**, 11413 (1989).

135. Discrete Gauge Symmetry in Continuum Theories (with L.M. Krauss), *Phys. Rev. Lett.* **62**, 1221 (1989).

136. Gauge Theory of Deformable Bodies, in *Proceedings of IUPAM Swansea Conference*, pp. 220–233, ed. B. Simon, A. Truman, and I.M. Davies (Adam Hilger, Bristol and NY, 1989).

137. Gauge Theories of Swimming, *Phys. World 2*, **36** (1989).

138. Adiabatic Effective Lagrangians (with J. Moody and A. Shapere), in *Geometric Phases in Physics*, by A. Shapere and F. Wilczek (World Scientific, 1989).

139. Enhanced Baryon Number Violation Around Cosmic Strings (with M. Alford and J. March-Russell), *Nucl. Phys.* **B328**, 140 (1989).

140. On Anyon Superconductivity, (with Y-H. Chen, E. Witten and B. Halperin), *Int. J. Mod. Phys.* **B3**, 1001 (1989).

141. Hydrodynamic Relations in Superconductivity (with M. Greiter and E. Witten), *Mod. Phys. Lett.* **B3**, 903 (1989).

142. Consequences of Time-Reversal-Symmetry Violation in Models of High T_c Superconductors (with B.I. Halperin and J. March-Russell), *Phys. Rev.* **B40**, 8726 (1989).

143. Lectures on Fractional Statistics and Anyon Superconductivity, in *Anomalies, Phases, Defects*, eds. M. Bregola, G. Marmo and G. Morandi (Bibliopolis, 1989).

144. Discrete Quantum Hair on Black Holes and the Nonabelian Aharanov-Bohm Effect (with M. Alford and J. March-Russell), *Nucl. Phys.* **B337**, 695 (1990).

145. The Interactions and Excitations of Nonabelian Vortices (with M. Alford, K. Benson, S. Coleman and J. March-Russell), *Phys. Rev. Lett.* **64**, 1632 (1990).

146. Spontaneous Fact Violation (with S. Giddings), *Int. J. Mod. Phys.* **A5**, 635 (1990).

147. Space-Time Approach to Holonomy Scattering (with Y.-S. Wu), *Phys. Rev. Lett.* **65**, 13 (1990).

148. Zero Modes of Non-Abelian Vortices (with M. Alford K. Benson, S. Coleman, and J. March- Russell), *Nucl. Phys.* **B349**, 414 (1991).

149. Infrared Behavior at Negative Curvature (with C. Callan), *Nucl. Phys.* **B340**, 366 (1990).

150. Some Global Problems in Gauge Theories (Variations on a Theme of Aharonov and Bohm), in *Quantum Coherence*, pp. 1–17 (World Scientific, 1990).

151. Heuristic Principle for Quantized Hall States (with M. Greiter), *Mod. Phys. Lett.* **B4**, 1063 (1990).

152. States of Anyon Matter, *Int. J. Mod. Phys.* **B5**, 1273 (1991).

153. *Fractional Statistics and Anyon Superconductivity*, a monograph and reprint collection, World Scientific (1990).

154. Anomalous Dimensions of Anisotropic Gauge Theory Operators (with D. Robertson), *Phys. Lett.* **B251**, 434 (1990).

155. Positron Line Radiation as a Signature of Particle Dark Matter in the Halo (with M.S. Turner), *Phys. Rev. D* **42**, 1001 (1990).

156. Perspectives on Particle Physics and Cosmology, *Physica Scripta* **T36**, 281 (1991), invited talk at Nobel Symposium #79: "The Birth and Early Evolution of Our Universe," Gräftàvallen, Östersund, Sweden, 6/90.

157. Inflationary Axion Cosmology (with M.S. Turner), *Phys. Rev. Lett.* **66**, 5 (1991).

158. Fractional Quantum Numbers: A Conceptual Introduction, *Trends in Theoretical Physics*, Vol. 2, eds. P. Ellis, Y. Tang (Addison-Wesley, 1991).

159. Relic Gravitational Waves and Extended Inflation (with M.S. Turner), *Phys. Rev. Lett.* **65**, 3080 (1990).

160. Anyons for Anyone, *Phys. World* **4**, 40 (1990).

161. Cosmological Implications of Axinos (with K. Rajagopal and M.S. Turner), *Nucl. Phys.* **B358**, 447 (1991).

162. Anyons, *Scientific American* **264**, 5, 58 (May 1991).

163. Cosmology and Broken Discrete Symmetry (with S. Trivedi, J. Preskill and M.B. Wise), *Nucl. Phys.* **B363**, 207 (1991).

164. Dynamical Effect of Quantum Hair (with S. Coleman and J. Preskill), *Mod. Phys. Lett.* **A6**, 1631 (1991).

165. Paired Hall State at Half Filling (with M. Greiter and X.G. Wen), *Phys. Rev. Lett.* **66**, 3205 (1991).

166. Growing Hair on Black Holes (with J. Preskill and S. Coleman), *Phys. Rev. Lett.* **67**, 1975 (1991).

167. Dual Dilaton Dyons (with A. Shapere and S. Trivedi), *Mod. Phys. Lett.* **A6**, 2677 (1991).

168. Limitations on the Statistical Description of Black Holes (with P. Schwarz, A. Shapere and S. Trivedi), *Mod. Phys. Lett.* **A6**, 2353 (1991).

169. Exact Solutions and the Adiabatic Heuristic for Quantum Hall States (with M. Greiter), *Nucl. Phys.* **B370**, 577 (1992).

170. Unification of Couplings (with S. Dimopoulos and S. Raby), *Physics Today* **44**, 25 (1991).

171. Quantum Hair on Black Holes (with S. Coleman and J.Preskill), *Nucl. Phys.* **B378**, 175 (1992).

172. Paired Hall States (with M. Greiter and X.G. Wen), *Nucl. Phys.* **B374**, 567 (1992).

173. Review of "Niels Bohr's Times," *Science* **225**, 345 (1991).

174. Disassembling Anyons, *Phys. Rev. Lett.* **69**, 132 (1992).

175. Black Holes as Elementary Particles (with C.F.E. Holzhey), *Nucl. Phys.* **B380**, 447 (1992).

176. Internal Frame Dragging and a Global Analogue of the Aharonov-Bohm Effect (with J. March-Russell and J. Preskill), *Phys. Rev. Lett.* **68**, 2567 (1992).

177. Quantum Mechanics, article in *World Book Encyclopedia*.

178. Paired Hall States in Double Layer Electron Systems (with M. Greiter and X.G. Wen), *Phys. Rev.* **B46**, 9586 (1992).

179. Application of the Renormalization Group to a Second Order QCD Phase Transition, *Int. J. Mod. Phys.* **A7**, 3911 (1992).

180. Remarks on the Phase Transition in QCD, in *Proceedings of the IFT Conference on Dark Matter*, *Int. J. Mod. Phys. D*, **03**, 63 (1994).

181. QCD and Asymptotic Freedom: Perspectives and Prospects, in *Proceedings of Aachen "20 Years of QCD" Conference*, ed. P. Zerwas and H. Kastrup, pp. 16–39 (World Scientific, Singapore, 1992), and *Int. J. Mod. Phys.* **A8**, 1359 (1993).

182. The End of Physics?, *Discover* (March 1993), p. 30.

183. Quantum Purity at a Small Price: Easing a Black Hole Paradox, in *Proceedings of Houston Conference on Black Holes*, eds. S. Kalara and D. Nanopoulos, pp. 1–21, January 1992 (World Scientific, Singapore).

184. Static and Dynamic Critical Phenomena at a Second Order QCD Phase Transition (with Krishna Rajagopal), *Nucl. Phys.* **B399**, 395 (1993).

185. Lectures 1–4 on Black Hole Quantum Mechanics, *The Black Hole 25 Years After*, eds. C. Teitelboim and J. Zanelli, World Scientific, p. 336 (1998).

186. A Philosopher in Spite of Himself (Review of *Dreams of a Final Theory* by S. Weinberg), *Physics Today*, April 1993.

187. Emergence of Coherent Long Wavelength Oscillations After a Quench: Application to QCD (with Krishna Rajagopal), *Nucl. Phys.* **B404**, 577 (1993).

188. Beyond the Standard Model, in *Proceeding of Texas/PASCOS 1992*, Berkeley, November 1992, *Annals of NYAS* **688**, 94–112 (1993).

189. Liberating Exotic Slaves, in *Quantum Coherence and Reality*, Proceedings of Aharonov's 60th Birthday, ed. J. Anandan, J. Safko (World Scientific, Singapore, 1995).

190. Fractional Statistics and Spin Charge Separation in $2 + 1$ Dimensions (with M. Greiter and Z. Zhou), unpublished.

191. 10^{12} Degrees in the Shade (preprinted as "Hot Stuff: The High Temperature Frontier"), *The Sciences*, January/February 1994, p. 22.

192. Geometric and Renormalized Entropy in Conformal Field Theory (with C. Holzhey and F. Larsen), *Nucl. Phys.* **B424**, 443 (1994).

193. Remarks on Hot QCD, in *Proceedings of Quark Matter '93*, Borlange, Sweden, June 1993 and *Nucl. Phys* **A566**, 123c (1994).

194. Status of QCD, in *Proceedings of Lepton-Photon Conference*, ed. P. Drell and D. Rubib, pp. 593–619, Cornell University, Ithaca, NY, August 1993 (AIP Press).

195. Non-Fermi Liquid Fixed Point in 2+1 Dimensions, (with C. Nayak), *Nucl. Phys.* **B417**, 359 (1994).

196. On Geometric Entropy (with C. Callan), *Phys. Lett.* **333B**, 55–61 (1994).

197. Exclusion Statistics: Low Temperature Properties, Fluctuations, Duality, Applications (with C. Nayak), *Phys. Rev. Lett.* **73**, 2740 (1994).

198. Renormalization Group Approach to Low Temperature Properties of a Non-Fermi Liquid Metal (with C. Nayak), *Nucl. Phys.* **B430**, 534 (1994).

199. Statistical Transmutation and Phases of Two-Dimensional Quantum Matter, in *Proceedings of 150th Anniversary of Boltzmann's Birth*, Academi Lincei, Rome.

200. Some Applications of a Simple Stationary Line Element for the Schwarzschild Geometry (with P. Kraus), *Mod. Phys. Lett.* **A9**, 3713 (1994).

201. Self-Interaction Correction to Black Hole Radiance (with P. Kraus), *Nucl. Phys.* **B433**, 403 (1995).

202. Geometric Entropy, Wave Functionals, and Fermions (with F. Larsen), *Annals of Physics*, **243**, 280 (1995).

203. Effect of Self-Interaction on Charged Black Hole Radiance (with P. Kraus), *Nucl. Phys.* **B437,** 231 (1995).

204. A. Spin, Electron Spin, Spin and Statistics; B. Fermions and Bosons, *Macmillan Encyclopedia of Physics*, 1996 Edition, pp. 1509–1511; 1511–1513; 1513–1514; and 547–549.

205. A. Symmetry Laws (Physics), Vol. 18, p. 89.

    B. Symmetry Breaking, Vol. 18, p. 86.

    C. Anyons, Vol. 1, p. 807.

    D. Geometric Phase, Vol. 8, p. 53.

    E. Conservation Laws, Vol. 4, p. 368.

    McGraw-Hill *Encyclopedia of Science & Technology* (8th Edition, 1997).

206. Review of Penrose's *Shadows of the Mind. Science* **266**, 1737 (1994).

207. Space-Time Aspects of Quasiparticle Propagation (with R. Levien and C. Nayak), *Int. J. Mod. Phys.* **B9**, 3189 (1995).

208. Quantum Hall States of High Symmetry (with C. Nayak), *Nucl. Phys.* **B450**, 558 (1995).

209. Physical Properties of Metals from a Renormalization Group Standpoint (with C. Nayak), *Int. J. Mod. Phys.* **B10**, 847 (1996).

210. Asymptotic Freedom, Lecture on receipt of the Dirac Medal, published by ICTP, Trieste, Italy (1994).

211. From the Standard Model to Dark Matter (invited talk at 5th Annual October Maryland Astrophysics Conference), published in *AIP Conference Proceedings* **336**, Issue 01.

212. Realization of the Fredkin Gate Using A Series of One- And Two-body Operators (with H.F. Chau), *Phys. Rev. Lett* **75** 748 (1995).

213. Quantum Numbers of Hall Effect Skyrmions (with C. Nayak), cond-mat/9505081. (Superseded by Quantum Numbers of Textured Hall Effect Quasiparticles, Item 220.)

214. Indirect Neutrino Oscillations (with K.S. Babu and Jogesh Pati), *Phys. Lett.* **B359**, 351 (1995).

215. Renormalization of Black Hole Entropy and of the Gravitational Coupling Constant (with F. Larsen), *Nucl. Phys.* **B458**, 249 (1996).

216. Spin-Singlet to Spin Polarized Phase Transition at $\nu = 2/3$: Flux-Trading in Action (with C. Nayak), *Nucl. Phys.* **B455**, 493 (1995).

217. Spin-Singlet Ordering Suggested by Repulsive Interactions (with C. Nayak), cond-mat/9510132. (See Possible Electronic Structure of Domain Walls in Mott Insulators, Item 223.)

218. Internal Structure of Black Holes (with F. Larsen), *Phys. Lett* **B375**, 37 (1996).

219. Remarks on the Phase Structure of QCD, *Particle Theory and Phenomenology Proceedings*, Iowa State University, May 1995, ed. Lassila, *et al.*, p. 47 (World Scientific, Singapore).

220. Quantum Numbers of Textured Hall Effect Quasiparticles (with C. Nayak), *Phys. Rev. Lett.* **77**, 4418 (1996).

221. Aspects of d-Density Order, in *Proceedings of Pacific Conference on Condensed Matter Theory: Complex Materials and Strongly Correlated Systems*, Seoul, Korea, Dec. 2–5, 1995.

222. QCD Interference Effects of Heavy Particles Below Threshold (with P. Kraus), *Phys. Lett.* **B382**, 262 (1996).

223. Possible Electronic Structure of Domain Walls in Mott Insulators (with C. Nayak), *Int. J. Mod. Phys.* **B10**, 2125 (1996).

224. A crack in the Standard Model?, *Nature* **380**, 19–20 (7 March 1996).

225. Remarks on the Current-Carrying State of Hall Superfluids, in *Proceedings of 1st Jagna International Workshop on Advances in Theoretical Physics*, Jagna, Bohol, Philippines, January 1995.

226. Classical Hair in String Theory I: General Formulation (with F. Larsen), *Nucl. Phys.* **B475**, 627 (1996).

227. $2n$ Quasihole States Realize 2^{n-1}-Dimensional Spinor Braiding Statistics in Paired Quantum Hall States (with C. Nayak), *Nucl. Phys.* **B479**, 529 (1996).

228. Experimental Consequences of a Minimal Messenger Model for Supersymmetry Breaking (with K.S. Babu and C. Kolda), *Phys. Rev. Lett.* **77**, 3070 (1996).

229. Particle Physics for Cosmology, published in "Critical Dialogues in Cosmology" in celebration of the 250th Anniversary of Princeton University, 24–27 June 1996. ed. N. Turok (World Scientific, Singapore).

230. Classical Hair in String Theory II: Explicit Calculations (with F. Larsen), *Nucl. Phys.* **B488**, 261 (1997).

231. Populated Domain Walls (with C. Nayak), *Phys. Rev. Lett.*, **78**, 2465 (1997).

232. From Asymptotic Freedom to Unification to Supersymmetry (and Beyond), chapter in *Physics in 2000 and Beyond*, World Scientific.

233. Asymptotic Freedom, Lecture on receipt of the Dirac Medal, October 1994, published by ICTP, Trieste, Italy.

234. Resolution of Cosmological Singularities (with F. Larsen), *Phys. Rev.* **D 55**, 4591 (1997).

235. Review of "In Search of the Ultimate Building Blocks" by G. 't Hooft, *Nature* **385**, 217 (16 Jan. 1997).

236. The Future of Particle Physics as a Natural Science, in *Critical Problems in Physics* in celebration of the 250th Anniversary of Princeton University, November 1996, eds. V.L. Fitch, D.R. Marlow, and M. Dementi, Princeton University Press; also in *Int. J. Mod. Phys. A* **13**, 863, (1998); also in *Magazine of Physics, Science & Ideas* **1**(2), 12–25 (Dec. 1996).

237. The Future of Particle Physics, in *Proceedings of the 11th Nishinomiya–Yukawa Memorial Symposium "Physics in the 21st Century"*, eds. K. Kikkawa, H. Kunitomo, and H. Ohtsubo (World Scientific, Singapore, 1996).

238. Comments on the high-Q2 HERA anomaly (with K.S. Babu, C. Kolda, J. March-Russell). *Phys. Lett.* **B402**, 367 (1997).

239. Cross-Confinement in Multi-Chern-Simons Theories (with L.J. Cornalba), *Phys. Rev. Lett.* **78**, 4679 (1997).

240. Review of *"The Inflationary Universe"* by Alan Guth, *Science* **276**, 1087 (16 May 1997).

241. Review of *"The Fabric of Reality"* by David Deutsch, *Physics World* **10**, 51 (June 1997).

242. Mass Splittings from Symmetry Obstruction (with L. Cornalba), *Phys. Lett.* **B411**, 112–116 (1997).

243. Some Examples in the Realization of Symmetry, *Nucl. Phys.* **B68** (*Proc. Suppl.*), 367 (1998).

244. Panning for Gold at the K Stream, *Nature* **389**, 671 (16 Oct. 1997).

245. An Action for Black Hole Membranes (with M. Parikh), *Phys. Rev. D* **58**, 064011 (1998).

246. QCD at Finite Baryon Density: Nucleon Droplets and Color Superconductivity (with M. Alford and K. Rajagopal), *Phys. Lett.* **B422**, 247–256 (1998).

247. A Chern-Simons Effective Field Theory for the Pfaffian Quantum Hall State (with E. Fradkin, C. Nayak, and A. Tsvelik), *Nucl. Phys.* **B516**, 704–718 (1998).

248. Colour Takes The Field, *Nature* **390**, 659 (18/25 Dec. 1998).

249. Neutrino Deficit Challenges Conservation Laws, *Nature* **391**, 123 (8 Jan. 1998).

250. Why Are There Analogies between Condensed Matter and Particle Theory? *Physics Today*, **11** (Jan. 1998).

251. Suggested New Modes in Supersymmetric Proton Decay (with K.S. Babu and J. Pati), *Phys. Lett.* B423, 337–347 (1998).

252. Riemann-Einstein Structure from Volume and Gauge Symmetry, *Phys. Rev. Lett.* **80**, 4851 (1998).

253. Liberating Quarks and Gluons, *Nature*, **391**, 330–331 (22 Jan. 1998).

254. Back to Basics at High Temperature, *Physics Today*, **11** (April 1998).

255. Beyond The Standard Model: An Answer and Twenty Questions, in *Erice 1997: highlights for subnuclear physics, 50 years later*, pp. 291–327 (1997).

256. Color Superconductivity and Signs of Its Formation (with M. Alford and K. Rajagopal), in *Proceedings of Riken-BNL Workshop*, November 1997.

257. Quantum Field Theory, in the American Physical Society Centenary issue of *Rev. Mod. Phys.* **71**, S85–S95 (1999); also in More Things in Heaven and Earth — A celebration of Physics at the Millennium, ed. B. Bederson (Springer-Verlag, New York, 1999).

258. *CP* Violation, Higgs Couplings, and Supersymmetry (with K.S. Babu, C. Kolda and J. March-Russell), *Phys. Rev. D* **59**, 016004 (1999).

259. Color-Flavor Locking and Chiral Symmetry Breaking in High Density QCD (with M. Alford and K. Rajagopal), *Nucl. Phys.* **B537**, 443–458 (1999).

260. From Notes to Chords in QCD, in *Proceedings of QCD at Finite Baryon Density Conference*, April 1998, Universitaet Bielefeld, Bielefeld, Germany, *Nucl. Phys.* **A642**, 1c–13c, (1998).

261. Projective Statistics and Spinors in Hilbert Space, arXiv:hep-th/9806228 (1998).

262. Particle Physics: The Standard Model Transcended, *Nature* **394**, 13–15 (2 July 1998).

263. Global Structure of Evaporating Black Holes (with M. Parikh), *Phys. Lett.* **B449**, 24–29 (1999).

264. Imaginary Chemical Potential and Finite Fermion Density on the Lattice (with M. Alford and A. Kapustin), *Phys. Rev.* D **59**, 054502 (1999).

265. Nuclear and Subnuclear Boiling, *Nature* **395**, 220–221 (17 September 1998).

266. Beyond the standard model: This time for real, *in Proceedings of XVIII International Conference on Neutrino Physics and Astrophysics*, Takayama, Japan, June 4–9, 1998, *Nucl. Phys. Proc. Suppl.* **77**, 511–519 (1999).

267. Fermion masses, neutrino oscillations, and proton decay in the light of SuperKamiokande (with K.S. Babu and J. Pati), *Nucl. Phys.* **B566**, 33–91 (2000).

268. High Density Quark Matter and the Renormalization Group in QCD with Two and Three Flavors (with T. Schäefer), *Phys. Lett.* **B450**, 325–331 (1999).

269. Continuity of Quark and Hadron Matter (with Thomas Schäefer), *Phys. Rev. Lett.* **82**, 3956–3959 (1999).

270. The Persistence of Ether, *Phys. Today* **52**, 11–13 (January 1999).

271. The Long Life of a Thoughtful Teacher (Review of *Geons, Black Holes and Quantum Foam: A Life in Physics* by J. A. Wheeler with K. Ford) *Science* **282** (1998).

272. Getting Its from Bits, *Nature* **397**, 303–306 (28 Jan. 1999).

273. Reply in sonnet form, to Pinotti's letter to the editor regarding Numerical Simulation (Item 254), *Physics Today* **113** (March 1999).

274. Quark Description of Hadronic Phases (with T. Schäefer), *Phys. Rev. D* **60**, 074014 (1999).

275. Cosmic Molasses for Particle Masses, *New Scientist* **2181**, 32–37 (10 April 1999).

276. Minimal Potentials with Very Many Minima (with M. Soljacic), *Phys. Rev. Lett.* **84**, 2285–2289 (2000).

277. Reaching Bottom, Laying Foundations, *Nature* "A Celebration of Physics" (special issue for American Physical Society 100th anniversary), pp. 4–5 (April 1999).

278. Superconductivity from Perturbative One-gluon Exchange in High Density Quark Matter (with T. Schaefer), *Phys. Rev. D* **60**, 114033–1 (1999).

279. And You're Glue *Nature* **400**, 21–23 (1 July 1999).

280. What QCD Tells Us about Nature — and Why We Should Listen, keynote talk at PANIC'99, Uppsala, Sweden, June 10, 1999, *Nucl. Phys.* **A663 & 664**, 3c–20c (2000).

281. The Recent Excitement in High-Density QCD, invited talk at PANIC '99, Uppsala, Sweden, June 1999. *Nucl. Phys.* **A663 & 664**, 257c–271c (2000).

282. Reply to Walter L. Wagner, regarding Mukerjee's Article on the Relativistic Heavy Ion Collider (RHIC) at Brookhaven National Laboratory ["A Little Big Bang," March 1999], Letters to the Editors, *Scientific American*, **8** (July 1999).

283. Hawking Radiation as Tunneling (with M. Parikh), *Phys. Rev. Lett.* **85**, 5042–5045 (2000).

284. Review of Speculative "Disaster Scenarios" at RHIC (with W. Busza, R. L. Jaffe and J. Sandweiss). (Report of a Committee charged by Dr. John Marburger, Director of Brookhaven National Laboratory, to review potentially catatrophic processes that might be initated by heavy ion collisions at the Relativistic Heavy Ion Collider.) *Rev. Mod. Phys.* **72**, 1125–1140 (2000).

285. QCD in Extreme Conditions, Lectures given at CRM Summer School, "Theoretical Physics at the End of the XXth Century," June 27–July 10, Banff, Alberta, Canada. Published in *CRM Series in Mathematical Physics*, eds. Y. Saint-Aubin and L. Vinet (Springer, 2000), pp. 567–636.

286. Mass without Mass I: Most of Matter, *Physics Today* **52** (1999).

287. Maxwell's Other Demon, *Nature* **402**, 22–23 (4 November 1999).

288. Charged Stripes from Alternating Static Magnetic Field (with O. Tchernyshyov), *Phys. Rev.* **B62**, 4208 (2000).

289. Mass without Mass II: The Medium is the Mass-age, *Physics Today*, 13–14 (January 2000).

290. Is the Sky Made from Pi? (Review of two books, *Just Six Numbers: The Deep Forces that Shape the Universe* by Martin Rees; and *The Nine Numbers of the Universe* by Michael Rowan-Robinson) *Nature* **403**, 2479–2481 (20 January 2000).

291. Radical Conservatism and Nucleon Decay, invited lecture at NNN99 Workshop, September 23–25, 1999, at SUNY-Stony Brook, NY. Published in *AIP conference Proceedings of NNN99*, **62–73** (1999) .

292. Backyard Exotica, *Nature* **404**, 452–45 (30 March 2000).

293. Neutralino Dark Matter in Focus Point Supersymmetry (with J. Feng and K. Matchev), *Phys. Lett.* **B482**, 388–399 (2000).

294. Saltatory Relaxation of the Cosmological Term in String Theory (with J. Feng, J. March-Russell and S. Sethi), *Nucl. Phys* **B602**, 307–328 (2001).

295. Weinberg on Supersymmetry; Another Landmark Work (Review of *The Quantum Theory of Fields, vol. 3: Supersymmetry* by Steven Weinberg), *Physics Today* **53**, 5, 55–56 (May 2000).

296. QCD Made Simple, *Physics Today*, **53**, 8, 22–28 (2000).

297. Prospects for Indirect Detection of Neutralino Dark Matter (with J. Feng and K. Matchev), *Phys. Rev. D* **63**, 4502–4504 (2001).

298. Josephson Effect Without Superconductivity: Realization in Quantum Hall Bilayers (with M. Fogler), *Phys. Rev. Lett.* **86**, 1833–1836 (2001).

299. The Condensed Matter Physics of QCD (with K. Rajagopal), in *Handbook of QCD*, ed. M. Shifman, World Scientific, pp. 2016–2151 (2001).

300. Enforced Electrical Neutrality of the Color-Flavor Locked Phase (with K. Rajagopal), *Phys. Rev. Lett.* **86**, 3492–3495 (2001).

301. Voyaging in Hilbert Space, *Fortschr Phys.* **48**, 9–11, 769–770 (2000).

302. Future Summary, *Int. J. Mod. Phys. A* **16**, N10 1653–1677 (2001).

303. Precision Precession, *Nature* **410**, 28–29 (2001).

304. When Words Fail, *Nature* **410**, 149 (2001).

305. The Dirac Equation, in *It Must Be Beautiful: The Great Equations of Modern Science*, ed. G. Farmelo (Granta Books, 2002), pp. 102–130. Also in *Int. J. Mod. Phys. A* **19**, 45–74 (2004).

306. Learning from QCD, in *Proceedings: EPIC 2000 Workshop, AIP Conference* **588**.

307. Observability of Earth-Skimming Ultra-High Energy Neutrinos (with J. Feng, P. Fisher, and T. Yu), *Phys. Rev. Lett.* **88**, 161102 (2001).

308. The Minimal CFL-Nuclear Interface (with M. Alford, K. Rajagopal, and S. Reddy), *Phys. Rev. D* **64**, 074017 (2001).

309. Unified Field Theories, in *The Encyclopedia of Physical Science and Technology Vol. 17 – Third Edition*, ed. R. Meyers, pp. 339–349 (Academic Press, 2001).

310. Scaling Mount Planck 1: A View from the Bottom, *Physics Today* **54**, 6, 12–13 (2001).

311. Newton Rules (for now), *Nature* **410**, 881–882 (2001).

312. Quark-Gluon Matter, in *McGraw-Hill Yearbook of Science & Technology*, 298–299 (2002).

313. Review of *ITEP Lectures on Particle Physics and Field Theory*, Vols. 1 and 2 by M. Shifman, *Physics Today* **53N8**, 46–48 (2000).

314. What is Quantum Theory? *Physics Today* **53N6**, 11–12 (2000).

315. Quantum Statistics, in *Macmillan Encyclopedia of Physics, Supplement: Elementary Particle Physics* (2002).

316. The World's Numerical Recipe, *Daedalus* **131**, 142–147 (2001).

317. Universality, *Nature* **415**, 265 (2001).

318. Scaling Mount Planck 2: Base Camp, *Physics Today* **54**, 11, 12–13 (2001).

319. Particle and Astroparticle Searches for Supersymmetry (with J. Feng and K. Matchev), SNOWMASS-2001-P309 (Nov. 2001).

320. Reply to C. Alden Mead (Question of Fundamental Constants), *Physics Today*, **54**, 11–15 (2001).

321. Fermi and the Elucidation of Matter, in *Fermi Remembered*, ed. J.W. Cronin, 34–51 (University of Chicago Press, 2004).

322. Obituary of William Edward Caswell (with C. Callan), *Physics Today* **54**, 12, 74–75 (2001).

323. Four Big Questions with Pretty Good Answers, delivered at *Symposium in Honor of Heisenberg's 100th birthday*, December 6, 2001. In *Fundamental Physics — Heisenberg and Beyond*, ed. G.W. Buschhorn, J. Wess (Springer, 2004).

324. The Social Benefit of High-Energy Physics, in *Macmillan Encyclopedia of Physics, Supplement: Elementary Particle Physics* (2002).

325. Scaling Mount Planck 3: Is That All There Is? *Physics Today* **55**, 8, 10–11 (2002).

326. Depilating global charge from thermal black holes (with John March-Russell), CERN-TH-2001-378, hep-th/0203170.

327. Some Basic Aspects of Fractional Quantum Numbers, Commentary for the volume *Selected Papers of J. Robert Schrieffer*, eds. N.E. Bonesteel, L.P. Gor'kov (World Scientific, 2002), 135–152.

328. Interior Gap Superfluidity (with W. Liu), *Phys. Rev. Lett.* **90**, 047002 (2002).

329. QCD and Natural Philosophy (plenary talk at UNESCO TH2002 Conference), *Annales Henri Poincaré* **4**, S211–S228 (2003).

330. The Future of High Energy Physics (Summary talk at ICHEP 2002 — Rochester Conference), *Nucl. Phys.* **B117** (Proc Suppl.), 410–430 (2003).

331. Opportunities, Challenges and Fantasies in Lattice QCD (Keynote talk at LATTICE 2002), *Nucl. Phys.* **B119**, (Proc. Suppl.) 3–12 (2003).

332. Life's Parameters, *Physics Today*, **56**, 2, 10–11 (2003).

333. Inaugural Editorial Letter, *Annals of Physics*, **303** (2003).

334. Review of *Galileo's Finger* by P. Atkins, *Nature* **422**, 377 (2003).

335. Breached Pairing Superfluidity: Possible Realization in QCD (with E. Gubankova and W. Vincent Liu), *Phys. Rev. Lett.* **91**, 32001 (2003).

336. Analysis and Synthesis I: What Matters for Matter, *Physics Today* **56**, 5, 10–11 (2003).

337. Analysis and Synthesis II: Universal Characteristics, *Physics Today* **56**, 7, 10–11 (2003).

338. Diquarks and Exotic Spectroscopy (with R.L. Jaffe), *Phys. Rev. Lett.* **91**, 232003 (2003).

339. The Origin of Mass, *Physics@MIT* 24–35 (2003).

340. Review of *Quantum: A Guide for the Perplexed* by J. Al-Khalili, *Nature* **424**, 997–8 (2003).

341. The World's Numerical Recipe, in *The Best American Science Writing 2003*, ed. Oliver Sacks, 96–101 (Harper-Collins, 2003).

342. Analysis and Synthesis III: Cosmic Groundwork, *Physics Today* **56**, 10, 10–11 (2003).

343. Thermal Decay of the Cosmological Constant into Black Holes (with A. Gomberoff, M. Henneaux, and C. Teitelboim), *Phys. Rev. D* **69**, 083520 (2004).

344. Spin-Orbit Ordering, Momentum Space Coexistence, and Cuprate Superconductivity (with W. Vincent Liu) (2003).

345. Spin dependent Hubbard Model and a Quantum Phase Transition in Cold Atoms (with W. Vincent Liu and Peter Zoller), *Phys. Rev. A* **70**, 033603 (2004).

346. Systematics of Exotic Cascade Decays (with R.L. Jaffe), *Phys. Rev. D* **69**, 114017 (2004).

347. From Concept to Reality to Vision (speech accepting EPS High Energy Physics Prize), *Eur. Phys. J.* **C33**, S1–S4 (2004).

348. A Perspective on Pentaquarks (with R.L. Jaffe) (plenary talk at EPS conference), *Eur. Phys. J.* **C33**, S38–S42 (2004).

349. Analysis and Synthesis IV: Limits and Supplements, *Physics Today* **57N1**, 10–11 (2004).

350. The Universe is a Strange Place (keynote talk at *SpacePart 03: 2nd International Conference on Particle and Fundamental Physics in Space*, Washington, DC), *Nuclear Physics B Proceedings Supplements* **134**, 3–12 (2004).

351. A constructive critique of the three standard systems, in Advanced Studies Institute: Physics at LHC-Praha-2003, Prague, CR, *Czech. J. Phys.* **54**, A415–A427 (2004).

352. From 'not wrong' to (maybe) right, *Nature* **428**, 261 (2004).

353. Total Relativity: March 2004, *Physics Today* **57**, 4, 10–11 (2004).

354. Stability Criteria for Breached Pair Superfluidity (with Michael McNeil Forbes, Eleana Gubankova and W. Vincent Liu), *Phys. Rev. Lett.* **94**, 017001 (2004).

355. Quarks, Diquarks and Pentaquarks (with R.L. Jaffe), *Physics World*, **17**, 25–30 (2004).

356. Answers to "What is the physicist's concept of symmetry?", "Could we tell if left and right were reversed?", in Access Science @ McGraw-Hill, www.accessscience.com.

357. Yang-Mills Theory In, Beyond, and Behind Observed Reality, in *50 Years of Yang-Mills Theory*, ed. G. 't Hooft, pp. 255–69, 2004.

358. A Model of Anthropic Reasoning, Addressing the Dark to Ordinary Matter Coincidence, solicited article for *Universe or Multiverse*, ed. B. Carr (Cambridge University Press, 2004).

359. Whence the Force of $F = ma$? 1: Culture Shock, *Physics Today* **57N10**, 11–12 (2004).

360. Diquarks as Inspiration and as Objects, in *Kogan Memorial: From Fields to Strings* Vol. 1, ed. M. Shifman, pp. 77–93 (World Scientific, 2004). Also in "Deserfest: A Celebration of the Life and Works of Stanley Deser", ed. J. Liu, M. Duff, K. Steele, and R. Woodard, p. 322 (World Scientific, 2004).

361. Breached Superfluidity via p-Wave Coupling (with E. Goubankova and E. Mishchenko), *Phys. Rev. Lett.* **94**, 110402 (2005).

362. Doing science gave me freedom, in "One Hundred Reasons To Be a Scientist", 40th anniversary issue, Abdus Salam International Centre for Theoretical Physics, pp. 250–251 (2004).

363. In Search of Symmetry Lost, *Nature* **433**, 239–247 (2004).

364. Hadron Systematics, Diquark Correlations, and Exotics (with A. Selem) (2004). [Superseded by 400.]

365. Reply to letters commenting on Reference Frame article "Analysis and Synthesis IV: Limits and Supplements", *Physics Today* **57**, 9, 14–15 (2004).

366. Whence the Force of $F = ma$? II: Rationalizations, *Physics Today* **57**, 12, 10–11 (2004).

367. Gapless Surfaces in Anisotropic Superfluids (with E. Gubankova and E. Mishchenko), *Phys. Rev. B* **74**, 184516 (2006).

368. Whence the Force of $F = ma$? III: Cultural Diversity, *Physics Today* **58**, 7, 10–11 (2004).

369. A Relationship Between Hawking Radiation and Gravitational Anomalies (with S. Robinson), *Phys. Rev. Lett.* **95**, 011303–1 (2005).

370. Asymptotic Freedom: From Paradox to Paradigm (Lecture on Receipt of Nobel Prize), *Les Prix Nobel* **100–124** (Almqvist & Wiesell International, Stockholm, Sweden) (2004).

371. Shelf Life (Interview), *Physics World* **1747** (Nov. 2004).

372. Treks of Imagination (Review of *The Road to Reality* by Roger Penrose), *Science* **307**, 852 (2004).

373. New Physical Laws Suggested by Symmetry (Lecture on receipt of King Faisal International Prize), *Articles in Medicine and Science V*, **83** (2004–2005).

374. Gravitational Correction to Running of Gauge Couplings (with S. Robinson), *Phys. Rev. Lett.* **96**, 213601 (2006).

375. The Origin of Mass World Year of Physics Essay, *Frontline* Vol. 22 (2005); also *Mod. Phys Lett. A* **21** 701–12 (2006). (Modified from 339.)

376. An Emptier Emptiness? *Nature* **435**, 152 (2005).

377. Happy 100th Birthday, Special Relativity, www.accessscience.com (2005).

378. My Favorite Scientific Picture, *Science et Vie (Science and Life)* (June 05, 2005).

379. Reductionism is Dead, Long Live Reductionism, MIT-CTP 3658.

380. Asymptotic Freedom: From Paradox to Paradigm, *Rev. Mod. Phys.* **77**, 857 (2005); *PNAS* **102(24)**, 8403–13 (2005); *Int. J. Mod. Phys.* **A20** (2005). (See item 370.)

381. Advantages and Distinguishing Features of Focus Point Supersymmetry (with J. L. Feng), *Phys. Lett.* **B631**, 170–176 (2005).

382. General Issues Connecting Flavor Symmetry and Supersymmetry (with E. Bilgin, B. Patt, and D. Tucker-Smith), *Phys. Lett.* **B634**, 69–73 (2006).

383. Example of a Hidden Flavor Sector (with B. Patt and D. Tucker-Smith), hep-ph/0509295.

384. Journal Club: Promise that anyon particles hold for quantum computing excites the physicist who named them, *Nature* **437**, 299 (2005).

385. On Absolute Units, I: Choices, *Physics Today* **58**, 10, 12–13 (2005).

386. An explorer and surveyor (tribute to H. Weyl), *Nature* **437**, 1095 (2005).

387. The Universe is a Strange Place, in *Lepton-Photon Interactions at High Energies, International Symposium XXII Proceedings*, 447–61; also in *Int. J. Mod. Phys.* **A 21**, 8–9 (2005). (Different from 353.)

388. Enlightenment, Knowledge, Ignorance, Temptation, in *Universe or Multiverse?* (Summary talk given at Conference "Expectations of a Final Theory", Cambridge University), ed. Bernard Carr (Cambridge University Press, 2005).

389. Dimensionless constants, cosmology and other dark matters (with M. Tegmark, A. Aguirre, and M. Rees), *Phys. Rev. D.* **73**, 023505 (2006).

390. On Absolute Units, II: Challenges and Responses, *Physics Today* **59**, 1, 10–11 (2006).

391. From Electronics to Anyonics, *Physics World* **19**, 22 (2006).

392. Hawking Radiation of Charged Black Holes via Gauge and Gravitational Anomalies (with Satoshi Iso and Hiroshi Umetsu), *Phys. Rev. Lett.* **96**, 151302 (2006).

393. *Fantastic Realities: 49 Mind Journeys and a Trip to Stockholm* (World Scientific, Singapore, 2006).

394. Hadron systematics and emergent diquarks (with A. Selem), *in Ringberg 2005, New Trends in HERA Physics*, eds. G. Grindhammer, B.A. Kniehl, G. Kramer, and W. Ochs, World Scientific, pp. 337–356 (2006).

395. Stability conditions and Fermi surface topologies in a superconductor (with E. Gubankova and A. Schmitt), *Phys. Rev. B* **74**, N6 (2006).

396. Anomalies, Hawking radiation and regularity in rotating black holes (with S. Iso and H. Umetsu), *Phys. Rev. D* **74**, 044017 (2006).

397. On Absolute Units, III: Absolutely Not, *Physics Today* **59**, 5, 10–11 (2006).

398. Higgs-field Portal into Hidden Sectors (with B. Patt), hep-ph/0605188 (2006).

399. My Favorites [Discussion of favorite books], New York Academy of Sciences Update **19** (May/June 2006)

400. Hadron Systematics Exposing Diquark Correlation (with A. Selem), MIT-CTP-3762 (2006).

401. On Magic Moments, *SEED* (November 2006), MIT-CTP 3766.

402. Archaeopteryx Looks Up: Speculations on the Future of Human Evolution, New York Academy of Sciences Update **20**, pp. 10–13 (Sept/Oct 2006).

403. Reasonably Effective 1: Deconstructing a Miracle, *Physics Today* **59**, 11, 8–9 (2006).

404. Did the Big Bang Boil? *Nature* **443**, 637 (2006).

405. Resonating with Feshbach, Physics@MIT 32–35 (2006).

406. Pappalardo Sonnet, *Physics@MIT 25* (2006).

407. Quantum Chromodynamics, *SciDAC Review* (Fall 2006).

408. The Big Questions, *New Scientist*, 50th Anniversary Special 99 (November 2006).

409. Hard-core Revelations, *Nature* **445**, 156 (2007).

410. La musica del vuoto (Music of Void), *Di Renzo Editore* (2007)

411. Reasonably Effective II: Devil's Advocate, *Physics Today* **60**, N5 8–9 (2007).

412. W Poszukiwaniu Harmonii (translation into Polish of *Longing for the Harmonies*), translators E. Łokas and B. Bieniok (Prószyński i S-kq, 2007).

413. Fundamental Constants, in "Visions of Discovery, in honor of Charles Townes' 90th Birthday" ed. R. Chiao, Part II 75–104 (2007).

414. Quantum Chromodynamics: Lifestyles of the small and simple, *Nature Physics* **3**, 375–6 (June 2007).

415. Physics Will Not Achieve a Theory of Everything, in "What Are You Optimistic About?", ed. J. Brockman (Harper Perennial, 2007).

416. Anticipating a New Golden Age (Invited Lecture at SUSY 07, Karlsruhe) in *SUSY 07 Proceedings: Perspectives on LHC Physics* ed. G. Kane and A. Pierce (World Scientific, 2008); also in *Int. J. Mod. Phys.* **A23**, 1791–1811 (2007); also in *European Physical Journal C* **59**, 85 (2007).

417. Big Troubles, Imagined and Real, in *Global Catastrophic Risks*, ed. N. Bostrom and M. Cirkovic (Oxford University Press, 2008), p. 346.

418. Near-Zero Modes in Superconducting Graphene (with Pouyan Ghaemi), *Phys. Scr.* **T146**, 014019 (2012).

419. My Wizard, *Physics Today* **61**, N1 (2008).

420. *The Lightness of Being: Mass, Ether and the Unification of Forces* (Basic/Perseus, 2008).

421. Axion Cosmology and the Energy Scale of Inflation (with Mark Hertzberg and Max Tegmark), *Phys. Rev. D.* **78**, 083507 (2008).

422. QCD Meets BCS Meets QQ, in *QCD Down Under 2*, p. 7, MIT-CTP 3945.

423. Forecasting the Fate of Mysteries: Our Modern Answer to the Pyramids, *Newsweek* (September 2008).

424. The Beginning of a New Golden Age in Understanding the Laws of Nature, *Po drogach uczonych* (Polska Akademia Umiejetnosci, Krakow 2008), p. 763.

425. New Kinds of Quantum Statistics, in "Spin — Poincaré Seminar 2007", ed. B. Duplantier, J.M. Raimond and V. Rivasseau, pp. 61–69 (Birkhauser Verlag AG, 2009).

426. Mass by Numbers, *Nature* **456**, 449 (2008).

427. Introduction to *Philosophy of Mathematics and Natural Science* by Hermann Weyl (Princeton University Press, 2008).

428. Running Inflation in the Standard Model (with A. De Simone and M.P. Hertzberg), *Phys. Lett.* **678B**, 1–8 (2009).

429. "National Greatness" Versus Real National Greatness, *Science News* (October 2008).

430. A Slice of SciFoo, *Edge, The Third Culture* (2008).

431. Majorana Returns, *Nature Physics* **5**, 614–618 (2009).

432. Journal Club: A theoretical physicist examines exotic particles lurking in new materials, *Nature* **458**, 129 (2009).

433. What is Space? *Physics@MIT* 30 (2009).

434. Quantum Field Theory, in *Compendium of Quantum Physics* eds. D. Greenberger, K. Hentschel and F. Weinert (Springer, 2009).

435. The Social Benefit of High-Energy Physics: Challenges, Transformations and Development, in *Transformations — Risk, Crisis, Adaptation*, ed. V.I. Ionesov, 102–122 (Samara, 2009).

436. Prelude to *Compressed Baryonic Matter, The CBM Physics Book*, eds. B. Friman, C.H. Öohne, J. Knoll, S. Leupold, J. Randrup, R. Rapp and P. Senger Lecture Notes in Physics **814**, 1–10 (Springer, 2011).

437. Some Calculable Contributions to Entanglement Entropy (with Mark P. Hertzberg), *Phys. Rev. Lett.* **106**, 050404 (2011).

438. Beyond the Standard Litany: LOSP, Higgs Portal, Lattice Lattice Gauge Theory, European Physical Society Europhysics Conference on High Energy Physics, pos.sissa.it/084/001 (2009).

439. The Mind's New Eye, *Project News Syndicate* (March 2010).

440. Effective Action, Boundary Conditions and Virasoro Algebra for AdS (with Achilleas P. Porfyriadis), gr-qc/1007.1031 (July 2010).

441. BCS as Foundation and Inspiration: The Transmutation of Symmetry, *Mod. Phys. Lett.* **A25**, 3, 3169–3189 (2010); also in *BCS: 50 Years*, ed. L. Cooper and D. Feldman, pp. 535–558 (World Scientific, 2010).

442. A Landmark Proof (Viewpoint on "Plasma analogy and non-Abelian statistics for Ising-type quantum Hall states"), *Physics* **V4**, 10 (2011).

443. Introduction to "Quantum Matter", *Phys. Scr.* **T146**, 014001 (2012).

444. Quantum Beauty: Real and Ideal, in *Beauty*, eds. L. Arrington, Z. Leinhardt and P. Dawid, pp. 43–71 (Cambridge University Press, 2013).

445. MIT 150 Infinite History Interview, infinite.mit.edu/video/frank-wilczek (October 2011).

446. Classical Time Crystals (with A. Shapere), *Phys. Rev. Lett.* **109**, 160402 (2012).

447. Quantum Time Crystals, *Phys Rev. Lett.* **109**, 160401 (2012).

448. Hidden Layers, in *This Will Make You Smarter*, ed. John Brockman (Harper Perennial, 2012).

449. Introductory Remarks, in *Nobel Symposium 148: Graphene and Quantum Matter*, eds. A. Niemi, F. Wilczek, E. Ardonne and H. Hansson, *Physica Scripta*, **2012**, T146 (2012).

450. Happy Birthday Electron, *Scientific American* (June 2012).

451. A Long View of Particle Physics, in *The Theory of the Quantum World (Solvay Conference Proceedings)*, eds. D. Gross, M. Henneaux and A. Sevrin (World Scientific, 2013).

452. Final Editorial Letter, *Annals of Physics* **327**, 7, 1785 (2012).

453. Branched Quantization (with A. Shapere), *Phys. Rev. Lett.* **109**, 200402 (2012).

454. Quantum Physics: Majorana modes materialize, *Nature* **486**, 195–197 (June 2012).

455. Origins of Mass, *Central European Journal of Physics* **D12**, 00144 (June 2012).

456. Foreword to *Radioactive Transformations* by Ernest Rutherford, pp. ix–xli (Yale University Press) (2012).

457. Constraints on Chronologies (with A. Shapere), gr-qc/1208.3841 (August 2012).

458. Models of Topology Change (with A. Shapere and Zhaoxi Xiong), hep-th/1210.3545 (October 2012).

459. A watershed: the emergence of QCD (with D. Gross), *CERN Courier* (2013).

460. The Modern Concept of Substance, Bulletin of the *American Academy of Arts and Sciences*, Bulletin Vol. LXVI/No. 2, 29–34 (Winter 2013).

461. What's Next: Follow Beauty (Viewpoint), *New Scientist* **46** (March 2013).

462. Reply to Bruno's Comment, *Phys. Rev. Lett.* **110**, 118902 (2013).

463. Particle Physics: Minimalism Triumphant, *Nature* **496**, 439–441 (April 2013).

464. Why Does the Higgs Particle Matter? *Big Questions Online*, bigquestionsonline.com/content/why-does-higgs-particle-matter (April 2013).

465. The enigmatic electron, *Nature* **498**, 31 (2013).

466. Ken Wilson: A Scientific Appreciation, *Proceedings of the National Academy of Sciences of the United States of America*, **110**, 32, 12855–12856 (2013). DOI: 10.1073/pnas.1312463110.

467. Review of *The God Problem: How a Godless Cosmos Creates* by Howard Bloom, *Physics Today* **66**, 7 (July 2013).

468. Algebra of Majorana Doubling (with Jaehoon Lee), *Phys. Rev. Lett.* **111**, 226402 (2013).

469. Multiversality, *Class. Quant. Grav.* **30**, 19 (July 2013).

470. Superfluidity and Space-Time Translation Symmetry Breaking, *Phys. Rev. Lett.* **111**, 250402 (2013).

471. Using Cosmology to Establish the Quantization of Gravity (with L. Krauss) *Phys. Rev. D.* **89**, 047501 (2014).

472. Emergent Majorana Mass and Axion Couplings in Superfluids, *New Journal of Physics* **16** (2014).

473. Majorana and Condensed Matter Physics, Chapter 14 in *The Physics of Ettore Majorana* (Cambridge University Press) (2014).

474. From B-Modes to Quantum Gravity and Unification of Forces (with L. Krauss), gr-qc 1404.0634, April (2014). Awarded First Place in 2014 by Gravity Research Foundation Awards for Essays on Gravitation, *Int. J. Mod. Phys. D* **23**, 1441001 (2014).

475. Inflation Driven by Unification Energy (with M. Hertzberg), *Phys. Rev. D.* **95**, 063516 (2017).

476. Entanglement Enhanced Intensity Interferometry (with J. Cotler), quant-ph/1502.02477 (February 2015).

477. Entangled Histories (with J. Cotler), quant-ph/1502.02480 (February 2015).

478. Bell Tests for Histories (with J. Cotler), quant-ph/1503.06458 (March 2015).

479. Physics in 100 Years (2015), arXiv:1503.07735 [physics.pop-ph].

480. Particle Physics: A Weighty Mass Difference, *Nature* **520**, 303 (2015).

481. Unification of Force and Substance, *Phil. Trans. R. Soc. A* **374**, 20150257 (2016).

482. Oscillatory Attractors: A New Cosmological Phase (with J. Bains and M. Hertzberg), *JCAP* **05**, 011 (2017).

483. Superheavy Light Quarks and the Strong P, T Problem (with G.D. Moore), hep-ph/1601.02937 (January 2106).

484. Experimental test of entangled histories (with J. Cotler, L.-M. Duan, P.-Y. Hou, D. Xu, Z.-Q. Yin and Chong Zu), quant-ph/1601.02943 (January 2106).

485. Superfluidity and Symmetry Breaking: An Anderson Living Legacy, in *A Lifetime of Emergence* (P.W. Anderson 90th Birthday), ed. P. Chandra and P. Coleman, pp. 187–213 (World Scientific, 2016).

486. Physics in 100 Years, *Physics Today* **69**, 4, 32 (2016).

487. Particle Physics and Condensed Matter: The Saga Continues, The Royal Swedish Academy of Sciences, *Physica Scripta* **2016**, T168.

488. Statistics of fractionalized excitations through threshold spectroscopy (with S.C. Morampudi, A.M. Turner and F. Pollmann), *Phys. Rev. Lett.* **118**, 227201 (2017).

489. Theory Vision LHCP 2016, PoS (LHCP2016) 047 (2016), hep-ph/1609.06941.

490. Temporal Observables and Entangled Histories (with J.S. Cotler), quant-ph/1702.05838 (February 2017).

491. *A Beautiful Question: Finding Nature's Deep Design* (Penguin, 2015).

492. A Model of Comprehensive Unification (with M. Reig, J.W.F. Valle and C.A. Vaquera-Araujo), arXiv:1706.03116 (June 2017).

493. What is the Value of Imagination and Wishful Thinking in Science?, drive.google.com/file/d/1-A9nZOefVHw7qSGD7iOLpnQairj1hUzO (July 2017)

494. Dilute and Dense Axion Stars (with L. Visinelli, S. Baum, J. Redondo and K. Freese), *Phys. Lett.* **777B** (Feb 2018), pp. 64–72.

495. Experimental Test of Entangled Histories (with J. Cotler, L.-M. Duan, P.-Y. Hou, Da. Xu, Z.-Q. Yin and C. Zu), *ScienceDirect* 387, pp. 334–347 (Dec 2017).

496. A Friendly Ghost Story, in *Ludwig Faddeev Memorial Volume: A Life in Mathematical Physics* (eds. A. Niemi, K.K. Phua, L. A Takhtajan and M.-L. Ge), 33 (World Scientific, 2018).

497. Light, the Universe and Everything — 12 Herculean Tasks for Quantum Cowboys and Black Diamond Skiers, *J. Mod. Optics* **65**, 11 (2018), pp. 1261–1308.

498. Chiral Casimir Forces: Repulsive, Enhanced, Tunable (with Q.-D. Jiang), *Phys. Rev. B* **99**, 125403.

499. SO(3) family symmetry and axions (with M. Reig and J.W.F. Valle), *Phys. Rev. D* **98**, 095008 (2018).

500. The Universality of Intelligence, in *Possible Minds: Twenty-Five Ways of Looking at AI*, ed. John Brockman (Penguin, 2018).

501. Has Elegance Betrayed Physics? *Physics Today* **71**, 9, 57 (2018).

502. Axial Casimir Force (with Q.-D. Jiang), *Phys. Rev. B* **99**, 165402 (2019).

503. Quantum Atmospherics for Materials Diagnosis (with Q.-D. Jiang), *Phys. Rev. B* **99**, 201104 (2019).

504. Superdensity operators for spacetime quantum mechanics (with J. Cotler, C.-M. Jian and X.-L. Qi), *Journal of High Energy Physics*, **2018**, 93 (2018).

505. Truncated Dynamics, Ring Molecules and Mechanical Time Crystals (with D. Jin, A. Niemi and X. Peng), *Phys. Rev. A* **99**, 023425 (2019).

506. The Evolving Unity of Physics, *Nature Reviews Physics* **1**, 5–7 (2019).

507. Tunable Axion Plasma Haloscopes (2019) (with M. Lawson, A.J. Millar, M. Pancaldi and E. Vitagliano), *Phys. Rev. Lett.* **123**, 141802 (2019).

508. Color Erasure Detectors Enable Chromatic Interferometry (with L.-Y. Qu, J. Cotler, F. Ma, J.-Y. Guan, M.-Y. Zheng, X. Xie, Y.-A. Chen, Q. Zhang, and J.-W. Pan), *Phys. Rev. Lett.* **123**, 243601 (2019).

509. Spectroscopy of spinons in Coulomb quantum spin liquids (2019) (with S. C. Morampudi and C. R. Laumann), *Phys. Rev. Lett.* **124**, 097204 (2020).

510. Regularizations of Time Crystal Dynamics (with A. Shapere), in *Proceedings of the National Academy of Sciences*, PNAS (September 17, 2019) **116** (38) 18772–18776.

511. Crystals in Time, *Scientific American* **505**, 5, 28–36 (2019).

512. Quantum Independent-set Problem and Non-Abelian Adiabatic Mixing (with B. Wu and H. Yu), *Phys. Rev. A* **101**, 012318 (2020).

513. Gloria Lubkin (1933–2020), *Physics Today*, February 2020.

514. Moving Mirror Model for Quasithermal Radiation Fields (with R.R. Good and V. Linder) *Phys. Rev. D* **101**, 025012 (2020).

515. Quantum Overlapping Tomography (with J. Cotler), *Phys. Rev. Lett.* **124**, 100401 (2020).

516. Three Easy Pieces (in tribute to Roman Jackiw), contribution to *Roman Jackiw: 80th Birthday Festschrift*, eds. A. Niemi, T. Tomboulis, and K.K. Phua.

517. Geometric Induction in Chiral Superconductors (with Q.-D. Jiang and T.H. Hansson), *Phys. Rev. Lett.* 124, 197001 (2020).

518. Resonant Quantum Search with Monitor Qubits (with H.-Y. Hu and B. Wu), *Chin. Phys. Lett.* **37**, 5, 050304 (2020).

519. Black and White Holes at Material Junctions (with Y. Kedem and E.J. Bergholtz), *Phys. Rev. Research* **2**, 043285 (2020).

520. Freeman Dyson (1923–2020), May 2020, *Science* **368** (6492) 715.

521. The Noise of Gravitons (with M. Parikh and G. Zahariade), *Int. J. Mod. Phys.* **D29** (2020) 2042001.

522. *Fundamentals — Ten Keys to Reality* (Penguin Press, 2021).
523. Entanglement Enabled Intensity Interferometry of Different Wavelengths of Light (with J. Cotler and V. Borish), *Ann. Phys.* **424**, 168346 (2021).
524. Quantum Algorithm for Approximating Maximum Independent Sets (with H.-Y. Hu and B. Wu), *Chin. Phys. Lett.* **38**, 3 (2021) 030304.
525. Chromatic Interferometry with Small Frequency Differences (with L.-Y. Qu, L.-C. Liu, J. Cotler, F. Ma, J.-Y. Guan, M.-Y. Zheng, Q. Yao, X. Xie, Y.-A. Chen, Q. Zhang and J.-W. Pan), *Opt. Express* **28**, 32294–32301 (2020).
526. Signatures of the Quantization of Gravity at Gravitational Wave Detectors (with M. Parikh and G. Zahariade), *Phys. Rev. D* **104**, 046021 (2021).
527. Quantum Mechanics of Gravitational Waves (with M. Parikh and G. Zahariade), *Phys. Rev. Lett.* **127**, 081602 (2021).
528. Improved Spatial Resolution Achieved by Chromatic Intensity Interferometry, (with L.-C. Liu, L.-Y. Qu, C. Wu, J. Cotler, F. Ma, M.-Y. Zheng, X.-P. Xie, Y.-A. Chen, Q. Zhang and J.-W. Pan) arXiv: 2102.02060 (2021).
529. Adiabatic Construction of Hierarchical Quantum Hall States (with M. Greiter), *Phys. Rev. B* **104**, L121111 (2021).